C000246576

An affectionate history of
The Royal Victoria Infirmary,
a much loved hospital serving
Newcastle upon Tyne and the
North East of England for the
past century.

100 years
of the *RVI*

1906 - 2006

edited by John Walton & Miles Irving

The Newcastle upon Tyne Hospitals
NHS Trust

ISBN 10
0-9552654-0-1

ISBN 13
978-0-9552654-0-2

Published by Newcastle upon Tyne Hospitals NHS Trust

© 2006

Designed and printed by pottsprinters

Fortiter Defendit Triumphans

City of
Newcastle upon Tyne

Stained glass window in Peacock Hall.

Medal to commemorate laying of the Foundation Stone of the RVI,
20th June 1900. Courtesy of Mr P.V. Fallon.

RVI Centenary Book: *List of Contents*

Contributors

Barrett, A. Martin
MD FRCS
Consultant Paediatric Surgeon, RVI,
Newcastle upon Tyne Hospitals.
Chairman, RVI / Newcastle General
Hospital / Dental Hospital Medical
Staff Committee.

Barron, S. Leonard
MBBS FRCS FRCOG
Emeritus Consultant Obstetrician and
Gynaecologist, Princess Mary
Maternity Hospital and RVI. Former
lecturer in Obstetrics and Gynaecology,
University of Newcastle upon Tyne.
Former Chairman, Freeman Group
of Hospitals NHS Trust and then
Newcastle upon Tyne Hospitals
NHS Trust.

Brewis, R. Alistair
MD FRCP
Emeritus Consultant Physician, RVI.
Former Senior Lecturer in Medicine,
University of Newcastle upon Tyne.
Former Medical Director, Royal
Victoria Infirmary and Associated
Hospitals NHS Trust.

Burn, John
MD FRCP FRCPCH FRCOG
FMedSci
Consultant Clinical Geneticist,
Newcastle upon Tyne Hospitals
NHS Trust. Professor of Clinical
Genetics and Head of the Institute
of Human Genetics, University of
Newcastle upon Tyne. Clinical
Director, Northern Genetics Service.

Burt, Alastair D.
BSc MD FRCPath FiBiol
Professor of Pathology and Dean
of Clinical Medicine

Clouston, Ann OBE
ARRC TD DL SRN RCNT BSc(Hons)
Former Senior Nurse Operations RVI.
Former Commanding Officer, 201
(Northern) Field Hospital RAMC

Constable, Frank Leonard (Len)
KStJ TD QHP DL BSc MD
FRCPath
Emeritus Consultant Microbiologist,
RVI. Former Lecturer in Microbiology,
University of Edinburgh.

Craft, Sir Alan W.
MD FRCPCH FRCP FMedSci
Sir James Spence Professor of Child
Health, University of Newcastle upon
Tyne. Consultant Paediatrician, RVI.
Past President, Royal College of
Paediatricians and Child Health.

Davison, John M.
BSc MD MSc FRCOG
Former Consultant Obstetrician and
Gynaecologist, RVI and Princess Mary
Maternity Hospital. Consultant
Obstetrician and Emeritus Professor
of Obstetric Medicine. Former
Member of Scientific Staff, Medical
Research Council.

Driver, Joan
League of Friends, RVI.

Enever, Gary
R MA(Cantab) MBBS DA FRCA
Consultant Anaesthetist, Royal
Victoria Infirmary, Newcastle General
Hospital and Newcastle Dental
Hospital. Clinical Lecturer in
Anaesthesia, University of Newcastle
upon Tyne.

Feggetter, Jeremy
TD OStJ DL MB BS FRCS
Consultant Urologist, Freeman and
Wansbeck Hospitals. Hon Clinical
Lecturer, University of Newcastle
upon Tyne. President, Section of
Urology, Royal Society of Medicine.
Former Commanding Officer, 201
(Northern) General Hospital
(RAMC).

Fenwick, Leonard R.
CBE
Chief Executive, Newcastle upon
Tyne Hospitals NHS Trust.

Gallantry, James
BA(Hons) MSc
Assistant Project Manager, Newcastle
upon Tyne Hospitals NHS Trust.

Grey, Ken
JP BA DMS
Chairman, Newcastle Healthcare
Charity.

Gubbins, Barbara
Chief Executive, Children's
Foundation.

Hudspith, Helen
BA (Hons)
Honorary Play Coordinator, Radio
Lollipop, Newcastle.

Irving, Sir Miles
DSc(Hon) MD ChM FRCS
FACS(Hon) FMedSci
Chairman, Newcastle upon Tyne
Hospitals NHS Trust. Former
Professor of Surgery, University of
Manchester. Former National Director,
NHS Health Technology Assessment
Programme. Former President,
Association of Surgeons of Great
Britain and Ireland. Member of
Council, University of Newcastle
upon Tyne. Governor, University of
Northumbria.

Lamont, Helen
MBA RGN SCM ONC DipNurs
(London Univ) FETC
Deputy Director of Nursing and
Patient Services, RVI.

Lavelle, Ian M.
MB ChB DMRD FRCR
Emeritus Consultant Radiologist, RVI,
Freeman Hospital and St. Nicholas'
Hospital. Former Councillor and
Examiner, Royal College of
Radiologists.

Madeley, C. R.
MB ChB MD FRCPath
Emeritus Consultant Clinical
Virologist, RVI. Emeritus Professor
of Clinical Virology, University of
Newcastle upon Tyne.

Medows, Suzanne
RGN DipHE (Nursing Studies)
Practice Placement Facilitator, RVI.

Murray, John J.
CBE PhD MChD FDS RCS
FMedSci
Former Dean of Dentistry, University
of Newcastle upon Tyne and Professor
of Child Dental Health. Former
Senior Lecturer and Reader in
Children's Dentistry, Institute of
Dental Surgery, University of London
and Research Fellow in Children's and
Preventative Dentistry, University of
Leeds.

Proctor, S. J.
MBBS FRCP FRCPath
Professor of Haematological
Oncology, University of Newcastle
upon Tyne. Honorary Consultant,
Newcastle upon Tyne Hospitals NHS
Trust.

Proud, George
MD FRCS
Emeritus Consultant Surgeon, RVI.
Formerly Regional Advisor for
Surgery, Royal College of Surgeons,
England and Head of Northern
Office, Royal College of Surgeons.

Ross, W. M.
CBE MD FRCS FRCR FRCSE
FRACR
Emeritus Consultant Radiotherapist,
RVI. Past President, Royal College of
Radiologists.

Sadler, Chris
RSCN RGN BSc (Hons)
Committee Member, Fleming
Children's Trust.

Schapira, Kurt
MD FRCP FRCPsych DPM
Emeritus Consultant Pyschiatrist.
Former Hon Senior Research
Associate, Dept Pyschiatry, University
of Newcastle upon Tyne. Former
President, Section of Psychiatry, Royal
Society of Medicine. Former Sub-
Dean, Royal College of Psychiatrists.

Scott, John E. S.
MA MD FRCS FAAP(Hon)
Emeritus Consultant Paediatric
Surgeon, RVI. Former Senior Lecturer
in Paediatric Surgery, University of
Newcastle upon Tyne.

Shaw, David
CBE MB ChB FRCP FRCPE
Emeritus Professor of Clinical
Neurology and former Dean of
Medicine, University of Newcastle
upon Tyne. Former President,
Association of British Neurologists.

Shipton, Marjorie J.
BA(Hons) PGCE Cert Theol MA
Chaplain, RVI.

Skillen, A. W.
BSc PhD
Senior Lecturer in Clinical
Biochemistry, University of Newcastle
upon Tyne.

Stoddart, Joseph C.
MD FRCA FRCP
Consultant Emeritus in Anaesthesia
and Intensive Care, RVI. Founder
Member and one-time President of
the Intensive Care Society.

Tacchi, Derek
TD MD FRCOG
Former Consultant Obstetrician /
Gynaecologist, Princess Mary
Maternity Hospital and RVI. Former
Lecturer in Obstetrics and
Gynaecology, University of Newcastle
upon Tyne.

Walton, John (Lord Walton of
Detchant) Kt TD MA MD DSc
FRCP FMedSci
Former Professor of Neurology and
Consultant Neurologist, RVI and
NGH. Former Dean of Medicine,
University of Newcastle upon Tyne.
Former Warden, Green College,
Oxford. Former President, BMA,
GMC, RSM, World Federation of
Neurology. Crossbench Life Peer,
House of Lords.

Ward, Ian
Head of Planning, The Newcastle
upon Tyne Hospitals NHS Trust.

Wheatley, Sheila
Project Manager, WRVS.

Windle, Val
RGN SCM
Senior Patient Services Coordinator,
RVI.

The old Royal Victoria Infirmary Ambulance.

Acknowledgments

The Trust wishes to acknowledge the contributions of the following individuals and organisations without which this book would not have been published.

Donors

Platinum Donors
CHKS Ltd

Gold Donors
James Knott Trust
Dalkia Ltd
The Newcastle Healthcare Charity
The RVI League of Friends
Laing O'Rourke Ltd
Helena Biosciences Ltd

Silver Donors
Mr & Mrs M. Cooper
Price Waterhouse Cooper
Ridley Family Fund. Community Foundation (Tyne and Wear & Northumberland)
Catherine Cookson Charitable Trust

Bronze Donors
Phillips Medical Systems

The Editors and Authors
All the editors and authors have given their time generously and without reward of any kind other than the satisfaction of having contributed to the centenary celebrations in general and the book in particular. Lord Walton has been an outstanding Editor-in-Chief and the end product is a tribute to his hard work and skills, and his experience in writing and editing. Dr Alistair Brewis, as well as writing two chapters and contributing many illustrations, undertook a detailed review of the proofs. Using his immense knowledge of the RVI, he made an invaluable contribution to accuracy whilst simultaneously ensuring grammatical lucidity. We are grateful to many others who added small comments and contributions to ensure accuracy and completeness. The illustrations have been obtained from the archives of the RVI and from personal collections. Where copyright has been obvious we have sought permission for publication from the holders.

The Printers
Potts Printers have entered into this project with enthusiasm and the skilful use of the latest technology. The end product is a tribute to their professionalism and the high quality of their work. The Trust acknowledges the outstanding contribution of Potts Printers, specifically designer Sarah Beniston.

Proceeds from the Sale of this Book will be directed to the Charitable Funds of the Newcastle upon Tyne Hospitals NHS Trust for the support of research and patient amenities.

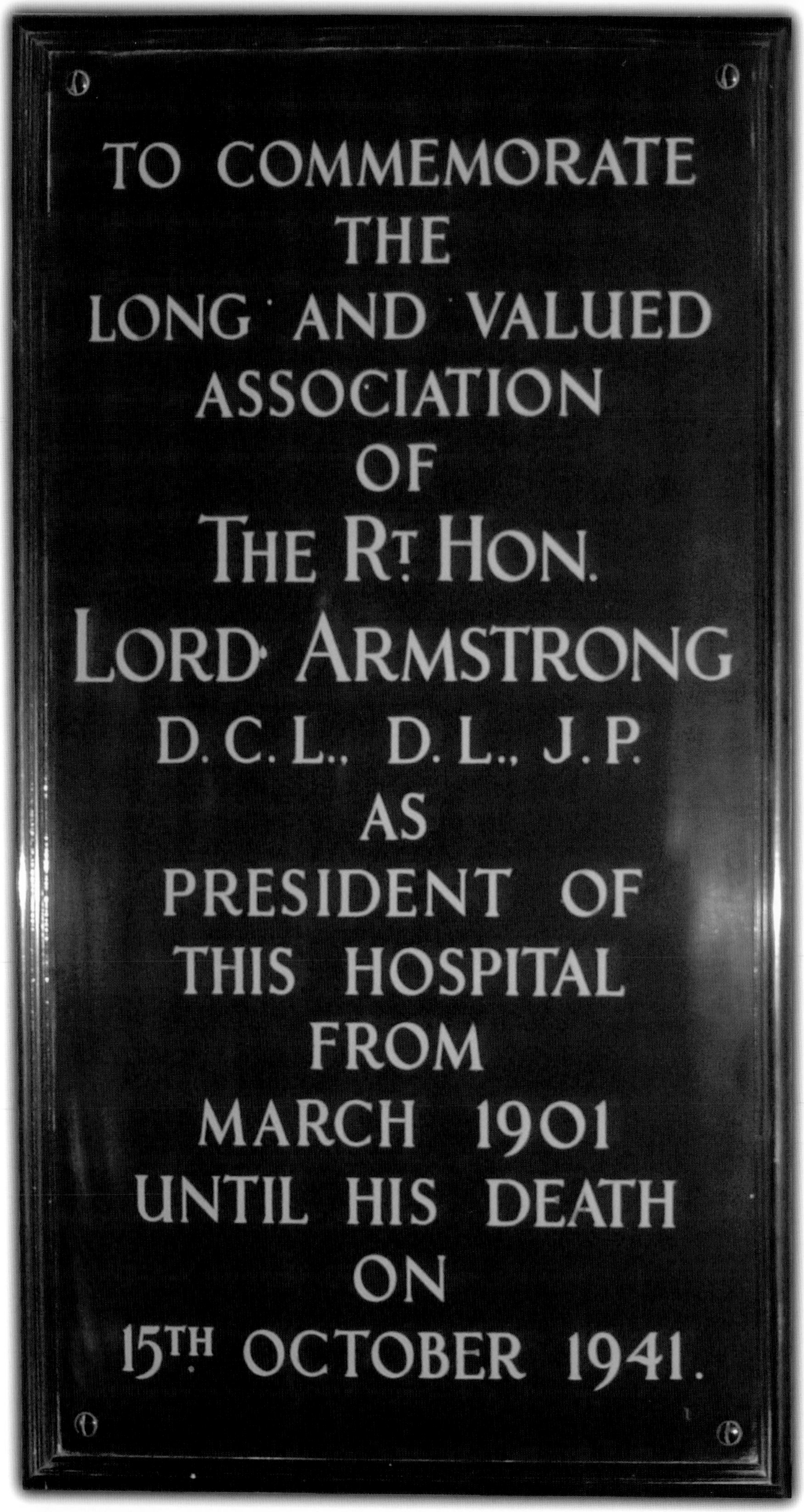

TO COMMEMORATE
THE
LONG AND VALUED
ASSOCIATION
OF
The Rt Hon.
Lord Armstrong
D.C.L., D.L., J.P.
AS
PRESIDENT OF
THIS HOSPITAL
FROM
MARCH 1901
UNTIL HIS DEATH
ON
15TH OCTOBER 1941.

Plaque in the RVI recording the contribution of Lord Armstrong.

Prologue John Walton

This book is certainly not a history of 20th Century medicine and medical services in Newcastle, as many notable figures in all of the caring professions worked in hospitals other than the RVI in Newcastle, and some made outstanding contributions to their particular disciplines, which were recognised locally, nationally and sometimes internationally. We must also make it clear that this volume is not, in the sense used by a professional historian, a scholarly history of the Royal Victoria Infirmary, since within the constraints of space imposed upon us it has not been possible for the contributions we solicited to be totally comprehensive.

In fact, the book contains a series of affectionate descriptions of developments in medicine, nursing and all other relevant hospital services in the century from 1906 onwards, describing not only the very significant changes which took place within that period in the delivery of medical care, but also the innumerable developments which took place in medicine, nursing and all of the related sciences and services. We have also included comments on other hospitals closely related to the RVI and its governance, and have discussed in depth the relationship between this well-loved hospital on the one hand and the Universities in Newcastle on the other, as well as the changes in governance of the hospital which resulted from the many private and subsequent governmental initiatives which followed the establishment of the National Health Service. Hence, we hope that we have paid due credit to the role played by voluntary organisations in assisting and complementing the work of the hospital, and chapters are included describing only a few of the major treasures still retained by the hospital, as well as others giving a pictorial history of developments throughout the relevant century. Yet another chapter deals with the architectural evolution of the hospital, with a glimpse into the future as plans for virtual reconstruction of the hospital now approach finalisation.

The chapters we have commissioned vary considerably in length, style and content, as we have allowed free rein to the authors to discuss their concept and vision of the historical developments which took place in their own particular fields of work over the century. We have made no attempt to impose a uniform editorial style, as we believe that all of the contributions are not only informative and interesting, as are the illustrations which accompany the text, but each reveals something of the personalities, personal interests and experiences of the individuals concerned. We have found the task of guiding the editorial process fascinating and indeed compelling, and believe that the resulting volume will be of great interest, not only to the medical staff of the hospital, but to former patients and many of those who have worked there, and also to the people of Tyneside and the Northern region who have held this hospital and its services in such high regard over many years.

John Walton, Newcastle upon Tyne 2005.
Editor-in-Chief

To the MEMORY of   Mr. JOSEPH SAINT,
Late TREASURER of the INFIRMARY   at NEWCASTLE upon TYNE;
This View of that Edifice, which he had ordered to be taken,   & engraved at his Expence, is most respectfully inscribd.

Chapter 1: *The Early Days 1751 - 1906* Miles Irving

Where it all began

In order fully to understand the centenary of the RVI it is necessary to consider the background leading to the establishment of the Infirmary on its present site. This period has already been described fully in the two histories written by G. H. and W. E. Hume[I] respectively. I have drawn heavily upon these accounts to provide this summary of events leading to the opening of the RVI in 1906.

Before the days of the establishment of the famous infirmaries across the North of England [Liverpool Royal Infirmary (1745), The Manchester Royal Infirmary (1752), The General Infirmary at Leeds (1767)], it was the city corporations that provided medical care for the poor. So it was in Newcastle upon Tyne where, from 1592, irregular payments were made to apothecaries for responding to the mayors' requests to attend selected sick patients. In 1599 the corporation employed a physician and this service continued until 1700 when the post was replaced by a surgeon.

Around 1750 there existed in Newcastle a small social club which was about to be dissolved because of the increasing age of the members and the associated attrition of the membership from their deaths. At the dissolution of the club the founding of an Infirmary as a memorial of their past happy associations was suggested. The idea was brought to the notice of the public by a letter over the signature BK which appeared in the Newcastle Courant on Saturday 5th January 1751, and was printed daily for a week. The identity of BK remains unknown but it is likely that there is a strong link with Mr Richard Lambert, a surgeon who suggest that there should be an infirmary. Subscription lists were opened in the coffee houses and elsewhere and there was an immediate generous response. The corporation gave a site on the Forth Banks, just to the south of where the International Centre for Life is currently situated, for the Infirmary to be built. However, the enthusiasm of the founders was such that they could not wait for the new building and it was decided to open a house in Gallowgate for the reception of patients. (*Fig 1.2*)

The Gallowgate House

On the 23rd May 1751 the subscribers and governors of the Infirmary assembled at the Exchange on Sandhill and accompanied by the Mayor Matthew Ridley (*Fig 17.1, p.183*) and "his brethren of the Magistracy in their formalities" proceeded to St Nicholas Church to hear a sermon by the Archdeacon of Northumberland.[II] After the service they proceeded to the house in Gallowgate whereupon seven patients were immediately admitted. The house accommodated 23 in-patients but the beds were so rapidly filled that rooms in neighbouring houses had to be rented. By using these rooms the space for patients was increased to 35-40 beds. Conditions must have been fairly spartan, for the Gallowgate house did not have a water supply and application had to be made to the mayor for "*leave to lay a pipe into the infirmary from that water that supplies the Newgate pant*".

Staffing of the new Infirmary was provided by four physicians and two surgeons (all unpaid). A secretary, an apothecary and a matron were also appointed. Proof that managerial overload is not a child only of recent times is evidenced by the size of the house committee which consisted of twelve persons from each of Newcastle, Northumberland and Durham.

Fig 1.2: Gallowgate and its Pant.

[I] History of the Newcastle Infirmary
G. H. Hume: Newcastle upon Tyne, Andrew Reid Ltd, 1906

[II] The Infirmary, Newcastle upon Tyne 1751 - 1951 a brief sketch
W. E. Hume: Newcastle upon Tyne, Andrew Reid Ltd, 1951

Six months after the occupation of the house in Gallowgate, the foundation stone of the new Infirmary was laid on the 5th September 1751 by the Bishop of Durham, the Rt Reverend Joseph Butler. (*Fig 17.4, p.184*) Two years later, on 8th October 1753, the building was completed and ready for the reception of patients.

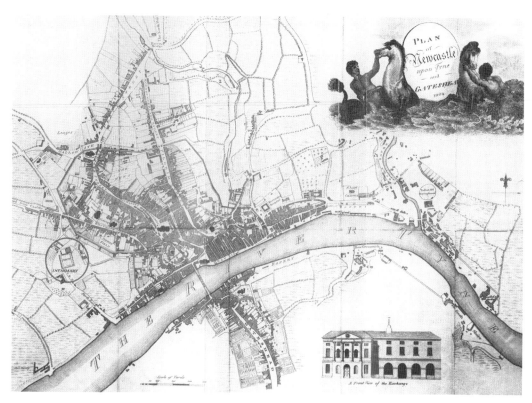

Fig 1.3: Map of Forth Banks showing site of Infirmary.

The Infirmary at Forth Banks (*Fig 1.3*)

The building formed two sides of a quadrangle, one side facing south, the other facing east. The southern block consisted of a basement and three storeys. On the ground floor were the chapel, board room, physicians' room, surgery and matron's parlour. On the first floor were three wards for men and on the top floor two further wards and an operating theatre. (*Fig 1.1*)

The east wing consisted of two floors, the ground floor had two wards, one of 16 beds and another with six beds. The first floor had three wards for women. The building was ready for occupation in 1753 exactly two years and one month after the laying of the foundation stone in September 1751 by Bishop Butler.

Also in 1753 a resident house apothecary, a house steward and a matron were appointed, as well as a porter and a brewer! Overall, provision was made for 90 patients, but overcrowding soon became a problem and it was not unusual for two patients to occupy one bed. Admission to the Infirmary as a patient was based on recommendations by subscribers to the institution. Each subscriber of one guinea could recommend one in-patient and two out-patients and so on, in proportion to the size of the subscription.

Rules for patients and staff were strict. (*Fig 1.4*) As is the case today, there was a complaints mechanism for dissatisfied patients, with cross infection and the food being the principal subjects of concern. A scandal arose around the case of a "clean" patient being

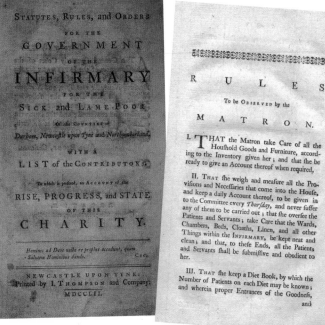

Fig 1.4: Rules for patients and staff.

required to share a bed with one with a contagious disease, whilst in May 1754 there was a complaint about the meat and the hospital's beer which was brewed on the premises. However, complaints were not well received by the House Committee who in this latter instance ordered the patients concerned to have toast and water for a week, though they did instruct the hospital brewer to increase the quantity of malt in the beer, and soon afterwards the quality of meat and beer given to patients was improved.

The nurse staffing was basic. Nurses were non-resident and mainly illiterate. Indeed, most nursing was done by the patients themselves, so that a disturbed or seriously ill patient was put in a room with a reasonably healthy patient who was instructed to provide care for that individual. Disorderly, dirty and drunken patients (and occasionally staff) were encouraged to mend their ways by having their name posted in the wards.

From 1751 to 1801 there was no alteration in the building but towards the end of the century, because of the overcrowding and the increasing problem of fever patients, it was decided to extend the infirmary.

Fig 1.5: The extended Infirmary in 1803.

After much argument it was decided to build a separate fever house with 20 beds outside the town wall and to reconstruct and extend the Infirmary. The new building began in 1801 and was ready for occupation by 1803 (*Fig 1.5*) but in the end the extension resulted in an increase of only 15 beds. Increasing demand meant that, despite the extra beds, the Infirmary was still overcrowded, a situation made worse by closure of the Lock Hospital as a result of lack of funds. All this time the Infirmary was in a relatively rural setting, but this was about to change with the opening of the Newcastle and Carlisle railway, which rapidly encroached on the ground to the South Front of the building. Inside the building history was being made. In September 1835 Mr Bains removed a bladder stone weighing 8 1/2 ozs and in May 1847 anaesthesia was used for the first time.

In 1851 the Infirmary was 100 years old and finding difficulty in meeting the requirements of the patients. Mr Thomas Michael Greenhow, who had been appointed as an honorary surgeon to the Infirmary in 1832, drew the attention of the house committee to the inadequacies of the Infirmary in 1845. Five years later he pointed out that the surrounding population had grown threefold and as a result John Dobson, the famous architect, was asked to look over the premises and the grounds with a view to enlarging the institution. In March 1851 he laid his plans before the re-development committee and within a month his plans were agreed.

A new block, known as the Dobson Wing and consisting of a basement and three storeys was added as a west wing to produce a fine looking Hospital. (*Fig 1.6*) The Dobson Wing was opened on January 18th 1855 and provided an additional 144 beds, but it was put to use before it was completed, for in 1853 there was a major outbreak of cholera and use was made of the unfinished Dobson Wing. (*Fig 1.7*) For the first time the general public were informed that

Fig 1.6: The Infirmary in 1855 showing the addition of the Dobson Wing to the left of the Southern Front.

SPASMODIC
Cholera
THE
BOARD OF HEALTH
Established at Newcastle-upon-Tyne,

Under the Authority of the Privy Council, cannot too
strongly impress on the Inhabitants of this Town the
Necessity of the instant Removal to the Hospital of
each Person attacked with the Disease. The Bed-
Clothes and Wearing Apparel of the Patient should
be steeped in Lime Water, and the Inside of the House
washed with hot Lime.

The Burial of the Dead should not, on any Account, be deferred for
more than twelve Hours after Death; the Coffin should not be borne by
Men to the Grave, but conveyed in Hearses, which have been provided
for that Purpose, and no Grave should be less than six Feet in Depth.

The Heads of Families are recommended not to permit their Servants to leave their Houses for the Purpose of Intercourse with their
Friends.

The Board of Health particularly request that all Medical Practitioners who may be called upon to attend Persons affected with this Disease residing in the County of Northumberland, out of the District of the
North Shields Board of Health, and within twelve Miles of Newcastle,
will report such Cases without Delay to this Board, at the Mayor's
Chamber, in the Guildhall, in Order that they may be reported to the
Central Board of Health in London.

By Order of the Board of Health,
JOHN BROWN, *Secretary.*

Mayor's Chamber, Newcastle-upon-Tyne,
December 15th 1831.

Fig 1.7: *Cholera warning leaflet.*

advice and treatment could be obtained at any hour of the day or night.
In 1854 an explosion on the Gateshead side of the river was followed by
a devastating fire in Newcastle and 23 victims of the fire were admitted
to the Infirmary in 24 hours. (*Figs 1.8, 1.9 & 1.10*)

Despite the newer and better facilities, infection was still rampant
throughout the Hospital, with erysipelas being a particular problem. It
was not until 1874 with the appointment of Dr Beatson, who had been
Lord Lister's house surgeon, and who introduced his methods, that the
situation improved.

In the succeeding two years, through the application of antiseptic
methods, the freedom of the Infirmary from Hospital Disease was
commented upon, and was manifested by the reduction in the quantity
from the three tons of linseed meal previously purchased annually for
the poulticing of infected wounds.

Fig 1.8: *The Gateshead Explosion.*

Fig 1.9: *The fire that followed.*

Fig 1.10: *Newcastle Quayside after the explosion.*

In 1885 the governors decided to build another block of 50 beds as an offshoot from the centre of the main block. The result was the Ravensworth wards (*Fig 1.11*) which were opened in 1885, allowing the accommodation of 270 patients and thus greatly relieving pressure on the Hospital.

Despite this, the medical staff were urging the building of another hospital on a different site. The Hospital was made a *free hospital* in 1887, the year of the Queen's Jubilee, and consequently the house committee sought permission from the Queen to designate the Hospital as a Royal Infirmary and, in 1887, the Infirmary became the Royal Infirmary for the counties of Newcastle upon Tyne, Northumberland and Durham. Despite these improvements the functioning of the Infirmary was seriously impeded by the continuing encroachment of the railway and the noise of the passing trains. (*Fig 1.11 & 1.12*)

Fig 1.11: Photograph illustrating the Ravensworth Ward and the closeness of the railway to the South of the Infirmary.

Fig 1.12: Aerial photograph showing the old Infirmary hemmed in by the railway.

Fig 1.13: The Royal Victoria Infirmary.

In 1896 the approaching Diamond Jubilee of Queen Victoria's reign suggested to the Mayor that a fitting local memorial of her reign should be built. It was thus decided that a new Infirmary should be constructed on Castle Leazes site and a suitable site was obtained from the Freemen and the Corporation. The foundation stone was laid by HRH Albert Edward Prince of Wales on 20th June 1900 who, as King Edward VII, opened the new Royal Victoria Infirmary on 11th July 1906 for the admission of patients. (*Figs 1.13 & 1.14*)

Fig 1.14: The last patient to leave Forth Banks arriving at the RVI.

This brief account of the period before 1906 would not be complete without mention of some of the individuals who pioneered medicine during this time. Prime amongst these is Matron Emily Aston who was in charge of both Hospitals, having successfully supervised the transfer from Forth Banks to the Leazes site. (*Fig 1.15*)

William Ingham (*Fig 1.16*) was born in 1753, the son of a Whitby surgeon. He came to Newcastle at the age of 14 to serve his apprenticeship with Richard Lambert. On completion of his apprenticeship he was sent to London to gain additional experience. When he returned to Newcastle he went into partnership with Lambert and they offered their services from a house in the Bigg Market. He was appointed surgeon to the Infirmary in 1779, where he served for 33 years.

Fig 1.15: Matron Emily Aston.

His portrait hangs in the Boardroom to this day. He died in 1817 and is buried in St Nicholas Cathedral. The Ingham Infirmary in South Shields was built and named after him in recognition of his services to the region. In 1853 Dr Edward Charlton (*Fig 1.17*) was appointed to the Infirmary. He later became Professor of Medicine and President of the College of Medicine. The following year George Yeoman Heath (*Fig 1.18*) was appointed as surgeon to the Infirmary, subsequently becoming Professor of Surgery and President of the College of Medicine. The famous Charles Gibb of Blaydon Races fame (*Fig 1.19*) was appointed Honorary Surgeon in 1855 and held this post until 1870.

Fig 1.16: William Ingham.

Fig 1.17: Edward Charlton.

Fig 1.18: George Yeoman Heath.

Fig 1.19: Charles Gibb.

Thus closed a pioneering chapter in the history of the development of hospital services. Those who implemented their vision of a hospital worthy of Newcastle and the north east will have been well satisfied with their endeavours. They would, however, have been even more thrilled to see their vision develop further still through the building of the Royal Victoria Infirmary on a prime site near the city centre and to follow its progress over the next 100 years.

Chapter 2: *The story of Nursing at the Royal Victoria Infirmary*

Helen Lamont, Val Windle, Suzanne Medows

Everything changes... Everything remains the same

Introduction

This chapter sets out to tell the story of nursing life in the RVI during the past one hundred years. It starts before the days of graduate training for nurses, nurse specialists, nurse prescribing, central heating, disposable bed pans, antibiotics, sterile dressing packs, and MRSA, to mention just a few of the many changes and developments during the period. However, whilst researching the story, it has become clear that, although the dates and characters have changed, many of the issues have not. Nursing has always been hard and rewarding work - there have always been bed shortages, waiting lists, concerns about infection, recruitment issues and, for most of the time, Matrons!

The traditions of nursing, emerging from religion and the *"local handywoman"*, were changed in this country through social reform led by Elizabeth Fry (1780-1845) and Florence Nightingale (1820 -1910) who, during the nineteenth century, were instrumental in bringing about improvements in health and social care. By 1906, nursing had achieved acceptance as a suitable profession for young women, and the image of the Charles Dickens character, *"Sairy Gamp"* (a drunken midwife in Martin Chuzzelwit 1844) had been dispelled.

Nurse Training

Following her experience in the Crimean War, Florence Nightingale set about reforming and improving standards of nursing, and established the first School of Nursing at St. Thomas' Hospital in 1860. Nurse training was therefore well established by the time the RVI was opened. Life was hard as a *"probationer"* in the early years, and this is noted by Mr. Dunstan, RVI House Governor, in a document commemorating the opening of the RVI Nurses' Home in 1929, which states: *"A nurse has to be highly trained and pass progressive examinations, the preparation for which, to a very great extent has to be done in her leisure time, which is indeed a strenuous ordeal, especially having completed a day's work in a busy hospital. It has recently been stated by the Matron of one of our principal hospitals that 50% of the probationers leave before the end of the first year on account of the strain and the many arduous duties which they are called upon to do".* (Fig 2.2)

However there was, and continues to be, recognition for some within the RVI. The Heath Awards, for excellence in the practice and theory of Nursing and Midwifery, were established in 1905, from a bequest made by George Yeoman Heath (Fig 1.18, p.21), a distinguished surgeon to the Infirmary from 1854. He also left £5000 to purchase the Northern Counties Nurses' Home in 40 Leazes Terrace for £1000, the remainder being invested in stock to produce an income from which the Nurses' teaching fees were paid, the decoration of the home paid for and a pound per nurse for holidays. In 1905 the house was sold and the Health Charity was founded in that year. In 1906 the first awards of a silver medal plus £10 were presented to the "top nurses". The award, in the form of the Heath Medal for excellence, continues to be made on an annual basis in recognition of the best learner nurses. (Figs 2.3 & 2.4)

Brenda McBride, author of *"A Nurse's War"*, commenced her training at the RVI in 1939, and her account of her four-year training, for which she was paid 36 shillings a month (£1.80), leaves no doubt as to the level of discipline at the time, with nurses not being permitted to speak to a tutor until they were spoken to. This discipline extended beyond the training school, as she describes in this account of going off duty at the end of a shift: *"we joined the stream of nurses filing through the conservatory, probationers' striped frocks giving way to staff nurse blue and everyone to the mauve of a Ward Sister. To break the precedent was almost a bread and water charge. Even the six week seniority between one training school and the next was most jealously guarded".*

An account of another 18-year-old, who began her nurse training in July 1948, describes how, following a personal interview with Matron to determine her suitability for nurse training, she was appointed for a three-month probationary period, six weeks of which were spent in the preliminary training school. On successful completion of

Dear Madam,

You are requested to be in readiness to enter this Hospital (on probation) not later than 7 p.m. on *2nd September 1935.*

UNIFORM   Two dress lengths of five yards each are enclosed; also pattern apron and collar. It is desirable that the material is shrunk before being made up. The dresses must be made with bodice and skirt joined together by a band of the same material.

THE BODICE to be made plain back and front without pleats . and to fasten down the front with flat buttons and to be lined.

THE SLEEVES As photograph enclosed, made with plain straight cuff of material, to reach the elbow but not to come below it.

THE SKIRT To be made to clear the ground by six inches. Two tucks are permitted to allow for shrinking. The back to be gathered at the waist without gore.

CAPS will be provided on arrival.

THE APRON Should be made of fine white linen or good quality linen faced longcloth and must be made to fit the individual wearer, the pattern apron being sent as a guide to shape only. The skirt of the apron should completely cover the dress in front, but must not come below it, and must be gathered into a band two inches wide, fastened with two buttons. The bib should fit neatly under the plain linen collar (not showing the dress at all) and be gathered into a band at the waist. The shoulder straps should be long enough to pin under the band of the apron. No pockets are permitted.

Fourteen aprons are required and suitable linen faced longcloth 45 inches wide, can be obtained from Messrs. Young and Sons, Royal Arcade, Newcastle-on-Tyne. The material should be well shrunk before being made up.

Twelve white linen collars (as pattern) are required.

Fig 2.2: Letter from Matron Charteris to a new probationer, 1935.

Jewellery and fancy combs are not permitted.

Black stockings and shoes must be worn. Walking shoes with fairly thick soles and medium heels, with rubber heels or tips are required. Suede or coloured shoes may not be worn in the wards.

Probationers are required to provide themselves with suitable warm underclothing, nightdresses or pyjamas and dressing gown, also bedroom slippers.

A pair of nail scissors and a pair of ordinary scissors, plainly marked with the owner's name are required.

Probationers are required to provide themselves with a suitable sized <u>trunk</u> with their full name (not initials) painted on the outside.

They must provide themselves with <u>two bags for soiled linen</u> (to be sent to the laundry) size 36 inches by 36 inches of strong material with their full names in letters not less than two inches in height across the lower part of the bag and a strong tape to tie up the upper part. <u>All clothing must be plainly marked with the owner's name</u> <u>(not initials)</u>

Every probatione r is required to provide herself with a copy of "Practical Nursing" by Cuff and Pugh (latest edition) "Notes on Nursing" by Florence Nightingale and "Anatomy and Physiology" by Evelyn C. Pearce, all of which can be obtained from the Scientific Press, 29, Southampton Street, London W.C. or from Local Stationers.

Kindly acknowldge the receipt of this letter and parcel. The pattern apron, collar and photograph should be returned as soon as possible.

When you arrive will you please go straight to the Nurses' Home.

Believe me,

Yours faithfully,

Matron.

this, she was given a contract for four years of practical work, with two state examinations after the first and third years. Her salary, after board and lodgings were deducted, was £12 per month. Lectures were attended in off duty time.

Fig 2.3: Heath Medal.

Fig 2.4: Prize Giving 1930. [1]

Royal Victoria Infirmary
Newcastle upon Tyne

This is to Certify that

HELEN ADDY

was received as a Student on the first day of October 1973 and has completed a term of 3 years training in the wards and departments of this hospital. She has fulfilled her duties, attended the required lectures and passed the usual examinations satisfactorily.

Anthony J Cass
Area Nursing Officer

Margaret A. Tatham
Principal Nursing Officer (Education)
Area Director of Nurse Education

Michael. Healey
Chairman of Newcastle Area Health Authority (Teaching)

Fig 2.5: RVI Hospital Certificate.

For many years, training was an "apprenticeship", continuing largely unchanged until the introduction of "Project 2000" training in the 1990s, and the move to higher education. This granted full student and supernumerary status to learner nurses who, until this time, were a major, and active, part of the nursing workforce undertaking direct patient care and often being left to take charge of wards and departments - a situation that would not be tolerated today. (*Fig 2.9*)

The RVI School of Nursing emerged, and retained responsibility for the training of State Registered and State Enrolled Nurses until 1976, when the local hospital schools of Nursing were merged to create the Newcastle School of Nursing. (*Fig 2.5*) In 1992 the responsibility transferred to what is now Northumbria University, which recruits 700 students per year to undertake degree and diploma level nurse training and who undertake clinical placements and experience in Trusts throughout the Northumberland Tyne and Wear Strategic Health Authority area.

The Nursing Workforce
When the RVI was opened, there were 17 wards, with 293 beds in occupation, and patients were cared for by a complement of 89 nursing staff. However, it wasn't long before increasing activity led to demands for additional beds and, consequently, more nurses. Table 2.1 illustrates

---

[1] Photograph courtesy of Miss Sheila Riley, who was herself a ward sister at the RVI for many years. This photograph includes Sister Riley's mother, also an RVI nurse.

the changing profile of activity and of the nursing workforce:

Date	In-patients	Out-patient Attendances	Operations	Nurses	Available Beds
1905	4,633	48,467	3,699	76	270
1907	6,445	93,244	5,678	103	366
1913	8,507	101,736	8,457	138	430
1928	14,469	388,897	15,836	197	572

Table 2.1: Information from document commemorating the opening of the RVI Nurses' Home Extension 1929

By 1922, 190 nurses were employed and a distinction was being made between sisters, staff nurses and probationers.[II] Also, for the first time "administrative nurses" were identified - so the Nurse Manager is nothing new. The profile of the nursing workforce in 1922[III] was as follows; Matron 1, Assistant Matron 1, Administrative 4, Ward and Departmental Sisters 25, Staff Nurses 25, Probationers 124 and Probationers on preliminary training 10.

Fig 2.6: Classroom scene.

As the nursing workforce developed, so did a career structure, with "Staff Nurses" being those who achieved State Registration, which was introduced in 1922, when nurses who had successfully completed a recognised nurse training programme were able to register with the General Nursing Council (GNC). (*Fig 2.6*) This existed from 1919 until 1982, when it was replaced, as the statutory body for nursing, by the United Kingdom Central Council (UKCC) for Nursing, Midwifery, and Health Visiting, at which time the "State Registered Nurse" designation was replaced by "Registered General Nurse".

The UKCC continued until 2001, when it was replaced by the Nursing and Midwifery Council, which assumed responsibility for the regulation of the professions in a more publicly accountable manner with a remit to *"protect the public, through professional standards"*.

These early State Registered Nurses were supported in their work, for many years, by Nursing Assistants (now Health Care Assistants). However, in 1943, in order to address the nursing shortages of the time, a second level of nurse was introduced, that of the State Enrolled Nurse. At the time of their introduction, many Nursing Assistants were awarded this title in recognition of their length of service, with new recruits being required to undertake a shorter, and more practically based, training than their State Registered counterparts. These two training programmes ran successfully alongside each other until Enrolled Nurse training was phased out in the 1990s.

II RVI Reports 1920-22.
III RVI Reports 1920-22.

ROYAL VICTORIA INFIRMARY

FOR THE SICK AND LAME POOR
of
THE COUNTIES OF NEWCASTLE-UPON-TYNE
NORTHUMBERLAND AND DURHAM

Established April, 1751

Foundation Stone, Newcastle Infirmary, laid by the Right Rev. Joseph, Lord Bishop of Durham (Bishop Butler), 5th September, 1751.

Opening, Newcastle Infirmary, 8th October, 1753.

Designated Royal Infirmary by permission of Her Majesty, Queen Victoria, 16th June, 1887.

Foundation Stone, Royal Victoria Infirmary, laid by Albert Edward, Prince of Wales, K.G., as the Representative of Her Majesty, Queen Victoria, 20th June, 1900.

Opening, Royal Victoria Infirmary, by His Majesty, King Edward VII., accompanied by Her Majesty, Queen Alexandra, 11th July, 1906.

Foundation Stone of the Nurses' Home Extension, laid by Sir Walter Runciman, Bart., on November 14th, 1929.

Fig 2.7: Taken from a Souvenir Booklet commemorating the opening of the RVI Nurses' Home Extension in 1929.

During the 1960s the Cadet Nurse was also a regular member of the nursing team, with school leavers who aspired to be nurses gaining experience and a wide understanding of hospital life during the years between them leaving school and being eligible to enter nurse training, for which they had to be 18. With the move of nurse training to Higher Education, the Cadet programme was also phased out, but has recently been successfully resurrected, in collaboration with Northumbria University, as a means of recruiting nurses, widening access to the profession and developing loyalty to the organisation and to nursing.

Male nurses and overseas nurses might be considered to be a modern phenomenon, but the RVI reports for 1946 and 1948 show that this is not the case. In 1946 the nursing establishment included 2 male staff nurses and 32 male probationer nurses, whilst the 1948 report states: *"the house committee have agreed to the introduction of colonial student nurses to the preliminary training school, provided that the numbers do not exceed four to six at any one time".*

The RVI Annual Report identifies that during 1951, the possibility of reducing the working week for nurses to 48 hours, based on a three shift system, was explored. It was considered that *"The implementation of this system would meet more fully the required educational and nursing standards".* However, it was also noted that this *"could only be realised when the financial requirements and numbers of nursing personnel were available"* - some things never change!

Today, the RVI nursing workforce is made up of 1500 qualified nurses and 400 health care assistants who care for patients in 800 beds on the RVI site as well as looking after out-patients and undertaking managerial and educational activities, and no doubt if these statistics are revisited in the future, there will continue to be a growing demand for beds and nurses.

Life at the RVI

Earlier sections described working life for nurses in the RVI, and this section looks at the social life and living conditions for nurses who dedicated (because this is what was expected) their lives to a career in Nursing. Even until the late 1960s, nurses had to choose between a career in nursing or marriage and for those who chose the career in nursing there were very strict expectations about their personal conduct. Although from an earlier period, this scathing comment, taken from a Nursing Register in the RVI archives, illustrates this nicely. *"Sister deteriorated very much indeed after she was trusted with responsibility. She had a very bad influence on her nurses and fellow workers. She set a bad example by entertaining the resident doctors in her sitting room. She is absolutely lacking in high principles and has no sense of personal responsibility"*. Presumably, she was encouraged to pursue her career elsewhere!

Fig 2.8: Nurses' Home.

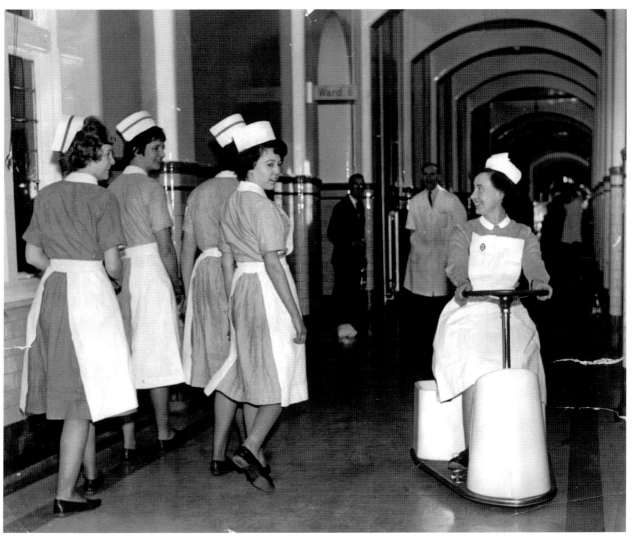
Fig 2.9: Sister on scooter.

Fig 2.10: The badge and uniform of a qualified RVI Nurse, worn with justified pride.

In 1905, before the vacation of the Infirmary on Forth Banks, the new Nurses' Home at Leazes was opened, and the nurses accommodated there. The nursing workforce quickly outgrew the available accommodation and by 1927 a special appeal was launched to provide additional accommodation for 150 nurses. This was made possible by a generous donation from Robert Runciman Bt. after whom the new wing, opened in 1929, was named. (*Figs* 2.7 & 2.8)

However, the RVI Reports of 1944-1947 describe that the accommodation was still inadequate for the needs of the expanding nursing workforce, and accordingly, Framlington House, in Framlington Place, was furnished and equipped as a student nurses' preliminary training school. The house provided accommodation for twenty student nurses, with a Sister Tutor in charge. Other properties in Framlington Place were also purchased and utilised as hostels for nurses, thereby relieving the pressure on the accommodation in the nurses' home.

Until the early 1970s it was a requirement for all student nurses to live in the nurses' home (perhaps this was no bad thing, as in 1973 the monthly rent for a first year student nurse was only £1.20) and meals were taken in the dining room, segregated from the sisters and consultants who ate in the much grander surroundings of their own dining room, complete with wood panelled walls, white tablecloths and waitress service.

Life in the Nurses' Home had its limitations - no men in the rooms (even fathers weren't allowed to visit), an early morning wake up bell (even if you were on a late shift), and a curfew of 10pm. Most managed to achieve this, as the alternative was to contact the night sister and request to be allowed in, which necessitated an interview with "Home Sister" the following day. Even during the emancipated "free love" culture of the 1960s and liberated 1970s, nurses remained under the close supervision of the Matron and Home Sister. However, there are many nurses who trained under this regime, still working at the RVI today, who have tales to tell about how, despite these restrictions, they still managed to live life to the full, without detection - the challenge all added to the excitement and camaraderie in the nurses' home - with fraternisation with resident doctors on "night rounds" being a common phenomenon.

The Matron - Then and Now (*Table 2.2*)

At the time of the opening of the RVI, and for many years thereafter, the Matron was undoubtedly viewed as a formidable figure, with wide ranging powers. A student nurse in 1948 describes her feelings when she saw Matron approach *"your knees went rather weak, you wondered if your cap was on straight, if your stockings had a ladder in them, and shoes were clean"*. The same student also describes that the Matron did a daily round of each ward and spoke to every patient.

Matron was responsible for 'hiring and firing' staff and in the early days of the RVI would write personally to each student nurse giving details of uniform and text book requirements and other essential information. (*Fig* 2.2) Matron's power also extended beyond the clinical areas, and catering records describe kitchen staff having to take the food orders to her office at the same time each week for her approval.

Following the Salmon Report (The report of the Committee on Senior Nursing Staff Structure) of 1968, the post of Matron became obsolete and the nursing administrative structure changed. However, the "Number 7s" (Nursing Officers), "Number 8s" (Senior Nursing Officers) and "Number 9s" (Principal Nursing Officers - formerly the Matron), established by the Salmon Report, did not have the same kudos as "The Matron" and, following a national government survey, and the publication of the NHS Plan (DoH 2000), the Matron's role was reinstated to be a "visible and authoritative presence". Whilst the role today is different to that of old, with the "Modern Matron" being responsible for a specific area, rather than the whole hospital, the Matron is still responsible for promoting high standards of care - although she no longer has to order the catering supplies!

1906 - Miss Emily Aston	Transferred as Matron from Forth Banks, with 11 years service, having been appointed on 7th November 1895, at a salary of £100 per annum. She resigned in August of 1906 and, during her term of office, the nursing staff increased from 30 to 72.
1906 - Miss McCall Anderson	Owing to illness she never worked in the Infirmary.
1907 - Miss Lucy W Wamsley	Resigned in 1912 on her appointment as Lady Inspector under the local Government Board.
1913 - Miss Esther Florence Corser Brown RRC	Served as Matron for fifteen years
1928 - Miss Annie Charteris	Served as Matron for eighteen years having been an RVI Probationer.
1946 - Miss G Lang-Davis	Resigned 1947
1948 - Miss Janet Thompson Hutton	Served as Matron for eleven years.
1959 - Miss Freda Shaw	At this time both of the Newcastle hospitals had "Matron Shaws". It is reported that the Matron at Newcastle General Hospital said that *"I am Miss Shaw, she"* (meaning the Matron at the RVI) *"is Miss Freda Shaw"!*
1972 - Miss F. M. Ovington	The records suggest that Miss Ovington was the last to hold the title Matron before the introduction of the "Principal Nursing Officer" and her succession by Mr Anthony Carr.

Table 2.2 **RVI Matrons 1906 - 1970s**

Nursing Today

Nursing has made significant progress during the lifetime of the RVI, with the development of a range of new nursing roles, including Nurse Consultants, Nurse Specialists and Nurse Practitioners. These have opened up exciting opportunities for nurses to widen their contribution to patient care, with professional boundaries becoming increasingly blurred. Nurses now assume responsibilities that were previously the domain of other professional groups, for example prescribing drugs and carrying out minor surgical procedures.

Developments in nurse education have kept pace with these "roles and practice" developments with "basic" nurse training now at diploma level. There are moves towards establishing an all graduate workforce, with many nurses achieving post graduate qualifications, including Masters Degrees, and in some cases Doctorates!

Fig 2.11: Helen Lamont, the matron in fact, if not in name, in the centenary year of the RVI.

However, throughout this on-going change, nursing has not lost sight of the need to maintain the ethos of nursing and the values that define it as the highly respected, and caring, profession that it is. It is with confidence therefore that the nursing staff within the RVI look forward to the changes and developments that the next 100 years will bring, and to a leap forward in standards of patient care at least as significant as that achieved since the RVI opened its doors in 1906.

Chapter 3: *A Century of Internal Medicine in the RVI*

Alistair Brewis

Introduction

When the Royal Victoria Infirmary opened on its present site in 1906 there were four Honorary Physicians responsible for the care of patients in the six medical wards and one Honorary Physician to the Skin Department. There had only been 29 earlier Honorary Physicians in the whole history of the Infirmary in Newcastle since its foundation in 1751. Now, a hundred years later, there are around 60 consultant physicians in post with responsibilities in medicine at the RVI, of whom about 40 spend all or most of their working week on the site. This striking comparison reflects the story of medicine over the same period, which is one of constant change and development, of increasing levels of activity, increasing specialisation and a hugely increased range of diagnostic and therapeutic facilities. This in turn reflects dramatic changes in the nature of disease borne by patients presenting for treatment and equally remarkable changes in their requirements and those of society as a whole. Astonishing modifications and additions have been made to the buildings to meet the changing requirements, and new facilities have been built on the site. This process has been almost continuous and is currently reaching a crescendo.

The scale of change and development makes it impossible to provide an account of the last 100 years of medicine at the RVI which is at the same time comprehensive and compact. However, an overall impression can be gained by reviewing medicine in three broad phases: firstly the period from the opening up to the start of the National Health Service in 1948, secondly the next period up to the 1970s and, lastly, from the 1980s to the present.

Fig 3.2: *View of a ward shortly after the opening. A central fireplace is visible behind the table. The beds at first seem vacant but closer examination shows that they contain patients - all lying rigidly at attention!*

From 1906 to 1948

From the outset the medical wards were situated on the first floor above the surgical wards, reproducing the arrangement which had existed in the old Infirmary on the Forth Banks. Of the six wards, each of around 30 beds, four were for male patients but only two for female patients. Within two years of its opening, the Annual Report of the RVI lamented the shortage of in-patient accommodation in medicine, particularly for female patients, in the face of increasing demand. The anomalous distribution persisted nevertheless for over 80 years, until the building of the Leazes Wing, and was the cause of persistent difficulties.

The wards themselves

The wards were high, light and airy and well spaced apart on classic late-Victorian 'Nightingale' lines. (*Fig 3.2*) Great emphasis was made of fresh air and cleanliness as an integral part of treatment, as well as a means of preventing spread of infection. In 1909 1,118 gallons of floor polish were applied. Heating in winter was achieved by means of a central fire in the ward - often taken charge of by a convalescent patient with stoking experience. The fires were set in the end of a central tiled block at about chest height with grilles on the top emitting heat from the surrounds of the fireplaces within. Flues from the fires ran beneath the floors to tall chimneys - the stacks of which can still be seen (in 2005) on either side of the wards. The fires were removed in the 1960s.

Left: Fig 3.1: The Main Out-patient Department in the 1970s.

33

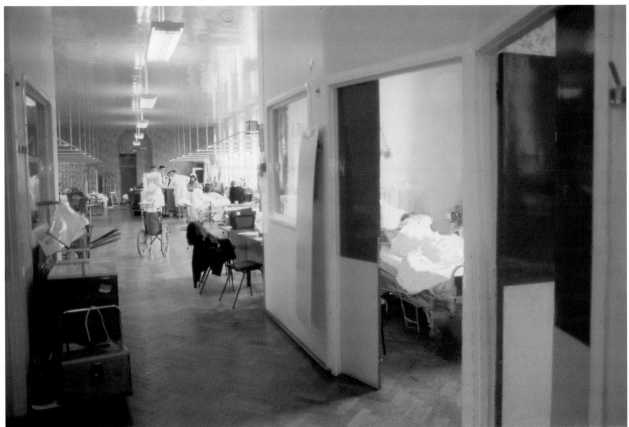

Fig 3.3: View near the entrance to Ward 14 showing the cubicles. A ward round is in progress in the distance.

The corridor connecting the ward entrance to the bedded area had small rooms leading off on either side. In the early part of the century these comprised the ward kitchen, the ward sister's room, a linen room, a clinical investigation room (urine testing and microscopy etc) and a patients' day room. There was some variation in use between the wards. Over the next 80 years or so these small rooms would see service as specialist research laboratories, secretarial offices, examination rooms, waiting rooms, teaching rooms, areas for storage and preparation of medicines and apparatus, and for conduct of special procedures of a sophistication unimaginable by the original designers. Initially the medical wards had no cubicled areas, although the shortage of beds on the female wards was partly met by one or two of the small rooms being used as single or double-bedded spaces. Later, four single cubicles were created on each ward at the entrance to the bedded area (*Fig 3.3*) and the balcony area at the end of the ward between the sluice and bathroom was enclosed, and the space used for two beds.

Naming and numbering of wards

On the opening of the RVI, wards were numbered but were principally known by names given to them in commemoration of prominent benefactors and famous clinical figures from the past.[1] By the 1930s the wards became known by their numbers. In 1995, as part of an initiative to improve signage in the hospital, ward numbering in the Victoria building was revised so that, on entry, a newcomer looking for a particular ward could follow a more logical branching series of options at each junction. The benefits to newcomers were less obvious to staff (and a significant proportion of the population of Tyneside) who already had a map of the 'old' numbering firmly imprinted on their

---

[1] The one hundred and fifty eighth Annual Report of the Royal Victoria Infirmary for the Sick and Poor of the Counties of Newcastle upon Tyne, Northumberland and Durham. 1907.

minds. The ward numbering used in this chapter refers to the 'old' numbering prevailing for most of the period under review.

The early Honoraries

The Honorary Physicians supported themselves entirely from the fees that they charged in their external private practices; their clinical and administrative services to the Infirmary were provided free of any charge. The Honorary Physician, of course, derived an enhanced standing in the medical community and attracted more patients for consultation by virtue of his (there was never a female Honorary Physician) appointment to the staff of the Hospital. Honorary service persisted for nearly 200 years until the introduction of the National Health Service in 1948. By today's standards the duties of the Honorary Physicians may seem light. Typically he would attend on two mornings each week to conduct a ward round and perhaps see a few out-patients before leaving for lunch. However, as patients were generally suffering from slow-moving illnesses (the average length of stay in the medical wards was about four weeks throughout the first decade of the century), this was considered to be perfectly adequate. The Honorary Physician might arrive by carriage, alighting under cover of the arched portico which still exists at the main entrance opposite Queen Victoria's statue, to be met by the House Physician, who might take his hat and coat and deposit it in the cloakroom before accompanying him to the wards. The early Honoraries were distinguished by having huge reputations for clinical expertise and experience, and for taking meticulous care in the examination of patients. A high proportion were sons of professional families in the north east, educated locally and even qualifying in medicine in the Newcastle School. Some were national figures. Sir Thomas Oliver (Honorary from 1879 and Professor of Medicine from 1911 to 1927) made notable contributions to the understanding of industrially related disease. George Murray, who moved to Manchester in 1908, had launched modern endocrinology by demonstrating that myxoedema could be cured by treatment with thyroid extract. Sir David Drummond (Hon until 1912) was another outstanding teacher and clinician who, like many of the physicians, had a sound background of pathology. At this time, physicians conducted most of the post mortem examinations and many had served appointments as pathologists or lectured in pathology soon after qualification in medicine. Even domiciliary post mortem examinations were undertaken from time to time. Sir David's son, Horsley Drummond, was held in equal regard and broke new ground by being the first physician to make daily visits to patients under his care. Like many holding senior appointments at the time, neither of the Drummonds was a Fellow of the Royal College of Physicians. The obituaries of the physicians of the time, Beattie, Parkin, Hall and others, emphasise their clinical expertise and diligence at the bedside and in teaching.

Early specialisation

All physicians, apart from the Honorary Physician to the Skin Department, were general physicians, as is evident from the wide variety of diagnoses recorded in every ward. Common diseases then are rare today, for example: subacute bacterial endocarditis, meningitis, chorea, and the various and grave medical complications of syphilis and tuberculosis. However, even in 1906 the beginnings of specialisation were evident. Records of lectures and clinical demonstrations in the Newcastle Medical Journal and the University of Durham Medical College Gazette reflect the interest of the Drummonds and George Hall in neurological disease, of Beattie in chest disease, Hume in cardiovascular problems and Oliver and Parkin in industrial disease. Psychoneurotic or 'functional' disease held particular fascination for several physicians in the days before clear definitions in the field of psychiatric medicine. Sir William Hume was an early appointment to the new RVI, becoming a full Honorary in 1908 at the age of only 28. He was the son of George Haliburton Hume, a respected Honorary Surgeon of the old Infirmary and its chronicler,[II] and the father of Cardinal

---

II Hume GH. The History of the Newcastle Infirmary. Newcastle upon Tyne: Andrew Reid, 1906.

Fig 3.4: Professor Sir William Hume.

Basil Hume. He made notable contributions to the early clarification of cardiac dysrhythmias using adaptations of instruments which transmitted the pulsation of arteries and veins to a moving pen which created a tracing on a moving strip of paper. He made advances in the analysis of the earliest form of electrocardiograph which was housed in the basement where, many years later, the pharmacy was located. He even introduced a wire link to the wards above so that recordings could be made in the patients' beds. It is staggering that he combined these developments with duties as clinician and teacher - becoming an influential Professor of Medicine and an inspiration to a generation of young physicians - all entirely voluntarily whilst supporting himself and his family by private consultant practice. (*Fig 3.4*) It is perhaps his example that set the tone in Newcastle, which persists to this day, for the full and unstinting contribution to the work of the hospitals by those physicians who also conduct medical private practice outside. Like his father, he too produced a short history of the Infirmary. [III]

Other medical staff

Each Honorary Physician was paired with an Assistant Physician, who generally had clinical charge of about four male and two female patients, at the discretion of the 'Honorary', and whose main duties lay in the out-patient department. The extent of the assistance afforded by the Assistant Physician on the wards was usually minimal. An Assistant Physician would not, for example, expect to be called to see one of the Honorary's patients whose condition had worsened and, indeed, would not dare to attend to such a patient for fear of causing offence. The times that each visited the ward would generally be different. The Assistant Physician was in effect an Honorary in waiting. In the early years the medical cover for the six wards was completed by one Senior House Physician (salary £50 per six months in 1906) and three House Physicians. The responsibilities shouldered by these junior doctors were immense. They dealt with all of the requirements of the in-patients and the medical (as opposed to surgical) needs of many out-patients and Accident Room and casual attendees. A House Physician felt deterred from ever calling in a Registrar for help and would never dare contact an Honorary or Assistant Physician, most of whom rarely attended any patient outside the usual times of attendance. The medical residence was situated on the first floor above the main (Peacock Hall) entrance in rooms on either side of the Board Room. In 1931 the men's medical residence transferred to a new stone-faced block off the long north south corridor, roughly opposite the tower of the Armstrong Building of the University. Within a short time of the opening the Board of Governors had appointed two Medical Registrars *"whose duties we hope will include the instruction of clinical clerks in the art of history taking"*. Further appointments were made over the years and on the arrival of the NHS there were four medical registrars.

By 1912 a Resident Medical Officer had been appointed. This post was held by a junior grade physician for some years at a time and the duties were wide. The RMO had his own living quarters and sitting room and oversaw medical admissions and the care of casual attenders in the Accident and Emergency Department (always referred to as the "Accident Room") as well as the unheralded needs of in-patients or their junior physicians. Holders of the post rapidly acquired a huge experience of acute medical problems of every description. During and after the Second World War, Dr John Craig was a notable and long serving example of the RVI RMO.

The later Honorary Physicians

By the 1940s the Honorary Physicians were Professor F. J. Nattrass and Drs. Armstrong and Ogilvie. A vacancy had been created in 1939 by James Spence's taking over the care of all children in the hospital in Wards 8 and 16 and

[III] Hume W. E. The Infirmary, Newcastle upon Tyne: Newcastle upon Tyne, Andrew Reid, 1951.

Fig 3.5: Professor Frederick Nattrass.

releasing his post as general Honorary Physician - a development of great significance for the specialty of paediatrics. Up to this time all of the physicians cared for children with medical illnesses on Ward 16 just as all the surgeons did likewise on Ward 8. Frederick Nattrass (*Fig 3.5*) became the first full time professor of medicine in 1941 at considerable financial sacrifice as the University appointment involved giving up a large consulting practice. A wise, considerate and kindly man, he was a respected authority over a wide range of medicine. He developed his interests in neurological disorders, in particular myasthenia gravis and muscular dystrophy, and led the organisation of teaching until the mid-fifties.

Dr C. N. ("Nat") Armstrong developed clinical endocrinology and became renowned for his scholarship in the area of intersex. A quiet, methodical, unassuming man, he was extremely shrewd, had a twinkle in his eye and frequently surprised those unwise enough to underestimate him. He had become the first Clinical Sub-Dean in 1939 and later became the first Postgraduate Dean and oversaw great advances in facilities for training in the Region as a whole. [IV] He continued to attend endocrinological seminars and other RVI events until shortly before his death, aged over 100. Dr Armstrong also introduced the wearing of white coats by students in clinical areas and this was gradually taken up by almost all medical staff.

Dr A. G. Ogilvie. ("the Og") was an energetic, hardworking physician with expertise in respiratory disease. From an early stage he recognised the insights to be obtained from measurement of pulmonary function and assiduously made his own ventilatory measurements for years. He conducted with D. J. Newell a pioneering epidemiological study of chronic bronchitis in Tyneside. He was greatly loved by patients, staff and students not least for his unconscious mannerisms and forms of speech. To his own staff he spoke in a sort of abbreviated short-hand and interspersed conversation with booming imaginative asides. These were usually expressions of wonder or delight but they could be difficult for any newcomer to understand. His sayings and the quainter episodes were faithfully recorded by his team over many years in a book of "Ogisms" - the existence of which he affected ignorance but which was eventually presented to him on his retirement.

A fourth Honorary Physician, appointed towards the end of this period, was Charles Ungley who had a major interest in clinical haematology. He was credited with playing a leading role in the international effort to understand the cause of pernicious anaemia in the period leading up to the identification of vitamin B12, and afterwards in delineating its use in treatment. He represented the first of a new breed of clinical scientist and based his research in a tiny laboratory just off the medical corridor between Wards 12 and 13.

Out-patients

One of the many significant improvements provided in the new RVI was a purpose-built Out-patient Department which had its entrance just within the main gates. Great care went into the design of the department and the outcome was regarded from the outset as a great success in practice. It had a central waiting hall surrounded by doors leading to consulting rooms which had examination rooms attached to them. An interesting feature was a narrow corridor peripheral to the consultation rooms which allowed staff to arrive and leave and also to pass from room to room *"behind the scenes"*.

[IV] Armstrong C. N. My seventy years in medicine in Northumbria. Inaugural Presidential Address to Durham and Newcastle upon Tyne Medical Graduates Association, 19th November 1986.

Fig 3.6: The Main Outpatient Department in the 1980s.

Before 1948 most medical out-patients were seen by the Assistant Physicians who were in turn assisted in various degrees by junior doctors. Attendance was often large with long waiting periods until the introduction of an appointments system in 1948. Clerical staff were then housed in a partitioned "appointments bureau" created in the waiting hall. (*Fig 3.1*) In time some of the rooms became subdivided and other adaptations were made, but the overall Victorian character was little changed until 1979, when a major refurbishment was undertaken. (*Fig 3.6*) After this it once more performed remarkably successfully despite the increasing demands of modern medicine and teaching.

Private patients

In-patient facilities for private patients were created in the 1930s from the single storey pavilions of the Ministry of Pensions Hospital which had been constructed at the north of the site to receive casualties from the First World War. This was called the Leazes Hospital. From Pavilion 1 at the bottom of the sloping corridor to Pavilion 3 at the top there was a matching gradation of privacy and amenities which was also reflected in the fees. Pavilion 1 was open and generally received workmen at a charge of one guinea per week; Pavilion 2 had small wards of four to six beds each and charged five guineas; Pavilion 3 comprised single rooms at a cost to the occupants of seven guineas per week. In time, Pavilion 1 became a surgical ward, Pavilion 2 was devoted to Eye Surgery and Pavilion 3 remained a private ward until its demolition in 1979. House Physicians' duties generally included assistance in the care of the physicians' private patients. During the 1980s private patients were cared for as necessary on the ordinary wards, generally where their medical needs were as compelling as those of other patients, but the arrangement was an uneasy one - and in medicine private patients were a rarity. In the 1990s, after the move of medicine to the Leazes Wing, cubicled private patient accommodation was created within the former Ward 15 which then reverted to the name it bore in 1906: the Bishop Ward.

Fig 3.7: Professor Sir George Smart.

From 1948 to the 1970s

Increasing specialisation

With the coming of the NHS the former Honorary and Honorary Assistant Physicians dropped the 'Honorary' from their titles and now received salaried payment for their services which reflected their contractual time commitment to the hospital. In time they were all referred to as Consultant Physicians. The pace of specialisation became more striking. The former Honorary Assistant Physicians were more specialised than the older physicians. Thomas Boon developed expertise in management of clotting disorders and had been instrumental in establishing the Blood Transfusion Service for the north east. He combined this with an entrepreneurial approach to the investigation and treatment of gastrointestinal disease and performed rigid gastroscopy decades before the invention of fibreoptic scopes. Henry Miller returned from the war with expanded expertise in neurology and psychiatry and had in-patient facilities on Wards 13 and 10 shared with Dr Ogilvie. After dermatology and paediatrics, neurology became the third specialty to break its links with general medicine when a dedicated cubicled medical and surgical unit was created from Ward 6 on the lower surgical corridor (see chapter 4).   The third former Assistant Physician was Hewan Dewar who shared clinical facilities with Dr Armstrong on Wards 14 and 15. He was to take up the mantle of William Hume and drive cardiological practice in the RVI to the forefront of international standards (see chapter 4).

In 1956 Professor (later Sir) George Smart (*Fig* 3.7) took over the chair of medicine and clinical facilities on Wards 9 and 15.   He was an amiable, enthusiastic and inspiring organiser and had major interests in metabolic medicine and rheumatology. He attracted to his unit academic staff who developed and researched the fields of diabetes, renal and hepatic medicine and established the services in these specialties. A Wellcome-founded Department of Medicine was constructed immediately above the medical corridor - a proximity which brought daily benefits to research, clinical care and teaching. His other lasting contribution was to spearhead the complete overhaul of the undergraduate curriculum and its elevation to a matter of high importance to all clinicians. Variations on the pattern that emerged are in place throughout the medical schools of Britain. He also persuaded his physician colleagues to rearrange themselves to best advantage along the medical corridor. He became Dean of Medicine and later moved to London to direct the British Postgraduate Medical Federation.

By the end of the second phase Professor David Kerr had succeeded to the Chair of Medicine. Originally appointed on the strength of achievements in hepatic medicine, Kerr oversaw the recruitment of new colleagues and drove forward the development of both renal and hepatic medicine. The achievements in these fields were based not only in his thoughtful academic approach but on teamwork and detailed attention to the detail of round-the-clock clinical care to which he was a prodigious personal contributor. The development of renal medicine, gastroenterology and other medical specialties is continued in chapter 4.

Fig 3.8: View of a medical ward showing the clerical station shared by nursing and medical staff.

Other medical staff - the medical 'firm'
In this phase the number of House Physicians on the medical corridor had increased to eight (each six months) and each two-consultant unit had a Senior House Officer, a Senior Registrar and usually a Registrar. SHOs were in post for at least a year and Registrars and Senior Registrars for longer, and up to the mid 1960s there was little or no formal

rotation in any of the posts. The on-call cover was largely arranged within the medical unit so that patients were virtually continuously under the care of staff they knew. The 'firm' with the related nursing staff all knew each other well and enjoyed a family feeling in their ease of communication and sharing of responsibilities. The focal point of the firm's clinical activities was generally the Sister's Room. This had evolved from the Sister's private parlour of the early years, complete with blazing coal fire and personal trappings such as china and lace table cloths, to a more communal meeting place - a function, however, always understood to be at the Sister's discretion. Towards the end of this period desk space was created near the entrance to the ward to allow nurses and medical staff to deal with the increase in paperwork. (*Fig* 3.8) Working proximity made interchange of information between junior medical staff and nursing staff very easy and most of their patients were directly in their vision.

For most of this middle phase of the story house physicians and surgeons had their homes in the residence with a separate dining room at the north end of the site and their social life, as well as their working life, was firmly centred in the hospital or nearby. In the mid-1960s the medical residence was relocated to part of what had been the Nurses' Home accessed through the conservatory. The residence to the north was used as an ENT out-patient department and eventually demolished in 1975 to make way for the relocation of the Accident and Emergency Department.

Characteristics of Newcastle medicine

Several characteristics of Newcastle medicine at the time were particularly noted by those with experience elsewhere. These included a climate in which cross-consultation was freely sought and promptly given and a readiness to discuss problems openly with juniors, nurses and students alike, with subjugation of considerations of rank to the problem in hand. Consultants newly appointed from other medical centres consistently commented favourably on the friendly helpful atmosphere they encountered. Under the leadership of Professors Smart and Kerr, the University Senior Lectureship appointments enjoyed clinical facilities equal to those of the NHS consultants, and the NHS consultants were involved in research and teaching to a level which matched the commitments of academic staff. Most physicians came to have mixed NHS/University contracts. An important feature of medical life in the Infirmary at the time was lunch held in the old library which for many years was known as the Consultants' Dining Room. Here consultants of different disciplines met each other regularly and enjoyed a habitually high level of debate and conversation on all manner of subjects - medical and otherwise. Problem cases might be discussed and lead to a joint consultation at the bedside immediately afterwards. Each medical unit tended to develop an informal working relationship with a particular surgical firm. This was particularly striking in gastroenterology, hepatic medicine, renal medicine and endocrinology so that joint services emerged. In the case of cardiology, respiratory medicine and increasingly in neurology, these surgical links were with units in other hospitals. Junior staff rotations were eventually constructed jointly with Newcastle General Hospital, which did much to foster good working relationships and cooperation, for example in absorbing the pressure of acute admissions. Unusually cordial working relationships existed between physicians throughout the region as a direct result of the regular meetings of the Association of Physicians of Region No 1 (as it was then known) founded by Sir William Hume and sustained by Hewan Dewar. Despite being the largest region geographically, the physicians were all known to each other to a degree which was rare elsewhere and which happily persists to this day.

The use of space

Over this middle period of the story the pressure on medical beds continued to become increasingly intense and the length of hospital stay continued to shorten. The overloading on the female side was partly compensated for by even shorter inpatient stays, by the use of centre beds arranged head-to-tail down the centre of the ward and by periodic conversion of a male ward to female occupation. All of these had undesirable consequences. Despite there still being only two female wards to four male wards, the numbers of female patients admitted remained close to the male total. The degree of specialisation gathered further pace and was most evident in the out-patient load. The facilities remained largely unchanged so that in time several specialised regional services were being run from Victorian ward bases. Laboratories, secretaries, and space for special procedures or additional out-patient clinics were crammed into small rooms or housed in ingeniously constructed quarters on rooftops or into any available recess (see chapter 4: Gastroenterology). The original open design of 1906 came into its own but had its limits.

From the 1980s to 2006

The familiar themes of increased specialisation and increased pressure on the in-patient services continued. This period saw a significant increase in the number of consultants, many of whom drew out specialisation in new directions. The nature of general medicine took on a new shape in response to these and other changes within the RVI but the biggest influences were perhaps those arising outside.

Important new influences on RVI medicine

Major changes to affect RVI medicine in this third phase were:

1. The opening of Freeman Hospital.
2. The union of the clinical and administrative services with those of Newcastle General Hospital and later Freeman Hospital.
3. The transfer of the medical wards to new accommodation in the Leazes and Claremont Wings.
4. Changes in the contracts of Junior Doctors with the advent of 'Junior Doctors Hours'.
5. The evolution of geriatric medicine and other specialties.
6. Changes in medical care in the community.

When the RVI opened in 1906 it already effectively shared the hospital provision in Newcastle with 'the Wingrove Hospital', as it was sometimes known, which had grown from an attachment to the Workhouse on Westgate Hill (opened 1870) into an expanding hospital of roughly equal size. Links between the two institutions were reinforced by a strong tendency for Honorary Physicians and Surgeons at the RVI to transfer to what was now Newcastle General Hospital (NGH) on reaching the obligatory resignation age of 60 and to continue to work as Consulting Physicians or Surgeons for up to another 10 years. From Sir William Hume onwards, RVI figures contributed to the development of an increasing array of specialist services at the NGH which increased the interdependence of the institutions. The History of Newcastle General Hospital, published in 1966[v], details its parallel development. Joint appointments, shared responsibilities for teaching and shared training programmes for junior doctors further strengthened the clinical and personal links, as did shared budgets when the management of the two hospitals - and later, in 1998, all three hospitals - came under the same authority. The opening of Freeman Hospital in 1977 saw the beginning of the transfer of some medical services from NGH to the other two sites and from the RVI to Freeman Hospital, a process of gradual rationalisation to two sites which continues today. The history of medicine in the RVI becomes that of medicine in Newcastle.

By far the biggest development of the century on the RVI site was the building of the Leazes Wing into the third floor of which all but one of the medical units transferred in 1992. (Fig 3.9 & 3.10) The move took place over the course of a single day during which the normal care of patients, including the admission of emergencies, continued without interruption despite the fact that, at the same time, the nursing teams and junior medical teams from four wards divided and re-formed in new combinations in three mixed-sex wards. New challenges were encountered, firstly in managing a pool of medical beds separated by a quarter of a mile of corridor and secondly in providing bedside care to patients who were now in L-shaped wards with a combination of six-bedded bays and single rooms rather than Nightingale wards. The significant benefits of improved equipment and fittings, additional lavatory, shower and bath facilities, and a greater degree of flexibility were traded off against paradoxically reduced patient privacy in the smaller spaces and difficult visibility of patients by staff and vice versa (Fig 3.11). In 1996 the remaining medical unit moved from the old wards to a floor of the newly opened Claremont Wing (built primarily to accommodate Opthalmology). The medical service was now all housed in modern accommodation but still split geographically.

---

v Hurrell G. The History of Newcastle General Hospital. Newcastle upon Tyne: Hindson and Andrew Reid, 1966.

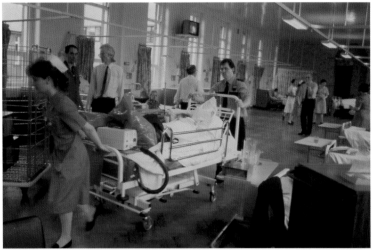

Distribution of acute emergencies to the split medical bed complement was eased by the introduction of an Acute Admissions Ward on the first floor of the Leazes Wing. Here rapid initial assessment and treatment could be concentrated more easily in the first 24 hours and patients could be more effectively distributed to units specialising in their particular disorders. The two-stage admission, however, inevitably involved interruption of the continuity of nursing and medical care and of communication with patients and relatives.

Fig 3.9: Transfer of patients from a medical ward to the Leazes Wing in 1992.

Fig 3.10: Move to the Leazes Wing: A vacated medical ward.

During the later part of this third phase of the history, the concept of the medical firm underwent marked change. This was largely a consequence of changes to the contract of all junior doctors which radically reduced the number of hours per week that a doctor was permitted to be on duty and which designated a significant proportion of 'protected' time which must be dedicated to education. The benefits of avoiding overwork and tiredness and supporting training were, however, balanced by a reduction in the experience gained and in the continuity of care. When doctors were on call they were necessarily covering the work of a large number of off duty doctors so that the patients they were called upon to attend - and the related senior staff - were likely to be unknown to them and vice versa. A night on emergency duty would be followed by an obligatory day off, effectively preventing any continuity of care or educational follow-up. Revised training programmes involved useful exposure to a larger range of specialties but, as this involved a shorter time in each post, seniors, juniors and nursing staff had less time to get to know each other. House Physicians became attached to wards rather than to consultant teams. Much more of the hands-on care and most of the continuity was now provided by consultants and by nurses whose role involved progressively more responsibility and specialisation.

In the same way that new treatments bring in their wake unexpected side-effects, new methods of organising medical care and training may be attended by unwanted snags. Part of the art of the Physician has always been to identify and minimise 'his' own adverse effects on patients and this seems an even wider challenge today.

By the 1980s few doctors now had their homes in the residence and increasingly they only stayed in the hospital overnight when immediately on call. Separate dining facilities had lapsed and off-duty social activities were firmly located outside the hospital. In the 1990s the residential facilities moved once again - to the Western Extension of the earlier Nurses' Home. In recent years residential quarters for House Officers have all been provided at Freeman Hospital.

In this phase the consultant dining room also ceased to exist and increasingly consultants took a working sandwich lunch in their offices or during meetings or seminars. The wearing of white coats by medical staff declined sharply during the 1990s and informal clothing became the norm. Doctors became distinguishable from other non-uniformed individuals only by their name badges and the wearing of a stethoscope, generally around the back of the neck. More of specialised medicine came to be centred on out-patient services. Most medical services were provided within a new out-patient clinic included in the Leazes Wing development. The old Main Out-patients continued to be used by some specialties and, in addition, specialised clinics and out-patient procedures were carried out in other areas of the hospital.

Welcome changes to the character of RVI medicine which have gathered pace over this third phase, have resulted from the increasing capacity of General Practice to deal with ever more complex forms of patient management and from much improved communication between general practice and hospital. The same period has seen a hugely expanded ability of nurses in the community to take on the care of patients who would formerly have required in-patient care. Increasingly extensive social support for the frail and incapacitated has also influenced the character of patients admitted and speeded up discharge to their own homes. A prominent theme throughout the century has been the gathering pace of specialisation, and this is reviewed in the next chapter.

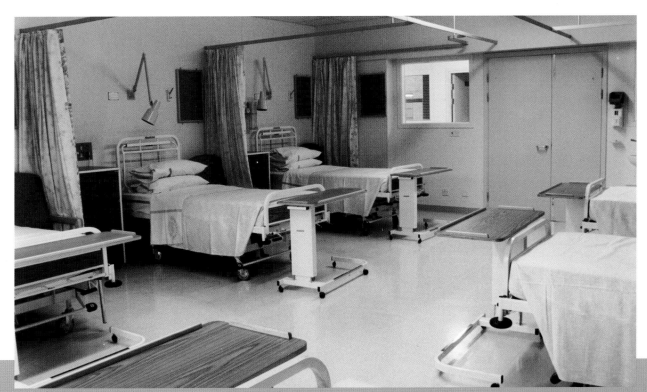

Fig 3.11: *View within a six-bedded bay in Leazes Wing looking towards the ward corridor which lies beyond the door. Opposite beds are much closer, visibility from the ward corridor is limited.*

Chapter 4: *The Medical Specialties*

Alistair Brewis, William Ross

At the time of the opening of the new Royal Victoria Infirmary the honorary and assistant physicians all took charge of the care of patients with almost any form of medical illness. Yet, even then, each exhibited special interest and expertise in a particular field of medicine and sometimes the zone of interest extended to several different fields. The early development of some specialties is reviewed in chapter 3. The period under review was notable for the steady march of this specialisation so that by the end of the century the special interest was the main, or even exclusive, focus of the physician's activities and the term 'general medicine' had become largely applicable to the period of preliminary assessment of unsorted emergency patients and the management of individuals with multiple diagnoses as encountered in geriatric medicine.

The separated specialties

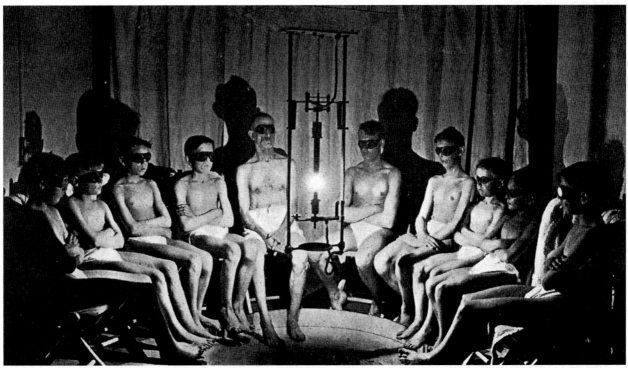

Fig 4.2: An 'Artificial Sunlight' treatment session in progress in the Skin Department in the first decade of the 20th Century.

Dermatology

The first specialty to be clearly defined by having single-specialty physicians and separate accommodation was dermatology. James Limont (who is notable as the first holder of the solitary House Physician post in the Infirmary in 1883) had created a department of dermatology in the old Infirmary to deal with high demand and the ward component of this was transferred to the twin Ward 11 (later gynaecology) at the west end of the corridor. The Skin Out-patient Department was on the lower ground floor in what later became Ward 21. He was soon succeeded as 'Honorary Physician to the Skin Department' by Sir Robert Bolam who directed dermatology for the next 30 years, attracted a staff of medical officers and made an impact as an administrator locally and nationally. Some idea of the scale of activity in the Skin Department emerges from pharmacy figures reported in 1910 which record that nearly two and a half tons of ointment were manufactured and supplied! At the time three quarters of all prescriptions were for out-patients and of these over half were repeat prescriptions. For many years there was enthusiasm for Grentz ray treatment for eczema and a number of other disorders and vast doses of ultraviolet light were administered in the 'Light Department' particularly to treat lupus vulgaris - tuberculosis of the skin. (*Fig 4.2*) A Department of Venereology was created in 1920 with a separate medical staff but also headed by Robert Bolam.

Sir Robert Bolam was followed by Dr Sydney Thompson and then Dr Mason Bolam, a highly regarded and kindly dermatologist who led the service with a small staff in the face of an ever-increasing out-patient load. The appointment

---

Left: Fig 4.1: Preparing for renal dialysis in 1959. Dr Walter Elliott is lowering the drum of an Alwall dialyser wound with a tubular membrane (which will be perfused with blood) into the dialysate chamber.

Fig 4.3: Professor John Ingram.

in 1959 of John Ingram, (*Fig 4.3*) already a prominent figure in the field, as the first Professor of Dermatology, gave an emphatic boost to the department which came to be regarded as the best in the country. In his time new ward accommodation replaced the out-patient department and a new purpose-built Dermatological Out-patient Department was constructed in one of the spaces between the wards with access along a narrow sloping corridor. Ingram was a master clinician and teacher and, although he conducted no significant research himself, he attracted to his team some of the best of the emerging dermatologists with a scientific leaning. This set the tone for the subsequent elevation of the laboratory and clinical scientific standing of dermatology, under professor Sam Shuster, to a level matching its clinical renown. In recent years dermatological beds were provided at Walkergate Hospital and then at Freeman Hospital but they are now all again concentrated on the RVI site in 'old Ward 1', formerly the male professorial surgical ward, and exactly above their earlier home in Ward 21 one floor below. This area in the basement now provides specialised out-patient treatments - for example PUVA, a form of ultraviolet treatment for severe psoriasis - activities echoing those being undertaken in the same place a hundred years earlier. There are now 12 dermatologists contributing to the service, two of whom hold University chairs.

Industrial Medicine

The threats to life and well-being posed by the shipbuilding, engineering, chemical and mining industries surrounding Newcastle attracted the attention of physicians from Sir Thomas Oliver onwards. This was to become the second specialty separate from medicine with physicians practising exclusively in the field. By 1948 R.C. Browne had been appointed as "Honorary Physician in charge of Industrial Medicine" and headed the University Department in this subject. Most of the clinical work of the department related to out-patients. A specialised pulmonary function laboratory was developed primarily for the investigation of occupational lung diseases and for many years provided a general service to the rest of the hospital from a laboratory on the medical corridor near Ward 13. The character of occupational lung disease changed over the years but it remains one of the areas of special local expertise and one of the services provided within the current department of Respiratory Medicine.

Fig 4.4: Professor Henry Miller.

Neurology

The earlier interest of physicians in the prevalent, disabling and clinically taxing neurological diseases and the development of neurosurgery and newer diagnostic tools prepared the ground for the separation of neurology from the rest of general medicine. Henry Miller, Newcastle's first exclusive neurologist, was an exciting character, an inspired clinician, a brilliant writer and speaker, a hilarious wit and a challenging tester of ideas. (*Fig 4.4*) He took risks which usually paid off but he was occasionally wrong - when he would generally be the first to recognise an error and was invariably contrite. He became successively Clinical Sub-Dean, Dean of Medicine and Vice-Chancellor of the University of Newcastle upon Tyne. His character and achievements are difficult to summarize but a short book published soon after his death[1] does some justice to this local medical legend. Henry Miller rapidly attracted a team of clinicians and scientists, such as E. J. Field, and research ranging from basic mechanisms to clinical and epidemiological studies resulted. John (later Lord) Walton shared the clinical facilities for some years although his principal commitment was to the Regional Centre at NGH. The two neurological units developed a friendly rivalry which both cherished for its stimulation of high standards - epitomised in weekly shared clinical conferences which have continued without a break to the present. David Shaw, appointed to the unit in 1964 with a special interest in cerebrovascular disease, led it forward when Professor Miller took on increasing university commitments before, some years later, himself becoming the third of a string of neurological Deans: Miller, Walton and Shaw. A characteristic of RVI neurology throughout has been its close ties with general medicine.

The unit on 'Ward 6' was for more than a decade after its opening a combined medical and surgical neurological one. George Rowbotham, a neurosurgical pioneer and founder of the Regional unit at NGH, operated weekly in the adjacent Theatre Main and was followed in this role in 1962 by Professor John Hankinson. In the later 1960s, however, it was found more efficient to focus neurosurgery on the NGH site. Within the next few years neurosurgery will return to the RVI when all of Newcastle's neurological and neurosurgical services finally combine in newly built accommodation.

Rheumatology

Up to the early 1960s patients with rheumatoid arthritis and related disorders were cared for within general medicine and predominantly by the Professorial unit. This changed with the arrival of Dr Malcolm Thompson who practised only rheumatology. He quickly developed a large out-patient following but, despite his determined promotion of the specialty, he was unable to secure more than two of the heavily overloaded medical beds. He broadened the concept of rheumatology to embrace Physical Medicine and took a prominent hand in the management and development of the physiotherapy services to the infirmary as a whole. With the help of a

[1] Lock S, Windle V, Eds. Remembering Henry. London: British Medical Association, 1977.

medical assistant and then a part-time consultant colleague he expanded the out-patient service and was assiduous in the conduct of clinical trials of new and revised treatments. In time he was joined by new consultants and after he retired there were three in post including a Reader in Rheumatology. After 1977 in-patient facilities were provided at Freeman Hospital and out-patient clinics were run on both sites until 1995 when rheumatology combined with orthopaedic surgery to form a comprehensive Musculoskeletal Service at Freeman Hospital.

Clinical Haematology

This latest specialty to emerge from general medicine was founded on the work of Ungley and Boon (see chapter 3). It was then nurtured within general medicine by Ronald ("RB") Thompson, an enormously learned author and editor of haematological works, and Alan Horler who, as well as pursuing specific haematological interests enjoyed the highest reputation of any general physician of his day. Towards the end of the 1980s accelerating advances in the treatment of leukaemias and lymphomas culminating in bone marrow transplantation greatly increased the complexity of the clinical and nursing load inherent in the management of vulnerable patients receiving potentially dangerous treatment. This demanded separate specialist teamwork, its own accommodation and protection from the unpredictable distractions of general medicine. Clinical Haematology finally broke loose. Achieving this, together with cooperative working by a network of Haematologists in the Region, has led to survival figures in previously lethal disorders which are unsurpassed anywhere. When most of medicine moved to the Leazes Wing, Clinical Haematology remained in 'old Ward 13' (which was re-named the John Hall Ward - which was its original name in 1906 commemorating one of the two most generous founding benefactors). Clinical haematology has always had one foot in the laboratories - research and service - and this stance remains evident today. The laboratory part of the story appears in chapter 11.

Geriatric Medicine

A welcome addition to medicine in the third phase was the development of geriatric services. The in-patient facilities were created in the vacated wards of the Victoria Building and from the outset close working links were established with the consultant geriatricians joining the acute medical teams with mutual benefit. The emergence of the specialty of geriatric medicine has partially compensated for the increasing specialisation elsewhere, although sub-specialisation within geriatrics is already emerging.

Although it remains very closely allied to acute medicine, the march of specialisation and its wide remit have led to its becoming, in effect, another of the separated medical specialties.

Specialties within general medicine

Cardiology

The story of cardiology in the RVI revolves round the enormous contribution of Dr Hewan Dewar throughout the middle phase of our story. Soon after appointment at the inception of the NHS he performed the first cardiac catheterisation in the North of England and later introduced angiocardiography with radiological colleagues. He continued to do both at the RVI for over 20 years. He introduced a pacemaker service, and set up a Coronary Care Unit in extended cubicle accommodation on Ward 14 at the RVI. He focussed his attention on coronary artery disease and was responsible for a prodigious output of highly regarded research which would have done great credit to a large specialist department, let alone a single-handed cardiologist who also carried a full load of general medicine, teaching and administrative work. Dewar's work on fibrinolysis applied to coronary artery disease was years ahead of the field

---

" Dewar H. The story of cardiology in Newcastle. Durham: Durham Academic Press. 1998.

at a time when little attention was paid to what was to form the most important treatment in acute myocardial infarction. He and two colleagues conducted a pioneering exploration, around 1978, of the effects of direct infusion of streptokinase into the coronary arteries in the early phase after acute myocardial function. Hewan Dewar has written an absorbing account of the story of cardiology in Newcastle which covers the parallel development at Newcastle General Hospital and later at Freeman Hospital.[11] His successors at the RVI have continued to bring the latest cardiological techniques and treatments to bear, particularly in refining management of coronary artery disease. There are close links with the Regional Cardiothoracic Centre at Freeman Hospital where catheterisation and angiographic facilities are concentrated. There are now five consultant cardiologists at work in the RVI.

Fig 4.5: A view of the staircase up to the medical corridor near the crossing showing the original tiling. The space was later filled when an endoscopy unit was built.

Endocrinology

The first treatment of myxoedema in the RVI by George Murray, which is generally regarded as the defining event which marked the birth of the specialty, and the contribution of Dr C. N. Armstrong have already been referred to in the previous chapter. Others in George Smart's Professorial Team added scientific strength to local clinical prowess and from this milieu emerged Reg Hall who went on to make an international name through research which effectively defined autoimmune thyroiditis and was one of two or three key figures to lead British endocrinology during the 1960s and 1970s. He developed a team which ran a specialist service covering the Region for some disorders. The general medical firm was based on Wards 10 and 12 adjacent to which a Programmed Investigation Unit (PIU) was developed where complicated tests could be coordinated so as to use the available resources to best advantage and avoid occupation of acute medical beds. Reg Hall was a much loved local product with a compelling enthusiasm for medical science but he had great personal warmth and never lost sight of the implications for patients. He was a rapid clear thinker able to focus completely on the matter under discussion, beguilingly unconscious of his own eminence in the field or of any gulf there might be between his own speed of thought and that of those around him. He left Newcastle in 1979 to take up the Chair of Medicine in the University of Wales, Cardiff. Endocrinology continued to be a local strength under those that followed him and continued the established pattern of close teamwork with surgeons with expertise in the field. The PIU was re-created on the medical floor of the Leazes Wing and in 1996 the endocrine/general medicine team moved to the Claremont Wing.

The need to foster expertise in the management of diabetes had been recognised by Professor Nattrass, who included it amongst his interests and later started the service at NGH after reaching the resigning age at the RVI. Clinicians in the professorial team continued to lead the development of a diabetic out-patient service, with innovations such as evening clinics, and introduced clinical guidance which was increasingly followed by other units in the RVI generally. Collaboration was particularly relevant and close in the management of patients undergoing surgery and childbirth. With the establishment of an endocrinological unit consultants with a major commitment to diabetes such as John Anderson and those who followed became part of that team. The withdrawal of general medicine from NGH further enlarged the diabetic service which became research focus of the Department of Medicine under George (later Sir George) Alberti who succeeded David Kerr as Professor of Medicine and was subsequently Dean and President of the Royal College of Physicians of London.

Gastroenterology

Even during the time of T. H. Boon much of gastroenterological medicine was undertaken by generalists. The development of new treatments, new investigative tools such as liver biopsy and especially the advent of fibreoptic endoscopic procedures gradually revolutionised the specialty. An endoscopy unit was ingeniously inserted into a space over the staircase to the medical floor at the crossing of the corridors in the centre of the Victoria Building. *(Fig 4.5)* Later a purpose-built suite was included in the ground floor of the new Leazes Wing as part of the Day Care Unit. For years gastroenterology (which included hepatology) was another of the specialties served by a single consultant but in the 1990s two more were appointed. Links with surgery were of course necessarily close, as were links with the service at Freeman Hospital, particularly after the establishment of liver transplantation.

Renal Medicine

Renal medicine grew into a specialty within the Department of Medicine with the advent of renal biopsy and renal dialysis in the late 1950s guided by Professor David Kerr (see chapter 3) and others, notably Dr Robert Uldall. Renal dialysis started in Newcastle in 1959 using the cumbersome Alwall dialyser which was situated in the basement in a small room near the entrance to what was later the Pharmacy. *(Fig 4.1)* A total of 36 attempts were made before a first successful dialysis was achieved - the dialysis itself took 36 hours. Technical improvements in dialysis saw its application to long term maintenance treatment based in the RVI and expanded to a dedicated unit in Rye Hill Hospital and also established in patients homes. Many developments in technique and in overcoming serious side effects emerged from the Newcastle unit. Close cooperation between medical and surgical teams was crucial to the success of the dialysis program as it was later to the introduction and development of renal transplantation and the achievement of outstanding results.

The early development of renal medicine has already been referred to in the previous chapter. With the opening of Freeman Hospital renal medicine became split with a single consultant providing most of the service at the RVI where renal transplantation was centred. Cross-cover arrangements and interchange of patients between the hospitals ensured close cooperation and maintenance of clinical and training standards. In recent years renal medicine has been re-combined, together with renal transplantation, at Freeman Hospital with outreach services to the RVI and NGH where necessary for the management of critically ill patients.

Respiratory Medicine

After Dr Ogilvie the RVI was served by further single-handed respiratory specialists who were general physicians with a prominent commitment to the management of respiratory disease. (The author of this chapter was one such physician-Ed) Cross consultation with other medical and surgical units formed a significant part of the responsibilities. In the 1990s when respiratory physicians from NGH transferred to the RVI a Department of Respiratory Medicine was created from the old Attic Laboratory above 'old Ward 16' and a specialised Respiratory Outpatient Department with an integrated pulmonary function laboratory was created from the former Ophthalmological Outpatient Department on the ground floor. There are now five consultants contributing to the specialty within the RVI and, as in cardiology, there are close links with the Cardiothoracic Centre at Freeman Hospital.

Radiotherapy and Oncology
W. M. Ross

In about 1930 a Department of Radiotherapy was established in the RVI as an 'adjunct' to the Department of Radiotherapy and was located at the end of the Radiology corridor. (*Fig 4.6*) It was headed by a lady doctor (Dr Bramhall), but Dr Donald Ramage, a radiologist, also practiced radiotherapy for a time. In 1934 Mr C. J. (John) Thurgar became Head of the Department, an appointment which he held until his retirement in 1973. He was joined by Dr M. M. Morrison, in 1948 by Dr L. M. Shorvon, in 1950 by Dr S. B. Wigoder by W. M. Ross in 1953 and in 1961 by Mr P. J. Van Miert. In 1945 Dr F. T. Farmer (subsequently an Honorary Professor) was appointed as Physicist to the Department and later headed an independent Medical Physics Department in which he was joined in 1947 by Dr M. J. Day.

Geographically, the department remained in diagnostic radiology until 1947, when it moved into part of the then Dental Hospital, a building on the RVI site where some offices and out-patient clinics remain.

In 1941-1942, the many air raid warnings over Newcastle necessitated the interruption of treatment involving the use of radium within body cavities (usually the uterus). The radium source had to be removed from the patient and placed in a borehole (situated between the diagnostic radiology department and Queen Victoria Road), and re-inserted into the patient after the all-clear signal had sounded. This proved unacceptably disturbing to patients and seriously affected the efficiency of the treatment. It was therefore decided that appropriate patients and their treatment should be transferred to Shotley Bridge Hospital, to which at the same time some of the deep X-ray therapeutic apparatus was also removed. The unit at Shotley Bridge, initially of 60, and eventually of 90, beds, continued as part of the RVI Radiotherapy Department until 1964.

In 1938, a small therapy department was opened at the Newcastle General Hospital, adjacent to the Diagnostic Department and also as an offshoot of the RVI department.

A major feature of the Radiotherapy Department at the RVI, in addition to providing deep x-ray therapy to in-patients and out-patients, was that regular out-patients clinics were held within the department, and many joint clinics with consultants in other specialties, as often patients required more that one form of treatment.

Closely associated with the department in such clinics were Mr Stanley Way (Gynaecological surgery) and Mr J.D.T. Jones

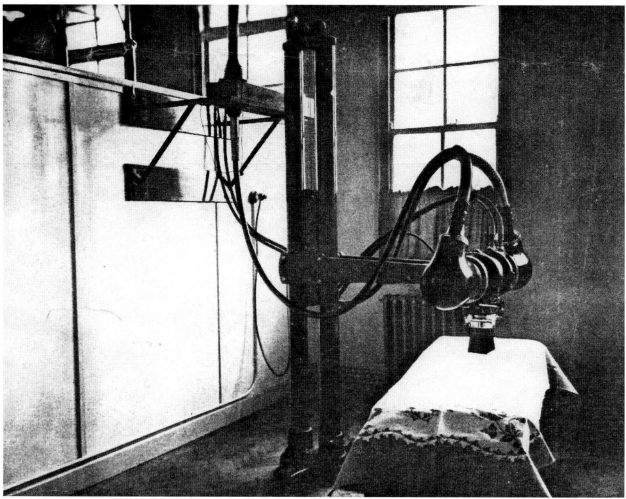

Fig 4.6: An early radiotherapy machine.

(General Surgery), while other joint clinics were held at different times with Mr J. I. M. Black (Otorhinolarygology), Professor F. H. Bentley, Professor I. D. A. Johnston and Professor D. N. Walder (all General Surgery), as well as with Mr Fenton Braithwaite and Mr J. R. G. Edwards (Plastic Surgery) and Professor Reginald Hall (Endocrinology).

Certainly, from 1945 (and possibly earlier), a weekly clinic was held at Cumberland Infirmary in Carlisle, the forerunner of a pattern of such clinics which eventually were established in every major hospital in the Northern region.

In 1948, the then Ministry of Health recognised that the Linear Accelerator was likely to be the external X-ray apparatus of the future and agreed to purchase five to be allotted to major centres, of which Newcastle was one, which were able to provide the necessary support, and in particular the appropriate buildings.

In Newcastle, Mr Thurgar and Dr Farmer received support from the North of England Cancer Research Campaign to fund the buildings. Initially, provision was made for superficial and deep x-ray therapy for out-patients, together with space for medical physics and clinical support staff. Eventually, the linear accelerator building was completed and the apparatus arrived late in 1953. Following acceptance testing, the accelerator was taken into clinical use in January 1954. (Strictly speaking, the first patient to be treated was a senior clinician treated in December 1953.) The accelerator eventually treated more than 250,000 patients over a period of 25 years (whereas today many machines are replaced after 10 years).

In 1950 Mr Way moved his work from Shotley Bridge Hospital to the Queen Elizabeth Hospital, although he retained his association with the RVI clinic. In 1964, the Regional Radiotherapy Centre at the Newcastle General Hospital (NGH) was opened with 90 in-patient beds, out-patients clinics and offices for all staff of the Radiotherapy Department and the Medical Physics Department, and so the RVI ceased to be the major centre, although deep X-ray therapy and out-patient clinic facilities continued.

Other specialties

Space does not permit an account of all of the medical specialties represented by the physicians working in the RVI or available to patients of the RVI from within the pool of multi-disciplinary expertise in Newcastle. Examples are Palliative Care, Clinical Genetics and Clinical Pharmacology.

The story of RVI medicine in the latest phase has increasingly been indistinguishable from the story of Newcastle medicine. The unification of the management and the clinical organisation of the Newcastle Hospitals and the gradual rationalisation of services to two sites takes the process further. Any future history will necessarily be a history of all of Newcastle's medical facilities. There will, however, still be benefit to be drawn from the pride that staff feel in working in a particular hospital and the from the inspiration that they, and indeed patients, can derive from reflection on a long history of achievement and ceaseless striving for improvement.

Chapter 5: *Surgery and the Surgical Specialties* George Proud

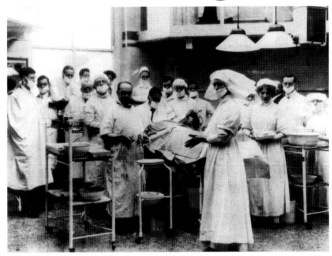

When the new Infirmary opened in 1906 a substantial part of the accommodation was designated for surgical service. Those entering by the main door and passing through what we now call Peacock Hall would have been on the level accommodating surgical cases. This entire level was given over to surgery. Turning left at the "cross-roads" - a T-junction then, for the corridor did not extend forwards - brought one to a single ward for male patients and four female wards, whereas a turn to the right led to three male surgical wards: at the end of the corridor there were two surgical wards for children. This level contained three operating theatres, one of which contained a main theatre plus a small theatre.

Fig 5.2: Professor Page and team. The theatre is what became Theatre Main. The viewing gallery is identified by the feet of spectators! The remnants of this were present until relatively recently.

During the 1914-1918 war additional surgical accommodation was provided by two temporary wards and towards the end of that war the Ministry of Pensions Hospital was built with three pavilion-style wards. These wards were incorporated eventually into the RVI and were upgraded to make them suitable for paying patients at the time the Pensions hospital transferred to Gateshead. This "Leazes Wing" of the hospital, complete with an operating theatre, remained until it was eventually demolished to make way for access to the New Medical School in 1994.

In 1933 a 48-bedded orthopaedic wing, complete with its own operating theatre, was opened and this remained until the latter part of the 20th Century. Changing orthopaedic surgical practice, with the extensive use of surgical implants, meant that the facility was below standard and elective orthopaedic surgery moved to new accommodation at Freeman Hospital and trauma orthopaedics moved to the General Hospital pending the re-provision of state-of-the-art facilities for orthopaedic trauma on the RVI site. It was no longer good enough to have an operating theatre which required the nurses or surgical registrars to clear the snow before the list began!

At the western end of the hospital two further surgical wards were provided as a second floor extension in 1933 - complete with their own operating theatre. By the middle of the century there were no fewer than fifteen surgical wards in the hospital plus, of course, facilities for gynaecology.

In addition, to ease the pressures on the surgical wards, convalescent homes at Ryton and Wylam became available before the Second World War. Despite this massive surgical facility there was constant pressure on the surgical beds. However, the convalescent homes were generally regarded as being the major reason why the average length of stay of 19 days in 1907 had been reduced to just over 11 days by 1947.

When the Leazes Wing of the RVI was completed around 1990, surgery transferred from the accommodation it had occupied since the RVI was opened into new state-of-the-art facilities. The surgical units lost their own individual operating theatres and all surgeons now had access to the operating theatres of the new operating theatre suite. In many ways this allowed for a greater efficiency. What was lost in the transfer to the new facility was the closely knit team approach which the previous structure allowed. Whilst an attempt was made to keep theatre nurse expertise in a specialised way, there was much more cross-over by the nursing staff. Instead of the surgeon always working with the same team, an element of surprise was now added to the working day: the composition of the team would be very variable. This was not liked by some, but gradually the new working arrangements settled down.

In 1906 the bulk of all surgery was carried out by general surgeons. George Haliburton Hume and Frederick Page laid the foundations for surgery at the RVI and Rutherford Morison took these forward on the RVI site. (*Fig 5.2*) He was appointed to the Infirmary in 1888 and retired from the RVI in 1913. His was an era when antisepsis had been introduced and anaesthesia was becoming safer - although that is only a relative term. Antibiotics were not available,

Fig 5.3: George Grey Turner.

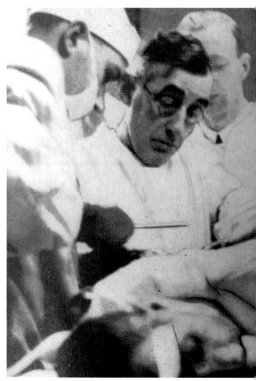
Fig 5.4: Grey Turner operating.

techniques of laboratory investigation were rudimentary to say the least, and many internal operations were conducted first to establish the diagnosis and then to treat. Many operations were bold - and so often were the surgeons. Rutherford Morison (*Fig 5.5*) was famous in his day and his surgery embraced many aspects (*Fig 5.12*). He remains famous today - his name was given to the pouch lying between the right kidney and the liver where abscesses might develop as a complication of, for example, acute appendicitis.

Grey Turner was another surgeon of this first part of the 20th century (*Fig 5.3*). Ultimately becoming Professor of Surgery at the Royal Postgraduate Medical Hospital in London, he described the skin discolouration which might occur in the loins as a consequence of acute pancreatitis. It was also Grey Turner who said that surgical training was incomplete if the surgeon was unable to remove the appendix of a Northumbrian miner in an operation conducted on the miner's kitchen table (*Figs 5.1 & 5.4*).

Very few names are included in this chapter. Editorial constraints prevent the naming of all of those who deserve to be here. However, one name above all needs to be included and that is F. C. Pybus. He graduated with a First Class honours degree in the same year that the RVI opened. Pybus traversed the era from appendicectomy at home to the outset of the antibiotic age. He was house surgeon to Rutherford Morison and registrar to Grey Turner. Pybus had a lifelong interest in cancer and the effects of atmospheric pollution. He was also a man who disliked unnecessary bureaucracy - he would have been a constant thorn in the side of the modern hospital manager (*Fig 5.6*).

My only contact with Pybus came shortly before he died. We were discussing antibiotics, each bemoaning their over-use, and the following day a book appeared which he had illustrated for Grey Turner in 1920. It was a surgical book and in there was a reproduction of a temperature chart of a patient undergoing an uncomplicated convalescence from surgery. A temperature rise on the second post-operative day was shown. *"That always happens"*, said Pybus, *"it is a normal response to trauma. It does not need antibiotic treatment!"* Today the patient will probably be given them. How true that statement of Pybus has been. During the Pybus era, specialisation began. Gynaecology was the first sub-specialty under Ranken Lyle at the time the RVI opened.

Fig 5.5: Rutherford Morison.

Orthopaedics

In 1933 a new block to the north of the main corridor, comprising two wards, an operating theatre, facilities for out-patients and a fracture clinic was erected for orthopaedic surgery. Incorporated into the building were facilities and accommodation for the department of physiotherapy. Immediately before and after the Second World

Fig 5.6: Frederick C. Pybus.

War the prominent orthopaedic surgeons were Mr C. Gordon Irwin and Mr J. K. Stanger. Gordon Irwin, in a lecture to clinical students in 1942, said, *"for the moment all you need to know about orthopaedic surgery is that I am Mr Gordon Irwin. The other great orthopaedic surgeon in the north of England is Stanger; I taught Stanger"*. Irwin and Stanger were assisted by Mr J. V. Todd who was Durham County Golf Champion before the 1939-45 war and subsequently OC of No1(N) General Hospital (TA) in the 1950s.

Both Irwin and Stanger were skilled operators but had little if any interest in research. Some time later the University established a full time Chair in Orthopaedic Surgery, the first holder of which was Professor Jack Stevens, Professor of Orthopaedic Surgery in Chicago, USA. Eventually, with further development of the RVI, the orthopaedic block was demolished to make way for new facilities, and elective orthopaedic surgery moved to the Freeman Hospital. ENT., plastic and ophthalmic surgery, as well as paediatric surgery, all developed on the RVI site. Other specialties were accommodated in other hospitals nearby - neurosurgery, thoracic surgery and some plastic surgery, for example.

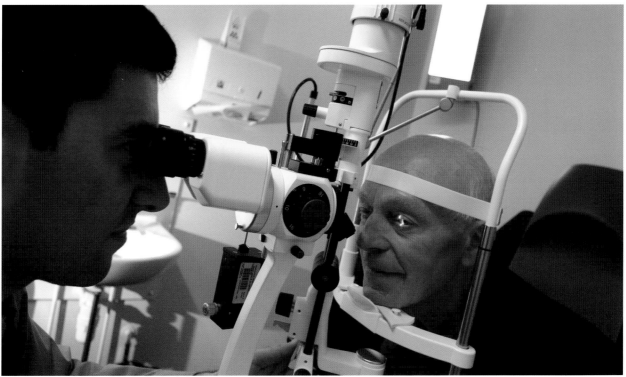

Fig 5.7: Modern ophthalmic diagnosis by the slit lamp.

Ophthalmology

Eye services in Newcastle date back to 1822 when the Newcastle upon Tyne Eye Hospital was founded. It proved so popular that two years later it moved to new premises in Prudhoe Street. In 1885, it moved again to St Mary's Place. By 1891 it was annually treating 7500 out-patients, and 382 in-patients in 12 beds. A description of the early development of these services in Newcastle has recently been published by Hart and McGhee[1] in an account of the life and times of a New Zealand born surgeon, Arthur Thomas Peterson, who devoted most of his professional life to the building of the reputation and prosperity of the Newcastle Eye Hospital. After his early surgical training he was appointed assistant surgeon to the Eye Hospital in 1924, and a full honorary surgeon in 1927. He achieved considerable fame and was elected president of the prestigious North of England Ophthalmological Society (a society still active today in its 93rd year). He died in 1947 at the age of 92. His name is perpetuated by a scholarship enabling New Zealand trainee ophthalmologists to further their training overseas. The Eye Hospital in St Mary's Place progressively enlarged to a point where it had 34

---

[1] Reference Arthur Thomas Peterson: the life and times of a New Zealand ophthalmologist. Hart, R.H. and McGhee. C.N.J. Clinical and Experimental Ophthalmology, 2004.32 71-74

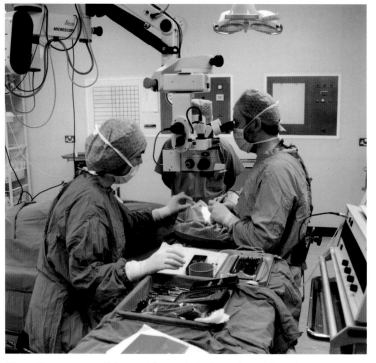

Fig 5.8: Cataract surgery. Today carried out under local anaesthetic and as a day case.

beds. It was closed in 1956 and subsequently demolished to make way for the new civic centre.

Eye services were then split across three sites, namely the RVI, the General Hospital and Walkergate Hospital. Whilst all these units had their strengths, the associated division and duplication of services led to inefficiencies and sometimes to in-fighting. Unification of eye services in Newcastle was brought about by the building of the Claremont Wing on the RVI site which was opened in 1997.

The new unit resulted in the bringing together of a critical mass of clinicians able to develop sub-specialist services, including retinal detachment surgery, oculoplastics, corneal transplantation and paediatric ophthalmology. The proximity to the University has fostered collaborative research and has dramatically improved the national and international profile of ophthalmic services in Newcastle. (*Figs 5.7 & 5.8*)

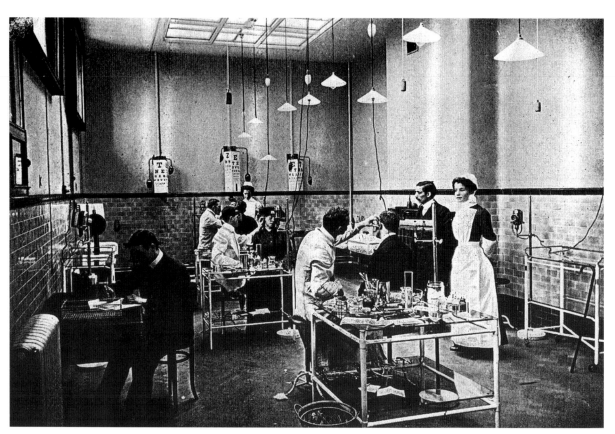

Fig 5.9: Early ENT Outpatients department.

Ear Nose and Throat Surgery

Between the two world wars Ear Nose and Throat Surgery (ENT) was regarded as relatively low key surgery with general surgeons operating on emergencies such as acute mastoiditis and ENT surgeons confining themselves to removing inflamed tonsils and adenoids. The Honorary ENT Surgeons to the Infirmary at this time were George Ridley, Samuel Whillis, William Wilson, and Robert Whillis (*Fig 5.9*). After the end of the Second World War the status of the service rose with the establishment of the NHS and the appointment of three consultants, Francis McGuckin, J. I. Munro Black and J. D. K. Dawes who between them oversaw the development of the ENT department to one that was internationally recognised. Considerable rivalry developed between the RVI unit and the Rye Hill ENT Hospital which subsequently moved to the Newcastle General Hospital. In the later 1960s ENT services were also established at Walkergate Hospital staffed by consultants from both the RVI and the General. It was around this time that a great leap forward occurred in ENT surgery with the development of the operating microscope, introduced to Newcastle by Francis McGuckin. This instrument allowed surgeons to operate inside the middle ear, a technique developed to a very high level by Desmond (Dizzy) Dawes who at one stage was President of the Otological section of the Royal Society of Medicine. The field of interest of ENT surgeons then began to expand and Munro Black expanded his repertoire and consequently established for himself a reputation as a surgeon for head and neck cancer that was second to none. In 1987 the two departments amalgamated on the Freeman Hospital site to create the Department of Otorhinolaryngology and Head and Neck Surgery which currently has academic leadership at professorial level and is the largest such department in the country.

Urology

In 1938 urology emerged as a separate specialty in Newcastle - the Department of Prostatic Surgery opened at Newcastle General Hospital under William Wardill. Rutherford Morison had a large urology practice, as did Grey Turner and many other general surgeons in these pre-war years. It has taken many years for the rest of the surgical world to catch up with this development. Even today, there are some who do not fully embrace this specialty, with some general surgeons still professing an interest in urology. In the 1970s the professorial surgical unit at the RVI regularly had as many as eight - or more - extra beds brought in to accommodate the cystoscopy list on a Tuesday.

Plastic Surgery

Plastic surgery developed an international reputation. One of its great personalities in the mid part of the century was Fenton Braithwaite. His cleft palate work was internationally known, and he gave his name to a skin grafting knife used by surgeons all over the world. His patients came from around the world. It was not unusual for a newly arrived international patient to present to the private ward in Pavilion 3 in the Leazes Wing at any time of the night, and for the house surgeon to have to see the patient pending Fenton Braithwaite seeing him/her the following day. By the early '70s one of Braithwaite's other interests, as medical officer for Newcastle United F. C., seemed to occupy much of his time.

Vascular Surgery

In the 1960s peripheral vascular surgery emerged as a specialty of general surgery, and a vascular unit was established at the RVI. This was well ahead of its time, but by the mid 1980s there were no fewer than five surgeons in the city, three at the RVI, with a predominantly vascular surgical practice. The impact on patient care and surgeon training was considerable. Even those patients who could not benefit from reconstruction procedures, and who needed amputations, were beneficiaries of this. They could expect to be home within about six weeks, compared with a previous time extending to a year or two in some instances. Vascular surgery is still emerging as a specialty in its own right, and is not yet as far down this road as urology, for some "vascular" surgeons still maintain a general surgical element to their work, but ultimately it does seem likely that the RVI's lead from the 60s will prevail in all hospitals.

Gastroenterological Surgery

Traditionally general surgery has centred heavily on gastroenterological surgery. That, too, has become split into several components with often surprisingly little overlap. Thus there are now colo-rectal surgeons, hepato-biliary surgeons, and upper gastro-intestinal surgeons. Other specialties are continuing to emerge - in particular one thinks of breast, endocrine and day-care surgery. There is now no longer a truly general surgeon.

Similar specialisation has occurred in other specialties, including paediatric surgery (see chapter 13), and these new working practices are taking surgery in to the RVI's second century. The general surgeons no longer have any responsibility to treat children, either electively or in the emergency setting, with only occasional exceptions - for example when a condition arises in a child which is more commonly seen in adults and only rarely in children. With the new buildings now well under way, soon neurosurgery will be on-site as well as orthopaedic trauma, once the building developments are completed to house them, along with the new accident and emergency unit. It does seem a little idiosyncratic that peripheral vascular surgery is remote from the accident and emergency facility - but that is how it has been for the last few years and the arrangement does seem to have worked satisfactorily with the peripheral vascular surgical unit now being sited at Freeman Hospital.

There have been other changes which have radically altered the way in which surgeons work. Medical treatments have reduced the need for many surgical procedures - for example, the management of peptic ulcer disease is now virtually a pharmacological exercise: burst peptic ulcers are rarely seen, despite having been one of the commonest of surgical emergencies only thirty years ago. Work done at the RVI and the University in Newcastle contributed greatly to this change. Similar change affecting other diseases is likely to continue into the long term future.

Day care surgery has radically altered the need for inpatient beds: it is now rare for patients to be admitted to have their hernia operation whereas only twenty or thirty years ago it was not unusual to have a patient in hospital for up to a week. Changes in surgeons' attitudes, changes in surgical techniques and, most important of all, improvements in anaesthesia have all contributed to the short stay for many operations.

Many internal operations are conducted by endoscopic techniques, with large incisions being exchanged for two or three tiny incisions. Most famous of all, endoscopic surgery is the operation to remove the gall bladder: a short stay of 24 hours or less is all that is now needed for many cases compared with a minimum stay of five to seven days only a relatively few years ago. No matter what the specialty, changes of this type have now been introduced and surgery is generally becoming less traumatic for the patient - or even no longer needed when drug treatments can be used instead.

Another change which has occurred, and which will continue its evolution into the future, is the team approach to patient management. Some surgical specialties have been managed in this way for some time. This is especially relevant to transplantation surgery - a specialty for which the RVI was renowned throughout the world - where patient management has been delivered by a combination of physician, surgeon, immunologist, and others, for many years. This has extended to many other surgical disciplines and one thinks now especially of gastro-intestinal surgery within

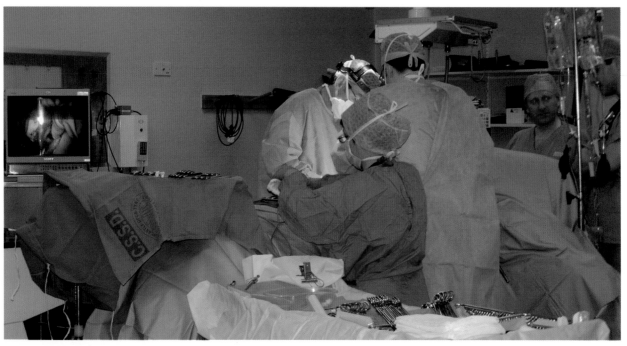

Fig 5.10: Cardio-pulmonary bypass operation.

the context of the RVI. Even cases of gastro-intestinal haemorrhage, which used to require emergency, and often very major, surgical intervention, are now managed either by a physician or surgeon - or radiologist - without the need for surgery. One must also not forget the increasing share of the work which is taken on by nurses, be it in the endoscopy clinic or in the out-patient department.

Although there is a feeling that such team working is revolutionary and new, one is reminded of the words of Henry Miller, written in 1968, when he was University Vice-Chancellor. *"We pay lip service to the nostalgic ideal of the 'good general physician' or the 'good general surgeon' - and when we need treatment ourselves we all seek out at once the most highly specialised attention that is available... The corollary of specialisation is team-work... this tendency will increase. The hospital supermarket of the future will comprise a series of large teams each including physicians and surgeons devoted to the medicine of a particular body system."*

Henry Miller was absolutely correct in his predictions and that trend, anticipated by him almost forty years ago, continues to gather pace. If anyone has any doubt about the changes along these lines, I recommend a visit to the breast clinic. Surgeon, specialist nurse, oncologist and pathologist will all be present and taking an active part in the patient's diagnosis and management.

It has not always been a story of glowing success for surgery. There have been low points. Surgery survived the introduction of the NHS, it survived the change in status from being managed as a University Hospital (up to 1974 it was part of the United Newcastle upon Tyne Hospitals group) to being managed by the Newcastle Area Health Authority (Teaching) but it struggled mightily when Trust status was introduced in about 1990. This change heralded what was likely to be lowest point of the first 100 years of the RVI as far as surgery was concerned.

The changes were never going to be easy at this time. Government decreed that money would follow patients and that is how hospitals would be funded from then on. However the cash pot was strictly limited and three hospitals in Newcastle was a very expensive option. Inevitably one would go to the wall - and that was to be the General with its ancient and often dilapidated buildings which were very expensive to maintain. Freeman Hospital was new and well maintained and in between was the RVI. Like the General, but unlike Freeman, the RVI also had an open access casualty department which made the planning of the increasingly scarce bed resource very difficult. Emergency cases took priority over elective cases and many emergency cases just arrived in casualty and a bed needed to be found for the patient. Freeman Hospital was insulated from this problem and could predict and plan its elective work. Management costs at the RVI were also very high.

All of this translated to the need to manage the emergency case and to save money by closing down the elective facilities in the RVI. Surgery, a predominantly elective specialty, suffered, and at one time there were only two or three adult surgical wards in the hospital, including plastic surgery. The general surgical facility was less than thirty beds, although by this time vascular and transplant surgery were now at Freeman Hospital. Often it was almost impossible to admit elective cases, the training of young surgeons was increasingly difficult and the University withdrew many of the undergraduates who were due to undertake their surgical instruction in the Infirmary.

However, other changes were also occurring and which further pitched clinician against management. This is best illustrated by the impact of change in renal transplantation. Renal transplantation, started by John Swinney at the General Hospital in the 1960s, was destined to be the jewel in the RVI's crown. Ross Taylor was appointed consultant transplant surgeon in 1970 and he developed the clinical transplant unit to a level that put it at one of the best in the UK - by whatever parameter it might be assessed - if not one of the best in the world. By the late 1980s/early 1990s the outcome of renal transplantation was at the very highest levels of success and the unit was also performing one of the highest rates of renal transplantation of any unit anywhere. It was as a direct result of the unit's success that cardiac transplantation was enabled to come to Newcastle and subsequently liver transplantation also. (*Fig 5.10*)

The last thing that should have happened to it was that anyone should seek to disturb its functioning. Yet that is exactly what happened. Somewhere in the corridors of management power it was decided that the unit would move to Freeman Hospital. The senior staff group on the unit was not part of the discussions and, as it turned it out, was not even to be part of the move should members of the group have wished to move. The changes were subject to a huge amount of criticism - from the Royal College of Surgeons, the Association of Surgeons, the British Transplantation

Society and others, as well as many individuals. Criticism was at its most eloquent from a surgeon commissioned to prepare a report on the future of surgery at the RVI. The target for his criticism was the manner in which the change was carried out. It is this last point which is the main reason for describing these happenings in such detail: change was now being made even to the most successful of units on a management whim without consultation with senior surgical staff members, or any proper clinical input at all.

This was probably the lowest point for surgery in the RVI throughout the entire century. Ten years down the line the transplantation unit is now functioning well again, in the Freeman Hospital, but the problems experienced in the years immediately following the changes could so easily have been avoided. However, what happened to renal transplantation is a clear message to all clinicians everywhere that management now is in charge exclusively and that is how surgery may be going into the next century of its existence. One hopes that the wise manager will know to consult his/her clinical colleagues.

Finally there is one aspect of surgery at the RVI which must not be overlooked and that is the close relationship the hospital has had with the University. Clinicians at the hospital were appointed to a Honorary Personal Chair of Surgery, but it was not until 1945 that a full-time Professor of Surgery (F. H. Bentley) was appointed by the University of Durham with clinical facilities being provided in the RVI.

Fig 5.11: *Tribute plaque in RVI to Andrew Gilchrist Ross Lowdon.*

Andrew Lowdon (*Fig 5.11*) followed him, taking up his post in 1954. He became Dean of Medicine in 1960 and was then responsible (with others) for one of the most seminal changes in medical undergraduate education ever implemented. Teaching would no longer be based on the old subjects of Anatomy, Physiology, Surgery etc, but would be integrated according to the subject being taught. These were pioneering changes, brought about by a surgeon whose clinical base was the RVI. They became world famous. Lowdon also initiated the Regional Registrar Research Prizes, emphasising the need for the trainee to undergo a period of research, or at least gain research experience, at an intermediate stage of training.

Andrew Lowdon died tragically early but the changes he initiated were developed by his successor Ivan Johnston: by the time of the early 1980s the University Department of Surgery had wide influence over the training of young surgeons and the appointment of new consultants. Many surgeons in the UK have good reason to be grateful for the strong academic grounding they received in Newcastle during their training. This included not only their work within the University but also their training at the RVI and increasingly, as the years passed, at hospitals in Newcastle and the region.

The pattern of surgical research also began to change. Whilst there was still the opportunity for clinical research, much of the research became the province of the molecular biologist rather than the surgeon. Thirty and forty years ago much of the research work was clinically based: for example, doctorates were awarded for work done on research into which type of selective vagotomy was best for peptic ulcer disease. Now, as the Royal Victoria Infirmary enters its second century, the research is more likely to be in identifying which gene test will be the best predictor of the most appropriate operation for a particular condition.

The 2006 surgeon is no longer the 1906 autocrat, but is a member of a team. (S)he will present clinical cases to all other members of the team - the physician, pathologist, radiologist, oncologist, nurse etc., for discussion and criticism, and will need to be able to defend what was done for, or is planned for, a particular patient on the basis of best clinical practice and clinical evidence. The surgeon can no longer defend what has been done by saying that *"it has always been done that way by me"* unless, of course, *"that way"* can be shown to be the best way. Evidence based surgery has taken over from anecdotally based surgery - and a good thing too!

In some ways, the relationship between the University and the Clinic is also changing. It appears to be reverting to where it was in 1906. Instead of appointing more University funded surgeons, and providing them with honorary clinical facilities, the University is now once more recognising distinction amongst the surgeons and awarding some of them honorary personal chairs. This is very constructive and strengthens not only the University but also the RVI's department of surgery. From the 1960s onwards there had been virtually no University appointments of this sort in surgery. One can think of a number of clinicians who ought to have been recognised in this way: it is now right and proper that this process is being cautiously reintroduced.

As the RVI enters its second century of existence surgery faces many challenges. It will survive - it has a background of great integrity on which to draw. Surgery, with its strong emphasis on gastro-intestinal surgery, breast surgery and endocrine surgery will flourish. Neurosurgery, ophthalmic surgery, orthopaedic and trauma surgery and plastic surgery will flourish. Surgery at the RVI will continue to embrace the best surgical changes as they occur - and it is likely to lead many of those changes. One measure of the hospital's achievements in a specialty is its popularity with trainees. A recent Higher Surgical Training post vacancy in surgery attracted around 40 appointable applicants. This is a good predictor of the hospital's future well-being.

Now that the City's surgical services are under one management there is the opportunity to co-operate and develop across the two sites: the harmful and uncontrolled competitiveness of the 1990s has gone. Rivalries will persist but that should be healthy. There is the opportunity for co-operation and development as never before. The future holds a great deal of promise. Surgery at the RVI may not have the physical presence it needed in 1906 (*Fig 5.12*), but in 2006 and beyond its importance to surgical care in the city, the country and beyond is in no way diminished.

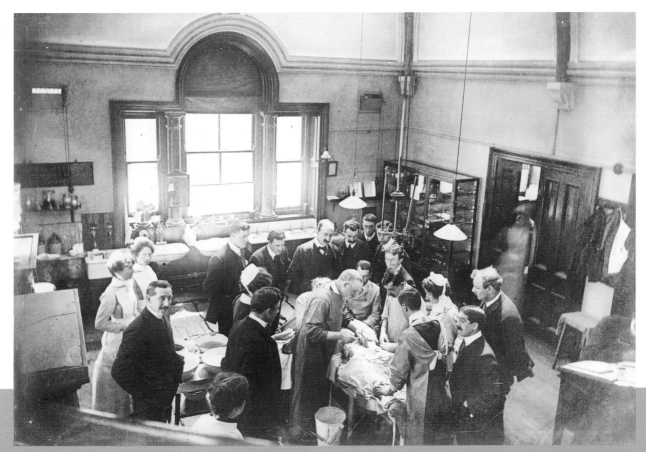

Fig 5.12: Operating in main theatre of the Old Infirmary conducted by Rutherford Morison on Saturday June 2nd 1906 just before the official opening of the RVI.

Chapter 6: *Obstetrics and Gynaecology* John M. Davison
from the Lying-In to the Leazes Wing

In writing this chapter, I was advised not to update earlier factual accounts of the Infirmary, but to offer a fresh focus on the evolution of my clinical specialty and the people involved from the early 1900s to the present day. However, two superb books must be mentioned because of their bearing on the history of Obstetrics and Gynaecology in association with and at the Infirmary. In his book, Mr Derek Tacchi[1] eruditely chronicles the development of the city's maternity services in an account brimming with names, dates, setbacks and Acts of Parliament affecting practice, while also stressing the development of the city's other Maternity Unit at the Wingrove (Newcastle General Hospital [NGH]), especially from 1939 onwards under Mr Linton Snaith and others. Sir William Hume's book *"The Infirmary 1751-1951: A brief sketch"*[II]. Chapter 4 specifically deals with 1906-1948 as the time of *"development of specialisms"*, the Infirmary's need *"to adapt to advances in knowledge"* and the *"perpetual demands for space"*, not envisaged at all in 1901, when planners *"could not foresee the great developments that would take place in the next years."*

The reality was that in 1906 there was no Obstetric or Gynaecological presence, or plans for such, at the Infirmary, let alone any concept of *"specialisms"* within its practice. Now, 100 years later, all the city's services on this specialty are more or less amalgamated on the Infirmary site in purpose-designed accommodation, the envy of other big cities and their NHS Trusts, with Newcastle leading the way in subspecialisation, as a high quality tertiary referral centre, while still providing for the needs and aspirations of local patients and their families with attractive, friendly and safe systems of basic care.

This happened because for decades generations of excellent clinicians, all shrewd but some with forceful personalities, having an indefatigable capacity for medical politics, were determined to combine the practice of Obstetrics and Gynaecology under one roof, thus providing a co-ordinated service for the city and its hinterland. Also, a major factor was the bond established between University and Infirmary at the turn of the century, so that this service was nurtured through successes and setbacks alike.

Traditionally, in 1906 in Newcastle, as elsewhere in the country, gynaecology was taught and practised by general surgeons. Indeed, there was resistance to the idea of a separate specialty linked to midwifery, so that its practice continued in an off-site out-patient setting overseen by physicians, and any surgery was performed by the surgeons. Physician accoucheurs were discouraged from undertaking operations other than vaginal procedures involved in childbirth and even the rarely performed caesarean sections were undertaken by surgeons. Few accoucheurs had any surgical training or a Royal College of Surgeons qualification and the British College of Obstetricians and Gynaecologists was not founded until 1929.

Fig 6.2: R.P. Ranken Lyle (1870-1950).

A man to be reckoned with

In 1899 a significant appointment was made by the University. Dr Robert Patton Ranken Lyle (*Fig 6.2*), a north Irishman by birth and recently Assistant Master at the Rotunda Hospital in Dublin, arrived in Newcastle as Lecturer in Midwifery and Diseases of Women and Children, a clear hint that things had to change. Indeed, at the gates of the new Infirmary site, Ranken Lyle purchased 23, St Thomas' Street (*Fig 6.3*) and personally equipped it as the *"Samaritan Free Dispensary for Women"*, where he gave advice and undertook surgery free of charge. By 1907 the Infirmary had appointed him Consulting Gynaecologist with a small number of beds. Later a 24-bedded gynaecological ward emerged on the second floor, close to the Conservatory and the Nurses' Home, where it stayed as Ward 11 until the move to the new Leazes Wing in 1993. In 1908 Ranken Lyle became the first Professor of Obstetrics and Gynaecology in the University of Durham (the University specifically included Gynaecology in the title) and slowly but surely, by force of personality and example, he dealt with the many prejudices against his subject.

[1] Tacchi D. (1994) Childbirth in Newcastle upon Tyne, 1760-1990
Bewick Press, Whitley Bay

[II] Hume W. E. (1951). The Infirmary Newcastle upon Tyne (1751-1951): A brief sketch.
Andrew Reid & Co. Ltd., Newcastle upon Tyne

Left: Fig 6.1: Detail from Fig 6.5 Midwife, Lying-In Hospital, New Bridge Street.

Fig 6.3: 2005 photograph of 23 St Thomas' Street, purchased and equipped in 1902 by Ranken Lyle, as the "Samaritan Free Dispensary for Women." It is now a private house but remarkably there is a hospital sign (H) outside, referring of course to the Infirmary, just visible, at the top of the street.

Fig 6.4: The Lying-In Hospital, New Bridge Street (1825-1923).

Midwifery in the city supervised by Infirmary staff

Concurrently, it was clear that the needs of Midwifery were not being adequately met by the 80-year-old 15-bedded Lying-In Hospital (with no operating Theatre) (*Fig 6.4*) in New Bridge Street (subsequently the BBC, now the Newcastle Building Society, opposite the Laing Art Gallery and Tiffany's Night Club). In 1900 when, at the behest of Ranken Lyle, the whole hospital had been papered, painted and refurnished, 32 women were delivered there (*Fig 6.5*) with another 165 supervised as domiciliary cases but by 1908, the figures were 227 and 1108,

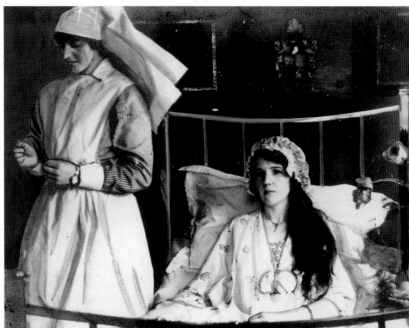

Fig 6.5: Midwife and patient, Lying-In Hospital, New Bridge Street.

respectively, and by 1920 there were over 1000 in each category, signalling the need for bigger premises. Ranken Lyle and the Committee of Management negotiated with the Corporation to use the vacated *"Ragged and Industrial School"* (built in 1854) in Jubilee Road, *(Fig 6.6)* sufficient for 90 beds and an operating theatre. Assisting Ranken Lyle was Dr Ernest Farquhar Murray, who in 1921, had been appointed University Lecturer and Honorary Assistant Obstetrician and Gynaecologist to the Maternity Hospital and the Infirmary. The Jubilee Road Hospital was officially opened in 1923 by HRH Princess Mary, The Countess of Harewood, who graciously allowed it to be named after her. The Princess Mary Maternity Hospital (PMMH), with an annual budget of £10,000, like all its Lying-In predecessors, relied on public generosity and annual grants from local Councils, tuition fees from pupil midwives and medical students, small stock market investments and the activities of a very

Fig 6.6: Princess Mary Maternity Hospital, Jubilee Road (1923-1939) former "Ragged and Industrial School."

active Ladies' Committee, *(Fig 6.7)* ably supported by Professor and Mrs Ranken Lyle, Sir Thomas Oliver and Lord Eustace Percy. A tradition was established that *"no case is ever refused admission"* and the hospital's catchment area extended from the Tweed to the Tees. The national maternal mortality rate in the 1920s was five deaths per 1000 maternities, but given the difficult cases it attracted or had referred, the maternal loss at Jubilee Road could be 70 deaths each year, the major causes being sepsis, haemorrhage and eclampsia. Invariably all were emergencies with inadequate antenatal

Fig 6.7: Young Peoples' Ball in 1932 in aid of PMMH.
Top Table includes: Ranken Lyle, Lady Allendale, Sir Thomas Oliver, Mrs Lyle. Standing: Dr & Mrs W. Hunter, Dr Mabel Campbell, Mr & Mrs H. Evers.

supervision and/or traumatic delivery at home; this prompted Farquhar Murray (*Fig 6.8*) to introduce a resuscitation service whereby specialist help went to the home before transfer to hospital; thus developed an Emergency Obstetric Service (later known as The Flying Squad), in 1935 at the PMMH (*Fig 6.9*), the very first in England. On Tyneside the peak Squad usage was in 1962 with 168 calls, gradually decreasing to 11 calls in 1985, it being "stood down" a few years later.

Fig 6.8: E. Farquhar Murray 1886-1959.

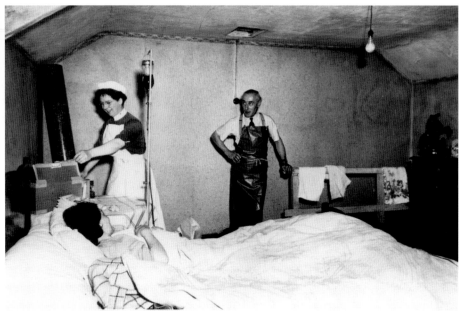

Fig 6.9: Flying Squad Call. F. E. Stabler and Sister Gordon with the situation under control.

The case for a new-build maternity hospital

In 1932 a Government inspection of the PMMH was complimentary, but when reassessed in 1934 the building was deemed "... *not designed for hospital purposes and without features of a well-planned maternity hospital*", so much so that "...*there should be the building of a new maternity hospital, preferably in association with the Infirmary or the General Hospital.*" The Infirmary House Committee immediately allocated 1½ acres of land on a 99-year lease and plans were ready by 1935, by which time Ranken Lyle had retired, to be succeeded in the chair by Farquhar Murray, who was renowned for his dogmatism. Controversies about the Infirmary's authority to release the land caused significant delays, the issue being resolved by the Freemen of the City and the Corporation. Disappointingly, in 1937 the Government offered only one-third of the costs for the new development and to raise the remainder (about £200,000) locally was going to be a long haul. Nevertheless, in July 1939 the Newcastle Medical Gazette was confidently reporting that "...*after many vicissitudes the Committee of the PMMH has at last received permission to proceed with the building of a new hospital on the north west corner of the Infirmary and a definite start will be made in preparing the ground for the foundations within the next few weeks.*" The project was shelved with the onset of the War but importantly, one benefit remained; the House Committee of the Infirmary agreed to meet regularly with the Committees of the city's five voluntary hospitals, one of which was the PMMH, now burgeoning with about 2500 in-patients per year and another 500 supervised as domiciliary cases.

To cope with the increasing clinical load Farquhar Murray and H. Harvey Evers, an Honorary Consultant, were ably supported by the continuing sequence of redoubtable matrons and two hardworking young doctors, Frank Stabler and William Hunter, who undertook most of the emergency work in both Obstetrics and Gynaecology, the latter still at the Infirmary. Wartime imposed more responsibilities on the medical students and the long-time Registrar, Stanley Way. As the Jubilee Road building was old and in a vulnerable area, the authorities were persuaded to evacuate it.

With a hasty reassessment of the city's midwifery needs, it was thought essential to maintain two hospitals, even though many women were evacuated to Gilsland (where deliveries peaked at 957 in 1943) and services at Dilston Hall near Hexham were already being augmented from the PMMH.

Fig 6.10: Abbott Memorial (girls) Orphanage, opened 1869.

The PMMH on the move

After some deliberation, the PMMH transferred to the Northern Counties Orphanage at Moor Edge (rented at £1100 p.a.) where the Girls' Section (the Abbott Memorial) was quickly converted into a 40-bedded unit. (*Fig 6.10*) The antenatal clinic and the district staff remained at Jubilee Road. By 1943, with the city's maternity bed provision considered insufficient, plans for a "temporary" hutted hospital at the NGH (costing £32,550) were abandoned, as the PMMH (*Fig 6.11 & 6.12*) was allowed to expand into the Orphanage's south wing Boys' Section (the Philipson Memorial). Between the two wings the Adamson chapel (dating from 1885) (*Fig 6.13*) was subsequently converted into a dingy

Fig 6.11: Lying-In Ward at PMMH, Moor Edge (1939-1945).

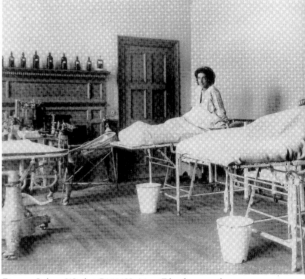

Fig 6.12: Labour Ward at PMMH, Moor Edge (1939-1950)

Fig 6.13: Memorial Chapel between the two orphanages connected to PMMH entrance hall in 1951.

entrance hall and reception area, long remembered by patients and staff alike. Medical students (each was required to deliver 20 babies before graduating) were housed in rotation in a prefabricated hut in the grounds.

The choice of the Orphanage (built in the mid-1800s) was thought by some senior Infirmary figures, notably Sir James Spence (the 'practical reformer', who encouraged a close association between obstetricians, midwives and the "new" neonatal paediatricians), to have been a tactical mistake, delaying provision of a new hospital for over 50 years. Although the War worsened an already critical financial situation, in 1945 a special payment of £3000 was found for yet more architects' plans for a maternity hospital at the Infirmary. These came to nothing but probably catalysed the official amalgamation of the PMMH with the Infirmary, the then House Governor becoming responsible for services, staffing and supplies, consolidated further by the 1946 National Health Service Act.

Fig 6.14: Flying Squad arriving at a house in Byker (1957). W. Hunter carries equipment from his car helped by G.P., medical student and Sister, who is carrying the 'blood box.'

During the war years and with the inception of the NHS, maternal mortality was considerably reduced and the trend continued downwards. Today it is 13.1/100,000 maternities, the leading overall cause being suicide, and for direct deaths, thrombosis and thromboembolism. Concomitantly, perinatal mortality has decreased over 50 years from 53/1000 to 9/1000 but, worryingly, unexplained, antepartum stillbirth remains the major contributor. Obviously, the Flying Squad (*Fig 6.14*) contributed but the advent of safe blood transfusion, antibiotics, better antenatal care with recognition of "high risk" pregnancies and better trained staff have been contributory too. Newcastle also made major strides in the antenatal and neonatal management of Rhesus isoimmunisation.

By the early 1950s the flamboyant and brilliant clinician Harvey Evers (*Fig 6.15*) had become Professor. He was the most popular teacher in the Medical School, had a fine taste in motor cars and owned his own private hospital *"Fernwood"*, in Jesmond, referred to as *"The Golden Gates"* by junior staff and students alike. The remodelled PMMH was re-opened by HRH Princess Mary, now the Princess Royal, and subsequently the antenatal clinic was transferred from Jubilee Road, occupying a building at the rear of the hospital, formerly used as a gymnasium.

Fig 6.15: H. Harvey Evers 1893-1979.   *Fig 6.16: F. E. Stabler 1902-1967.*

Harvey Evers retired in 1958 and the Senior Lecturer, J.K.(Jake) Russell was appointed Professor. Frank Stabler, (*Fig 6.16*) the Senior NHS Consultant was joined by Derek Tacchi in 1963 and in 1967 Leonard Barron succeeded Frank Stabler who retired. The NHS Consultants provided the backbone of the clinical department for the next 25 years, with Jake Russell and a stream of senior academic staff augmenting the service along with their research pursuits. By the 1970s 94% of Newcastle women were delivering in hospital, (*Fig 6.17*) the home confinement rate plummeting to 6% [having previously been 40% (1960s) and 65% (1930s)]; and private nursing homes closed, their heyday having been in 1950-1960s when 20% of Newcastle women delivered there.

Fig 6.17: The PMMH in the 1970s.

New academic developments

The academic department was considerably strengthened in 1965 with the move of the MRC Obstetric Medicine Unit from Aberdeen, becoming the MRC Reproduction and Growth Unit. Professors Angus Thomson and Frank Hytten and Mr W. Z. Billewicz were the nucleus of its staff. Their prefabricated building was at the rear of the PMMH on land which had miraculously been released by the "Schools and Charities Committee" thanks to inspired lobbying by Jake Russell and his colleagues and the then Dean, Professor A. G. R. Lowdon. This Unit became internationally renowned for work on the physiology of human pregnancy and the epidemiology of human reproduction. It had an excellent rapport with the clinical department, providing a superb environment for research training for young doctors.

Gynaecology at the Infirmary

Meanwhile Gynaecology continued at the Infirmary in the now 42-bedded Ward 11, with Out-patient facilities shared with medicine and surgery. Sister Carling ("*Mother Carling*") had been the doyenne of Nursing Sisters (1938-1967), famed for her personally devised postoperative recipes and her sitting room on the ward, into which favoured doctors were invited for morning coffee or afternoon tea. Before the proper establishment of their own departments with full complements of staff to deal with gynaecological patients, Radiotherapists, Clinical Oncologists and Family Planning Specialists all had access to facilities on Ward 11 and its single operating theatre. The ward itself had several internal rearrangements, principally to cope with day case admissions (the first at the Infirmary) and long stay cases, mainly gynaecological malignancies. Stronger links were forged, with Stanley Way's Gynaecological Oncology Unit in Gateshead and the Oncologists at NGH.

Yet more upgrading at the PMMH

Further upgradings at the PMMH took place in 1968-69, including a purpose-built special care baby unit and extensions to the delivery suite. Neonatology was now crucially important in obstetric practice (see chapter 10) and the booked "*high risk*" obstetric case load at the Princess Mary increased because of what the Neonatologists could offer. Also the concept of "*in utero transfer*" (IUT) became prevalent and the tertiary referral concept was born. The provision of a dedicated obstetric anaesthetic service and a Consultant Physician-based Maternal Medicine Clinic considerably enhanced the reputation and attraction of the PMMH. The advent of developments in ultrasound scanning was about to revolutionise obstetric practice. Between 1981 and 1984, with the modernisation of the antenatal clinic, operating theatre, wards, kitchens and dining room, no-one could really envisage the maternity hospital ever moving to the Infirmary. (*Fig 6.18*)

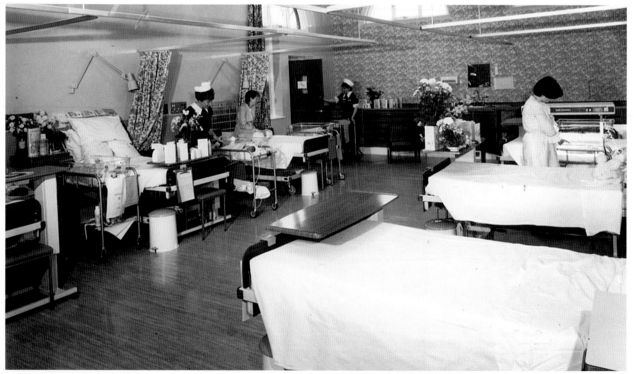

Fig 6.18: Postnatal Ward at PMMH (1980s). In the corner there is a door to a link corridor to the Special Care Nursery. What a contrast to Fig 6.11!

Prospects for a new Academic Department and its implications

One of the former MRC Research Registrars, William (Bill) Dunlop, became Professor in 1982, having been Senior Lecturer for the previous six years. With retirements and other changes in MRC personnel, the Unit became the MRC Human Reproduction Group, subsequently to be absorbed into the academic department. Building of the new Medical School had commenced and although space there had not been earmarked for Obstetrics and Gynaecology, a new home for research was allocated on the 4th floor of the Infirmary's new Leazes Wing, with laboratory and clinical area specifications already ratified.

NHS reorganisations (the first in 1974) and local reviews of hospital services and sites were ongoing because of the need to rationalise specialist services and Government directives. When Freeman Hospital was planned, the possibility of an Obstetrics and Gynaecology Unit there was considered but not pursued. With plans for the Leazes Wing *"on the boil"* and a new Medical School being built there was renewed impetus to strive for a new clinical department at the Infirmary. The Leazes Wing development had various phases and it was feared that any clinical relocation from the PMMH could be out of step with the now guaranteed academic move or would not occur at all, even though Gynaecology had just been afforded space on the new wing's 2nd floor.

The building of the Medical School proceeded apace with the much publicised prominent south-projecting flange of corridors (destined to link with the Leazes Wing) initially standing in isolation. By the time the Medical School was fully functional there was still much negotiation needed to ensure that Obstetrics would be given early consideration, to head off the worry that all the phases of the Leazes Wing project were not achieved.

Getting into the Leazes Wing

In 1989 it was mooted that 2nd floor space might be modified to accommodate a modern obstetric unit and special care nursery, although space for an antenatal clinic and a fetal medicine unit had yet to be identified, which eventually it was. The nettle was grasped, precipitating a weekend of frenetic "plan drawing" and calculations by all the Consultants at the PMMH. Thus was sealed its closure and translation to the Infirmary, along with the academic department. Concomitantly, there had been increased cooperation between the city's two Units (at the PMMH and NGH), long since working together to cover the Flying Squad, and officially from 1972 as the Division of Obstetrics and Gynaecology of Newcastle Area Health Authority (AHA), so that unification of all the city's services on the Infirmary site was seriously considered, to deal with the 5000 deliveries per year. Negotiations stalled, but momentum was rekindled with new plans for NHS Trusts, and the need for rationalisation of space on Infirmary and NGH sites as part of a city-wide review of the clinical disciplines. Serendipitously perhaps, Obstetrics and Gynaecology was high on the list and by 1992, a final decision was helped by two successive Government reports which advocated major changes in maternity services, to facilitate involvement of women themselves and seamless linkage with primary care. It was agreed by the Newcastle AHA, the Regional Health Authority, the Community Health Council, the Maternity Services Liaison Committee and the RVI Trust that the principles outlined in the Cumberlege Report could be best embraced in the city by unification and "level transfer" of the two units to the Infirmary site. Gynaecology moved in April 1993 and the doors of the two maternity units closed on 14th November 1993. Thus was born the Directorate of Womens' Services. Neonatology (the discipline which has singly contributed so much to the ongoing revolution of obstetric practice (see chapter 10) and Obstetric Anaesthetic services merged and transferred too.

Into the Leazes Wing and "Specialisms" at last

"Bedding-in" proved to be an interesting exercise and the two groups of Consultants *"thrown together"* wisely implemented the merger on the basis of what was really the forerunner of clinical governance with evidence-based guidelines for all areas of the Directorate, clinical audit (already enshrined in the specialty) as well as risk management and litigation awareness, utilising RCOG Working Party Reports and *"Green Top"* guidelines. Succession planning for future Consultant retirements was crucial to capitalise on the lead being shown to the country in subspecialisation.

A significant meeting was held on Maundy Thursday in 1997 when Consultant staff resolved to concentrate on practice in either Obstetrics or Gynaecology. Paul Hilton had earlier given up Obstetrics to concentrate on the development of Urogynaecology at the Infirmary. This Directorate-wide decision, however, was a huge change from the traditional approach where everyone was a generalist (capable of undertaking most things) and probably *"some sort of specialist on the side"*, to use a phrase coined by Professor Henry Miller nearly 40 years earlier when, in discussing *"The future of Newcastle Medicine"*, he predicted that the city did need specialists, accepting they might want to be "generalists on the side". So in 1997 the *"development of specialisms"* (to use Sir William Hume's terminology when describing the Infirmary from 1906-1948) was here to stay in Obstetrics and Gynaecology at the Infirmary. It should not be forgotten, however, that a ground-breaking step had been taken in 1990 with RCOG approval of the very first UK Fetal Medicine training programme, straddling the PMMH and the NGH, jointly directed by Professor Tom Lind and Dr Averil Snodgrass, who were also the Clinical Directors overseeing major negotiations. On the Infirmary site there soon followed approval for programmes in Urogynaecology and Reproductive Medicine. In the Directorate new Consultant appointments were tailored accordingly, while not forgetting the appropriate low technology care for women that needed and/or wanted it.

Progress and developments in the Directorate of Women's Services

Since 1993 there have also been many changes in the layout and facilities of the Directorate. The *"loss"* of some wards as part of the city's acute services review, was absorbed by pre-admission clinics, *"one-stop"* clinics, day unit assessments and better throughput of patients, early discharge strategies and considerable expansion of day case surgery. Dramatic changes specific to Gynaecology have included the widespread use of transvaginal ultrasound scanning, rationalisation of colposcopy services and development of family planning as a specialist service (linked to Community Gynaecology) as well as the medical management of miscarriage, termination of pregnancy and dysfunctional bleeding, in the latter case, almost completely replacing hysterectomy. The development of the Nurse Practitioner role in many areas has also helped to streamline patient care. As with surgery overall, minimal access (laparoscopic) surgery in Gynaecology has "exploded" on to the scene, so it is perhaps worth recalling that it was Derek Tacchi who first introduced the laparoscope into the Infirmary in 1964!

In the late 1970s Reproductive Medicine emerged as a potential subspecialty and the Infirmary's first assisted conception treatments were underway in the 1980s, based on Ward 11 in collaboration with the Endocrinologists. The first baby produced by in vitro fertilisation (IVF) was born in 1990 at a time when the only other option for couples was the private sector in London, so not surprisingly there was a rapid rise in the waiting list. The embryology laboratories expanded from converted toilets, to a sluice, to a vacated operating theatre in response to patient demand and amalgamated with the NGH donor insemination service. As *"newcomers"* the subspecialty had not figured in the Leazes Wing's vision initially, and so was left without a home. Finding space was impossible on the rapidly changing RVI site and when the opportunity arose to move to purpose-designed premises alongside the Regional Genetics Service at the new Centre for Life, Professor Alison Murdoch and her colleagues moved there in 1999. Since then the department has led the North East; over a thousand patients are seen each year and hundreds of babies have been born following treatment. Research plays a major role and the success of the embryonic stem cell and cloning programmes have launched the department on to the international stage.

Academic relocation and new clinical accommodation in Leazes Wing (*Fig 6.19*)

The University Department flourished and developed in its new home on the 4th floor of Leazes Wing. Programmes covered the molecular biology of trophoblast and myometrium as well as hypertension in pregnancy, physiological adaptation to pregnancy and the socio-economic health care considerations associated with prenatal screening, termination of pregnancy, antenatal ultrasound surveillance and preterm labour. Inevitably, the link with Fetal Medicine proved important, more so since Professor S.C.Robson, one of four Fetal Medicine Subspecialists, assumed the academic Headship in 1998. The 4th Floor accommodation was vacated in 2003 to make way for the development of a Clinical Research Facility and the academic department, now part of the School of Surgical and Reproductive Sciences, occupies refurbished space on the 3rd floor of the William Leech Building in the Medical School. Also in 2003 the Newcastle upon Tyne Hospitals NHS Trust financed a multimillion pound building programme and refurbishment scheme with

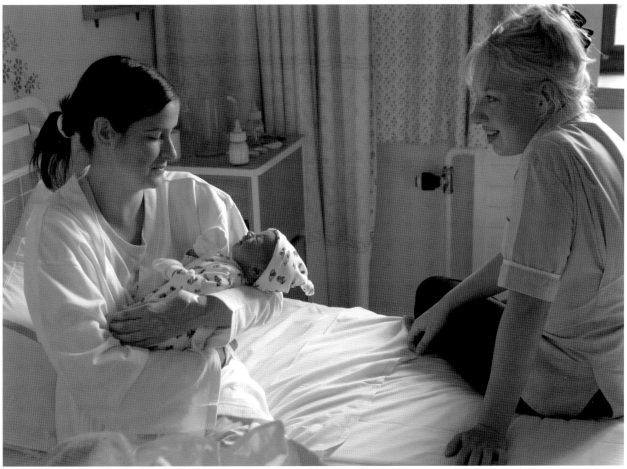

Fig 6.19: Postnatal Ward (2006).

new facilities for Fetal Medicine, a Maternity
Assessment Unit, (*Fig 6.20*) Antenatal Clinic and
a modern office block for all staff. (*Fig 6.21*) The
Delivery Suite was upgraded (including 'water
birth' facilities), (*Fig 6.22*) adapting to the aspirations
of the women and their partners and the two
operating theatres were relocated too. The
Gynaecology Ward was moved closer to the
Maternity Unit, the accompanying modifications
ensuring an even better environment for the
continuing evolution of the discipline. Sadly, the
Gynaecology Service had to cope with the
untimely and tragic death of Brendan Bolger in a
skiing accident in 2001. Through his talent and
diplomacy he had forged links with colleagues at
the Northern Gynaecology Oncology Centre in
Gateshead under John Monaghan, while ensuring
that a quality Oncology service was still offered at
the Infirmary.

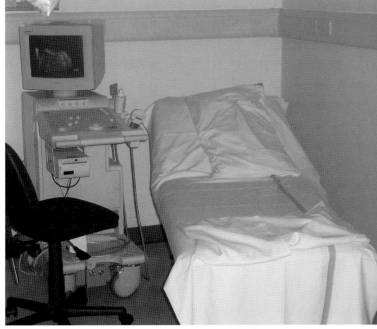

Fig 6.20: Assessment area in the Maternity Assessment Unit (2006).

Ever-changing maternity care provision and the role of the Infirmary

There have been substantial alterations to maternity care provision in recent years (*Fig 6.23*). Women with *"low-risk"* pregnancies are cared for entirely by midwives, who have also developed specialist roles, such as caring for pregnant teenagers, substance abuse problems, or multiple pregnancies. Midwives also undertake ultrasound scans and provide antenatal care for women with problems in the Maternity Assessment Unit. Antenatal clinics are more specialised and multidisciplinary, where Consultants and midwives focus on women with specific problems (i.e. twins clinics and clinics for women with previous *"placentation pathology"*). Junior medical staff hours have been reduced substantially, with specialist registrars (SpRs) working shift patterns at less than 56 hours per week. Consultants now provide a much greater proportion of medical maternity care, there being dedicated consultant cover on the Delivery Suite, perhaps with the prospect of having to *"live-in"* for on-call duties in the near future. Interestingly, the caesarean section rate now nears 20%, compared to 4.9% and 12.7% in 1946 and 1986, respectively.

It is likely that the RVI Maternity Unit will have an ever-greater role in the provision of maternity care throughout the local area and beyond. A review of maternity services facilitated by the Tyne and Wear Strategic Health Authority has proposed the creation of a network of maternity care, consisting of specialist, medical and midwifery-led units. It is possible that one or more of the existing local medical units will reconfigure to a midwifery-led unit, with a likely increase in the number of women choosing to deliver at the Infirmary, which will also be pivotal to the development of this network, providing leadership in its development, forging ever-closer links and working relationships with neighbouring units.

Fig 6.21: New facilities built into the Leezes Wing, 2003 housing offices and expanded clinical facilities.

Fig 6.22: Delivery Suite (2006). "Water birth facility".

Newcastle clinicians and national roles

Almost twenty clinicians who have trained at the Infirmary have become Professors, some locally but mainly elsewhere, and since Farquhar Murray first sat on the RCOG Council in 1929, Infirmary staff have continued to fulfil crucial roles in the College's affairs. As well as important committee and working party duties over the last 25 years, several have also occupied official College positions: namely Members of Council (Derek Tacchi, John Lawson (from the NGH), Tom Lind and Paul Hilton), Honorary Treasurer (Derek Tacchi), Vice President (John Lawson) and Honorary Secretary, Bill Dunlop, who became President for 3 years in 2001.

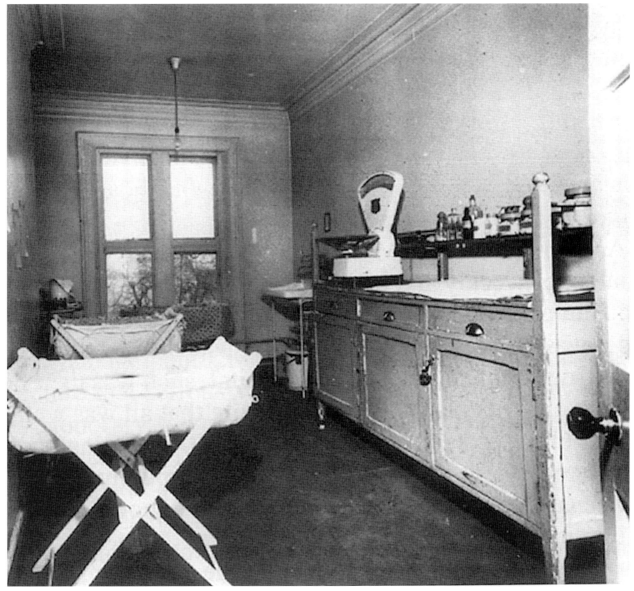

Fig 6.23: A reminder of how things were. Premature baby nursery, PMMH, Moor Edge, 1939-50. A striking contrast to the sophisticated accommodation for premature neonates now available in the RVI.

The Directorate's work is ever-changing but the current group of consultants, junior medical staff (although constantly changing) and dedicated, loyal midwifery and nursing staff are well able to advance Obstetrics and Gynaecology such that the Infirmary stays at the forefront of all that is best in clinical practice with flourishing academic activities alongside. Financial *"overspends"* are a constant headache and it is doubtful if these days the Trust could even contemplate reckoning with Ranken Lyle, who was often heard to say that *"...a hospital that has an overdraft is doing well."* Nevertheless, it does bring us full circle to the man who perhaps had the first vision of Obstetrics and Gynaecology under one roof and imbued his successors with that vision too.

Acknowledgements

Gratefully acknowledged is the permission given by Mr Derek Tacchi to use some illustrations from his book published by Bewick Press (Whitley Bay), now no longer in existence.

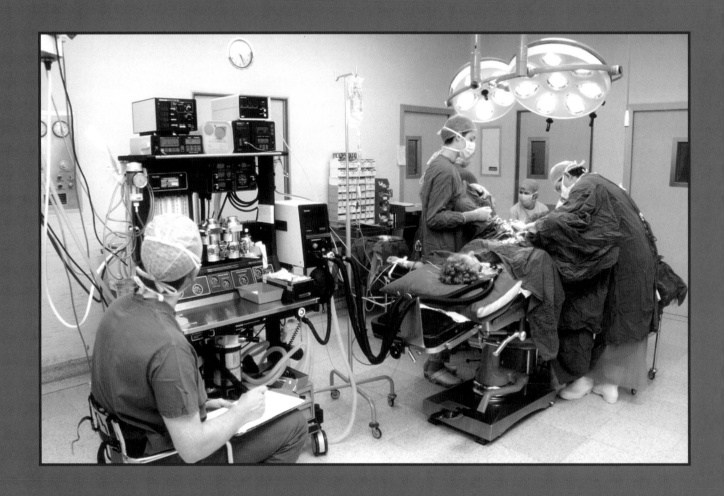

Chapter 7: *Anaesthesia and Intensive Care*
Joseph C. Stoddart

Developments in pain relief and safety in Critical Illness

When the Infirmary removed from the Forth Banks to its present site in 1906, anaesthesia was not a significant subject in the medical curriculum and Intensive Care (or Intensive Therapy) was not even considered as an entity. However, the Forth Banks Infirmary is now credited with having established the first Intensive Care Unit in the world, in 1801,[1] and at least one authority considers that the first person to receive the anaesthetic agent, chloroform, in England was a student in the Newcastle medical school during a demonstration, whilst the first death under chloroform anaesthesia in Britain occurred at Winlaton in 1848,[II] so the links with the region are well established.

At the end of the first year in the new site, the Anaesthetics Report in the Year Book was given by Dr W. Arnison who was named as the *"Anaesthetist to the Infirmary"*. The records of the next 30 years are limited to such annual reports, which included numbers of anaesthetics given, records of deaths (if any) and reports of the Coroner's inquests. The name attached to the report changed, but little information of value was given, with no mention of research, teaching or clinical advances in the subject.

Fig 7.2: Dr Philip Ayre.

Fig 7.3: Dr M. H. Armstrong Davison.

Many routine and most emergency anaesthetics were still being given by the resident staff, who had little or no training. This state of affairs was only acceptable because surgical demands and expectations were limited and there was no physical Department of Anaesthesia until 1947. Before this time there were a number of visiting anaesthetists who left their mark locally, many of whom also worked in other hospitals in the region, and towards the end of the 1930s Dr Philip Ayre (*Fig 7.2*) and Dr Armstrong Davison (*Fig 7.3*) joined the staff. Over the subsequent 40 years these and others altered the practice, teaching and status of anaesthesia. Dr Ayre is especially remembered for his T-piece technique and clinical skills which transformed the theory and practice of Paediatric and Neurosurgical Anaesthesia worldwide. This work was continued and developed by other RVI consultants, in particular Dr John Inkster, whose knowledge, inventiveness, and practical skills made paediatric anaesthesia into a specialty in its own right.

Dr Armstrong Davison, through his humour, intellect and forceful personality, combined with a willingness to try new methods, was responsible for attracting into anaesthesia many who subsequently became well known. He was also a historian of note who published the definitive text on the origin and significance of the Casket Letters in the trial of Mary Queen of Scots. Other members of the Department were instrumental in establishing and improving methods of providing obstetric analgesia and anaesthesia.

---

[1] Clark J. An account of the plan for the internal improvement and extension of the Infirmary at Newcastle. Newcastle. Edward Walker. 1801:13

[II] Bellamy Gardner H. Surgical Anaesthesia. London. Bailliere, Tindall and Cox. 1909. 15-16

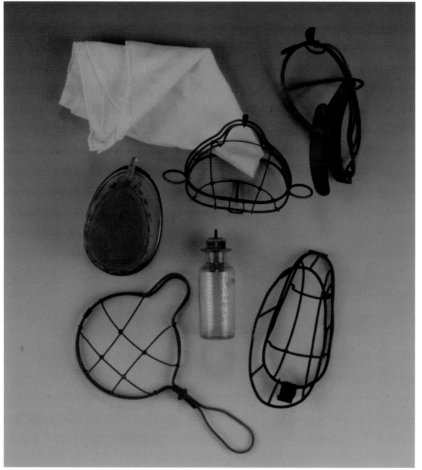

Fig 7.4: Anaesthetic masks at the time of the move, and for many years thereafter.

Fig 7.5: Professor E. A. ("Gar") Pask.

Great progress in anaesthesia and resuscitation techniques, some developing coincidentally, occurred during the Second World War. A most significant development was the recognition of the value and necessity of controlling a patient's breathing during upper abdominal and open chest surgery (controlled ventilation), sometimes when combined with the use of muscle relaxant (curariform) drugs, which were introduced in 1942. This greatly increased the anaesthetist's responsibility for his patient, while at the same time facilitating developments in surgery. Many of these techniques were introduced to the Infirmary (and elsewhere) by those anaesthetists who had served with the armed forces. In Fig 7.4 are shown some of the types of anaesthetic mask used until the late 1930s, contrasting with a modern anaesthetic machine which is shown in Fig 7.1.

Among them was Dr (subsequently Professor) E.A. "Gar" Pask. (Fig 7.5) After qualifying from Cambridge and the London Hospital, Pask became a Resident Anaesthetist in Oxford, and in 1942 joined the RAF and was posted to the Institute of Aviation Medicine, Farnborough. With his training and special interests in resuscitation and the effects of hypoxia, he became involved in research into many aspects of military aviation. These included the prevention of hypoxia during parachute descent from high altitude, the effects of exposure to extremes of temperature, and survival after immersion incidents, together with an investigation to establish the most effective form of artificial respiration. Because of the *"exigencies of the service"* which meant the pressures of wartime, most of the experimental work associated with these investigations was performed upon Pask himself. It often involved subjecting him to repeated deep anaesthesia, sometimes combined with muscular paralysis, immersion in a swimming pool while unconscious, exposure to simulated high altitude and similar hazards. He was awarded the OBE for this work, but his early death was at least in part the result of these activities.

At the end of the war he was invited to become Professor in several University Departments of Physiology, but he chose to return to anaesthesia, and became first, Reader, and subsequently, Professor of Anaesthesia in Durham University Medical School, with his clinical base in the RVI in Newcastle.

Here he undertook research in a variety of fields but principally into the development of satisfactory apparatus for producing controlled respiration together with elucidating its effects on cardiovascular and respiratory physiology. This was a very fertile period, and during it he had a succession of Departmental First Assistants who subsequently became Professors and Heads of Department both in the Infirmary and elsewhere.

The clinical consequences of this research programme resulted in the routine use of techniques of controlled ventilation in the operating theatre during surgical procedures, and also in the wards for the maintenance of breathing for patients with prolonged respiratory paralysis or weakness (e.g. those with tetanus, myasthenia gravis and polyneuritis), multiple injuries, severe sepsis and similar conditions. This demanded expertise not only in techniques of respiratory control, but also in resuscitation, the prevention and treatment of infection, nutritional support, pain relief and sedation, fluid and electrolyte balance. Such was the respect in which Pask was held that in 1956 the then Professor of Medicine set aside beds on his own ward for the use of the Department of Anaesthesia. This was a revolutionary step which formalised the connection between anaesthesia and intensive care in the Infirmary.

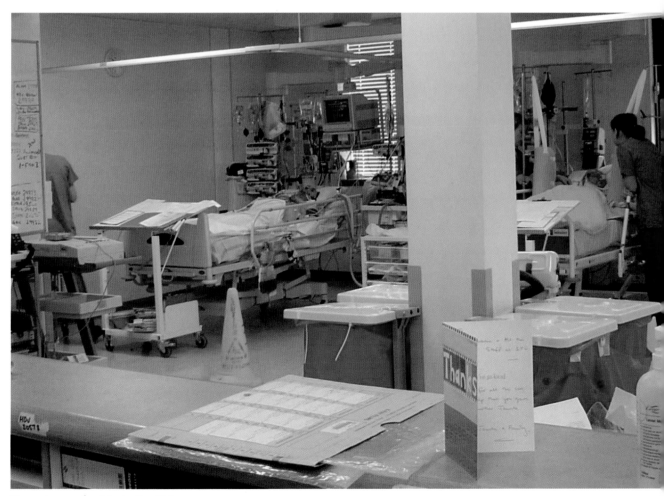

Fig 7.6: A corner of an Intensive Care Unit.

In his position as Head of the University Department of Anaesthesia, Pask was responsible for the organisation of undergraduate training. He was also a Vice-Dean of the Board of the Faculty (later Royal College) of Anaesthetists, and organised the Regional Post Graduate Training in Anaesthesia, and rapidly improved the quality and status of anaesthesia in the region, which had noteworthy results on recruitment into the specialty.

Although initially the Department shared the care of critically ill, dependent patients in many other wards in the hospital, this exposed the severe limitations presented by uncertainty concerning ultimate clinical responsibility, inadequate continuity of care and major difficulties with nursing. In 1970 a purpose-built 8-bedded Intensive Care Unit (ICU), one of the first in the country, was opened, which was under the supervision of a consultant anaesthetist. From the outset it was recognised that a period of exposure to the ICU (*Fig 7.6*) formed a vital part of the training of junior doctors from other specialties, and the resident medical staff of the ICU consisted of rotational trainees in medicine, surgery and anaesthesia. In addition to its clinical value, this also raised the awareness of the trainees to the skills and problems of their colleagues in other specialties. A structured system of post-registration nurse training was also begun. The next development was the establishment of a formal Senior Registrar training programme in intensive care, which was open to all specialties and which proved to be popular with those who wished to practice as Intensivists after obtaining a Consultant Post. With the alterations in post-graduate training, this was subsumed into the SpR (Specialist Registrar) training scheme, with the option of achieving a CCST (Certificate of Completion of Specialist Training) in Intensive Care.

A logical result of the anaesthetist's pharmacological training was to increase his contribution to the treatment of acute and chronic pain. Initially, this was limited to prescribing routine post-operative pain relief, but this was widely seen to be unsatisfactory, and in the Infirmary it was followed by the establishment of the "Pain" ward round during which an anaesthetist could determine the optimum safe drug (or drugs) regimen for individual patients in the surgical wards and elsewhere and the best route of their administration. One obvious result of this activity was the now routine use of Patient-Controlled-Analgesia apparatus which has been a blessing to many thousands of patients.

Following on from this came the Combined Pain Clinic, a development which originated in the USA. In the RVI Pain Clinic, anaesthetists and other specialists (usually a psychologist or psychiatrist and a pharmacologist), after a detailed assessment, decided (and still do) upon the most acceptable form of treatment for patients with chronic pain, which may be musculoskeletal in origin, such as from arthritis or following trauma, due to neuronal pathology or injury, or may be the result of malignant disease. In addition to the use of pharmacological agents, physical methods of treatment, acupuncture and other techniques are used, with the objective of achieving mobilisation or return to normal activity for patients who have been severely limited by pain. Although initially, patients could only be referred to the Pain Clinic by RVI consultants, its value was quickly recognised and referrals from general practice were soon accepted.

Three recent developments deserve notice. In the last ten years, the Royal College of Anaesthetists has initiated changes in postgraduate education which have resulted in the creation of Regional Schools of Anaesthesia, one of which is centred in the RVI. These have the responsibility of organising and supervising post-graduate training. Both of necessity and by design, this has required that trainees spend fixed periods in selected hospitals in the region, and can complete their training without having to travel to other regions. This has obvious advantages but also limits the variety and range of experience which would be obtainable from a period spent outside the region or overseas.

Another development has been the recognition that anaesthetic departments possess the expertise to accept responsibility for training cardiopulmonary resuscitation. This is a very heavy commitment in which medical and nursing students, paramedics, members of the armed services and others are taught on patients, models and simulators, in the department or in anaesthetic rooms, the skills of basic resuscitation, which may include airway management, external cardiac massage, endotracheal intubation, venepuncture and the insertion of intravenous lines, as well as cardiac defibrillation. It has also led to the establishment of a pilot scheme in which a selected group of trained nurses is being taught how to provide anaesthesia under the supervision of a consultant in the safe environment of an operating room suite.

To many of the previous members of the department, a less satisfactory development has been the absorption of the Department of Anaesthesia into the Faculty of Health Sciences. The sequelae include the disappearance of the University Chair of Anaesthesia, which historically was the second such chair in the United Kingdom, and with it the potential for discouragement of independent research, which in turn, reduces the attraction of the subject to graduates with an academic bent. Among other reasons, which include university economy, it has been claimed that this is one result of the present-day perfection of the science of anaesthesia, such that the impression has been gained that any future improvements can only be in minor alterations to agents, methods and apparatus, not requiring much research to establish. If this is indeed the case, it may suggest that trust in second sight has not been abolished by science and experience.

Postscript (Editor's note)

Despite the rule (all rules must sometimes be broken) that those still living should not normally be mentioned in contributions to history, I feel that it is essential to mention that Dr Joe Stoddart, author of this chapter, was the man primarily responsible for introducing intensive care to Newcastle while Dr John Inkster achieved an international reputation for his design of an anaesthetic apparatus for use in neonates, including premature infants.

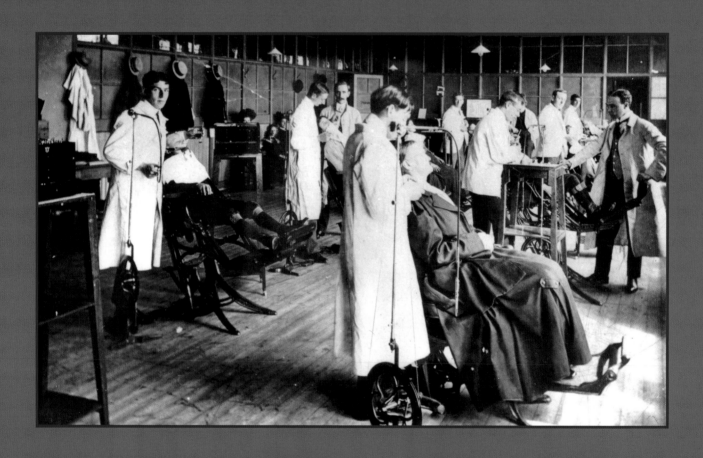

Chapter 8: *The Dental Hospital & School 1895 - 2005*

John Murray

The first Dental Hospital for Newcastle was opened by the Mayor on 22 April 1895 in Nelson Street, the seventh dental hospital to be opened in this country. It moved to larger premises in the Handyside Arcade (now Eldon Gardens), Percy Street in 1906. (*Fig 8.1*) With the support of Sir George Hare Philipson, physician to the Infirmary and Professor of Medicine, the University of Durham instituted a Licence in Dental Surgery in 1911.

The passing of the Dentists Act in 1921, which restricted the practice of dentistry to registered dentists and registered medical practitioners, resulted in an increased demand for student places. This put further pressure on the resources available in the Handyside Arcade. Application was made to the Royal Victoria Infirmary for part of the Orthopaedic Buildings to be let to the Dental Hospital. This had the support of the newly constituted Dental Board of the United Kingdom and Sir Robert Bolam, Registrar of the College of Medicine.

Developments on the RVI Site

At a special meeting of the Governors of the RVI on 5 December 1930, formal approval was given to the proposal to grant a 99-year lease to the College of Medicine to provide a Dental Hospital on the RVI site. The College, in conjunction with the Hospital, was going to arrange a joint appeal to the public to produce the funds required, but in the event this was not necessary because Sir Arthur Munro Sutherland came forward with a gift of £12,000. The new School buildings were officially opened by the Chancellor of Durham University, the Marquis of Londonderry, on 28 January 1932, who paid tribute to Sir Arthur's *"generous and magnificent gift"*. (*Fig 8.2*)

Fig 8.2: Architect's drawing of the Dental Hospital, 1931.

Sir Arthur expressed his thanks in a breezy speech *"Sir Robert Bolam has told you what I did"*, he said, *"but he has not said what he did in this matter. He asked me to meet him in London, and took me to see the dental hospital built by Mr Eastman, of Kodak fame. Then he asked me to go to Percy Street to see the best we had in the shape of a dental hospital here. At both places he rubbed it in that there were no proper dental hospital facilities between Leeds and Edinburgh. So what else could I do? As you all know, I am proud of Newcastle, and we are not going to let London, Edinburgh or Leeds beat us. I think you will be convinced after looking around, that Newcastle can now hold its own with any dental school in the country."* Thus, as a result of civic pride and personal generosity, the Newcastle upon Tyne Dental Hospital and Sutherland Dental School became firmly embedded within the Royal Victoria Infirmary. The building still stands, near the entrance to the multi-storey car park (*Fig 8.2*) at the time of writing, but may be demolished as part of the major RVI development.

The first Dean of the Dental School and Hospital, Mr Robert Markham, held the post from 1895 to 1907. He was succeeded by Mr J. J. Jameson who retired in October 1925. Mr Jameson was President of the British Dental Association in 1922, when the Annual General Meeting of the BDA was held in Newcastle. Mr Coltman, who had been elected to the staff of the Dental Hospital in 1900, was appointed Dean until his retirement in 1935. Up to this point all Dental Deans had been part-time appointments, but at this juncture Sir Robert Bolam played a further crucial part in the development of dental education in Newcastle. He suggested that with Mr Coltman's imminent retirement, the time had now come to consider the appointment of a full-time Principal. The new appointment would include the duties of Director of Dental Studies and Sub-Dean within the Faculty of Medicine. He also thought that it might be an advantage if the appointment carried with it some administrative functions on behalf of the Hospital Committee. The Dental Board of the United Kingdom made a definite offer of a grant towards the salary of a full-time Director of Dental Studies and this post was approved by the University.

Fig 8.3: *The Conservation Room of the Royal Victoria Infirmary Dental School and Hospital. On the right, towards the back is D. N. Allan, later to become Professor of Operative Dentistry in Newcastle.*

At the meeting of the Hospital Committee of Management on 4 June 1936, Sir Robert Bolam intimated that the Council of the College had appointed Mr Robert V. Bradlaw as Professor of Dental Surgery and Director of Dental Studies. The Hospital Committee agreed that he should also be given the status of Honorary Dental Surgeon and Director of the Dental Hospital. One year later, in 1937, the College of Medicine and Armstrong College were merged into King's College, Newcastle upon Tyne, in the University of Durham. The Dental School became the Dental Department of the Medical School, King's College.

Fig 8.4: *The exterior of the refurbished Medical School in Northumberland Road/College Street, which became the Sutherland Dental School on 29 May 1948.*

The Bradlaw Years

In spite of the difficulties caused by the start of the Second World War, Professor Bradlaw continued to drive the Dental School and Hospital forward. (*Fig 8.3*) The number of students admitted increased, so that by 1942 105 dental students were registered, the third highest in the country. The building was proving unable to cope with the increase in patients and students, so extensions and alterations were planned. By the end of the war, in 1945, 167 students had been enrolled.

In 1946, it was decided that, rather than extending the present building on the RVI site, the Dental School and Hospital should be moved into the former College of Medicine building, Northumberland Road and College Street, which had stood empty since 1941. (*Fig 8.4*) The official opening of the new premises of the Sutherland Dental School took place on 29 May 1948 and was performed by the Right Honourable Aneurin Bevan MP, Minister of Health. This was especially significant because the "new" Dental School and Hospital was the first hospital to be opened following the announcement of the National Health Service Act. Mr Bevan said that he was anxious that dentists in the National Health Service should have the greatest possible clinical freedom compatible with reasonable safeguards and maintenance of proper standards of treatment. (*Fig 8.5*) A great effort was required to improve the dental health of the nation. Mr Bevan also thanked Sir Arthur Sutherland for his gift of £50,000 for the provision of additional equipment. (*Fig 8.6*) The Dental Hospital continued to grow during the 1950s. Expertise in oral surgery, restorative dentistry and orthodontics increased but the expansion in student numbers, encouraged by Professor Bradlaw, resulted in clinical resources being stretched to the limit. (*Fig 8.7*)

Looking back over the thirty years between 1929-1959 it is apparent that the destiny of the Dental Hospital and School was determined to a great extent by two men. One, Sir Arthur Munro Sutherland, motivated by civic pride, provided substantial financial aid at two critical points, enabling the Hospital and School to be re-housed; the other, Professor Robert Bradlaw, drove this institution forward so that it became one of the best dental schools in the country.

Fig 8.5: Professor Bradlaw, The Right Honourable Aneurin Bevan, Sir Arthur Munro Sutherland and the Lord Mayor of Newcastle at the official opening of the New Dental School and Hospital on 29 May 1948.

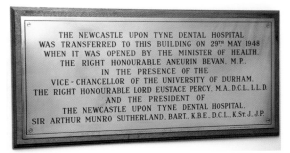

Fig 8.6: Plaque commemorating the opening of the Dental School and Hospital in 1948. (Now displayed in the entrance to the Dental Hospital in Richardson Road.)

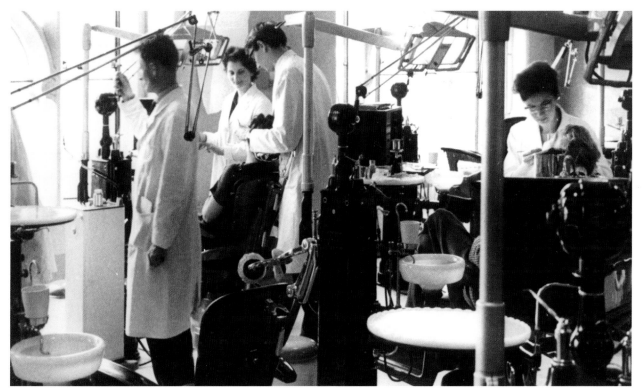

Fig 8.7: The Conservation Clinic in Northumberland Road/College Street in 1961.

Planning for a new Dental Hospital and School

The possibility of rebuilding the Dental Hospital and School at the northern end of the RVI site was first mentioned in 1957. When Professor Bradlaw left in 1959 to become Dean and Director of the Eastman Dental Hospital in London (the one Sir Arthur Munro Sutherland had visited in 1931) it was left to his successors, Professor Maurice Hallett, appointed Dean of the Dental School, and Professor Lovel, Sub-Dean and Director of the Dental Hospital, to drive forward the planning for a new dental hospital and school. The Rector of King's College, Dr C. I. C. Bosanquet, reported that a new Dental School and Hospital was to be constructed, in close association with the new Medical School, on land belonging to the Governors of the United Newcastle Hospitals. *"The new Medical School, Dental School and Hospital complex will be developed in such a way as to form with King's College a single large educational and hospital precinct."*

The next fifteen years were dominated by the need to negotiate, plan, design and build the new dental hospital and school. The Board of Governors and the University agreed not only to the dental hospital and school being built on the newly acquired eight acre site adjacent to the Royal Victoria Infirmary but also to its being incorporated in Phase 1 of the overall development plan. (*Fig 8.8*) In 1971 scale plans of the new building became available. Professor Hallett cut the first turf on Wednesday, 29 May 1974 to initiate the building programme. The building was "topped out" on 14 January 1976 and officially opened by the Chancellor of the University, his Grace the Duke of Northumberland, on 15 September 1978, accompanied by Professor Roy Storer, who had succeeded Maurice Hallett as Dean in October 1977. (*Fig 8.9*)

Fig 8.8: *Greenfield site at the north end of the RVI.*

Fig 8.9: *Entrance to the Dental Hospital in Richardson Road, opened on 15 September 1978.*

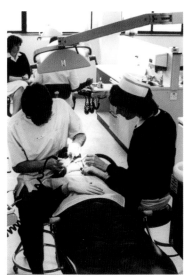

Fig 8.10: Conservation Clinic, Newcastle Dental Hospital 1985. Dental student, seated, treating a patient and supported by a dental nurse (close support dentistry). Compare this arrangement with that shown in Figs 8.1, 8.3 and 8.7.

Relationship between the RVI and the Dental Hospital

A formal relationship embedding the Dental Hospital within the RVI has existed since 1936 when the Hospital Committee of Management appointed Professor Bradlaw to be Director of the Dental Hospital. He was succeeded in that post by Professor Lovel in 1960 who worked tirelessly with Professor Hallett to ensure that the needs of the Dental Hospital were understood by architects. Hallett recalls one meeting *"that stands out indelibly amongst my recollections"*. In 1962 representatives of all the authorities concerned with the new Dental School and Hospital were called to the Ministry of Health in London to discuss the critical decision of 'to go or not to go'. After much discussion and, at times, fairly acerbic observations on the part of the Ministry architects, the chairman announced that if Professors Hallett and Lovel would agree to a building of less than 100,000 square feet, without circulation space, it would be approved. Hallet and Lovel had always been convinced that the absolute minimum of floor space for a student's operating cubicle, without circulation space, was 100 square feet. They never departed from that basic premise, despite many efforts to make them agree to some reduction and the Dental Hospital at Newcastle developed eventually around this cardinal figure. Hallett commented *"This in short was one of the most momentous experiences of my period of Deanship."*

The argument with architects, which two clinicians won in 1962, has benefited all who have worked in the Dental Hospital for the last twenty five years. The "circulation space" they battled for gave subsequent architects the opportunity to modernise and re-equip clinical areas to the exacting clinical standards required today. When the RVI Hospital Trust was created in 1995 the Dental Hospital became one of the eight clinical directorates. It was then incorporated as one of nineteen clinical directorates when the RVI, Freeman and General Hospitals merged to form the Newcastle upon Tyne Hospitals NHS Trust in 1998.

Recent developments at Richardson Road

The building, planned in the 1960s and built in the 1970s, has proved to be an excellent resource for the treatment of patients and the teaching of students. Because it was Phase I in the overall plan, it allowed dental hospital and school activities to develop whilst building work continued on the rest of the site. The Medical School was opened in 1984 and the Leazes Wing in 1992, so enabling the original plan of a medico-dental teaching hospital complex to come to fruition.

During the last 25 years parts of the building have been re-equipped to ensure that patients are treated in the best environment and that students have the benefit of using up to date dental equipment. The modern dental surgery of today is very different from that which students were used to in the previous dental hospitals in Newcastle. (*Fig 8.10*) The Oral Surgery facilities on the ground floor of the hospital were upgraded in 1998 to enable day stay surgery under general anaesthesia and sedation to be developed, in line with a government decision that general anaesthesia should not be available in dental practices, but concentrated in hospitals where all the appropriate facilities are available. A Dental Emergency Clinic was introduced to improve access to dental care and give students the opportunity to treat patients with acute problems. The entrance to the Dental Hospital was improved at the same time. (*Fig 8.11*) This unit was opened by the Secretary of State for Health, Mr Alan Milburn, on 9 March 2001, following in the footsteps of his

Fig 8.12: *Plaque commemorating opening of Initial Treatment Clinic.*

Fig 8.11: *Illuminated glass screen, by Bridget Jones and Sue Woolhouse, in the entrance hall of the Dental Hospital in Richardson Road.*

predecessor Mr Aneurin Bevan over fifty years ago. (*Fig 8.12*) The latest area to be redeveloped in 2003 was a Restorative Dentistry Clinic, comprising twenty dental chairs of the latest design, together with eight operating microscopes which enable many restorative procedures, particularly endodontic (root canal) treatment to be carried out to a higher degree of accuracy than ever before. (*Fig 8.13*)

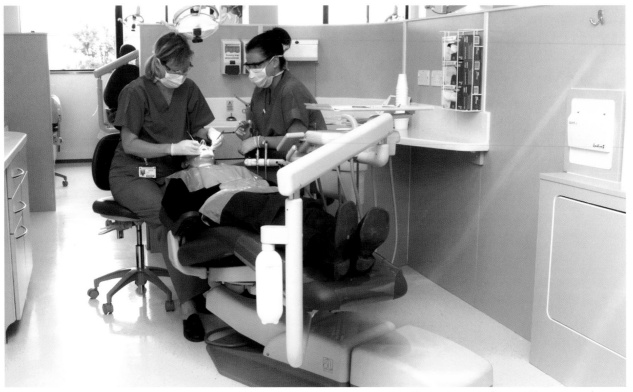

Fig 8.13: *Restorative Dentistry Unit, re-equipped in 2003.*

There are only ten dental hospitals in England. Thus the Newcastle upon Tyne Hospitals Trust should benefit from having a concentration of talent covering all the dental specialties. These specialties would not be in Newcastle to the same extent if there were not a dental school. Dental academics aim to provide excellent teaching and research in the discipline of dentistry, so bringing added value to the University and the NHS.

The Dental School has contributed consistently to the sporting activities of the Medical Faculty, especially the Medical Rugby Club. The records of 1939 included *"Congratulations to Professor Bradlaw on such a successful season as President of the Medical Rugby Club and Mr G. G. T. Tregarthen on the wonderful results he has had with the team."* Danie Serfontein (1952-1958) played for both Medicals and Durham University. He captained Durham to the UAU Championship in 1956. His commitment to rugby culminated in his appointment as President of the Rugby Football Union in 1992-93. W. D. G. Morgan (1955-61) played for the Medicals 1st XV, Northumberland and was Captain of the UAU Rugby Team, before gaining nine international caps for England. He was an England Selector from 1976 to 1985. David Caplan (1972-77) gained his first England cap in the match against Scotland in March 1978. Paddy Johns, a Newcastle dental student for three years from 1987-1989 before transferring to Dublin to complete his degree, gained many caps for Ireland in the 1990s. More recently almost half the Medicals team which won the Pilkington Shield at Twickenham on 4 May 1996 were dental students or recent graduates.

The Dental Hospital has progressed since it was founded 110 years ago. The General Dental Council reported in its Visitation to Newcastle in 2004 that *"clinical facilities are generally of a high standard... overall there is an impression of spaciousness, well maintained fabric, high quality equipment and attractive patient reception and waiting areas"*. The civic pride, articulated so clearly by Sir Arthur Munro Sutherland in the 1930s, is still evident today as the Newcastle Dental Hospital continues to develop in the twenty first century.

ROYAL VICTORIA INFIRMARY,

NEWCASTLE-UPON-TYNE.

OUT=PATIENT MENTAL CLINIC.

By arrangement with the Newcastle-upon-Tyne Corporation, an Out-patient Clinic has been established at the ROYAL VICTORIA INFIRMARY for the treatment of persons suffering from mental ailments, where those who require advice may have the benefit of skilled treatment which may in many cases prevent a complete breakdown in mental health. This is a new departure, the object of which is to encourage patients to seek treatment of mental illness in the early and curable stages. The holding of such a Clinic at a General Hospital emphasises the fact that mental ailments have much in common with bodily illness. This venture will no doubt prove to be a definite step in the right direction, and it is hoped that persons suffering in any way mentally will take full advantage of the Clinic, which will be open in the Out-patients' Hall of the Infirmary, on Friday afternoons from 2·30 to 3·30, commencing on 8th July, 1932.

Chapter 9: *Psychiatry in the RVI*
– from small beginnings   Kurt Schapira

The first public provision for the treatment of the mentally ill in Newcastle upon Tyne is recorded as early as 1763 when the Common Council raised a subscription for the building of a Lunatic Hospital. This was opened in 1764 and accommodated a mere 19 patients. The physician in charge Dr John Hall (1733- 1793) was a prominent Tyneside physician, son of a barber-surgeon, and educated at the Newcastle Royal Grammar School. He was a man of some enterprise and was also instrumental in the creation of a second hospital built in the next year.[1] The growth of the population over the next century resulted in ever-increasing demands and the creation of larger hospitals, which became known as asylums. These served the population of the region, and were euphemistically blessed with the names of saints. In the case of Newcastle, the new Borough Asylum was opened in 1869 and is now St. Nicholas Hospital in Gosforth, much diminished in recent years. In my time it was referred to by the local population as Coxlodge, the district in which it was located. Only patients suffering from serious mental illness were seen and admitted, often under compulsory detention for their own safety or that of others. Psychiatry at that time was considered a discipline whose patients were treated apart from those suffering from physical illness.

The birth of Psychiatry in the RVI is inauspiciously recorded in its Annual Report of 1932. It reports the opening of an Out-Patients Mental Clinic at the Infirmary on 8th July 1932, by arrangement with the Newcastle upon Tyne Corporation (*Fig 9.1*). The Clinic was held on Fridays at 2.30 to 3.30pm in the Out-Patients Hall of the Infirmary. The report goes on to say that *"the Clinic has proved of much benefit to the general public"* and that 386 attendances had been recorded up to the end of the year. The report concludes with the statement that *"it was gratifying to the Committee to know that their part in the establishment of this Clinic has received so much public appreciation"*.

The next important phase in the development of Psychiatry in the RVI was the creation of a University Department of Psychological Medicine in 1948, with the appointment of Professor Alexander Kennedy to the Foundation Chair. It proved to be an ideal appointment, since among his many gifts were negotiating skills combined with boundless energy. This resulted in a staggering number of new appointments, which surprised many, including those who had been on the committees which had agreed to their funding!

The new Department took over the Sutherland building, previously the Dental Hospital, facing King's Hall across Queen Victoria Road. (*Fig 9.2*) It housed the Academic Department and was also the nerve centre for all the NHS Psychiatric Services, providing a busy Out-Patient Department and a comprehensive Ward Consultation Service. In addition to creating new academic medical posts, psychologists and social workers were appointed to provide the infrastructure of a Department which was to become a Centre of Excellence, long before the term became a status to be aspired to. Links with Neurology were established within the hospital by the creation of an Electroencephalography Department under the aegis of John W. Osselton, which in time provided a Regional Service and which by its research achieved an international reputation.

A large part of the NHS work was very ably provided by Robert Orton, a canny Yorkshire man, whose diminutive size was combined with a vast appetite for clinical work and it was he, as Senior Lecturer and Honorary Consultant, who established the firm integration of psychiatry into the daily clinical life of the hospital. The early 1950s also saw the appointment of a number of the local Mental Hospital Superintendents as Associate Physicians in the Department, with some conducting an out-patient clinic once a week. Thus, links were established between the Teaching Hospital and the surrounding mental hospitals, links which were to grow over the years and which proved to be of great benefit to patients and in the training of undergraduate and postgraduate students.

---

[1] Le Gassicke, J, 1993
  History of Psychiatry on Tyneside in Medicine in Northumbria
  Publishers: The Pybus Society for the History and Bibliography of Medicine

---

Facilities for in-patients, however, were not available on site, and were provided in a building at Newcastle General Hospital that had previously served as the Poor Law Observation Unit. The new unit, which became known as the DPM (Department of Psychological Medicine) was a joint NHS / University venture and so became *pari passu* both part of the RVI and the General Hospital!

Alexander Kennedy was a towering figure in every respect, whose charisma did not disappoint the concept held by his medical colleagues and his students of what psychiatrists should be like. The Lambretta moped which precariously transported his large bulk at excessive speeds, as well as his skills exhibited in the boxing ring in the basement of the Medical School, were but two memorable aspects. Medical students of a respectable size (which included the writer), were at considerable risk of being invited to a few sparring rounds at lunch time. Refusal was not considered advisable. The idea of a whole hearted punch at any part of the professorial body was to say the least daunting, even though there would be no such hesitation in the reverse direction. The sight of Alexander Kennedy and 'Bobby' Orton who was Senior Lecturer, walking together down the long RVI corridor, separated from each other by an altitude of more than twelve inches became a familiar experience by which they are remembered by many of their colleagues. And then there were the many tales, particularly of Kennedy's war-time exploits, which ranged from the extraordinary to the incredible….

Kennedy was essentially a builder of 'empires', and having established an academic department, which also provided an integrated and effective service component for patients, he welcomed new challenges. Hence at the end of 1955, after only seven years, he left Newcastle for Edinburgh where he laid the foundations of an even larger department which in size and reputation grew to become another of the outstanding centres of psychiatry in the country.

He was succeeded by Martin Roth in 1956 as Professor and Head of Department who oversaw the growth and development of a department that achieved a national, and indeed an international, reputation. At the time, he was the youngest Professor of Psychiatry to be appointed, having gained his neurological expertise whilst working with Sir Russell (later Lord) Brain and in Psychiatry at the Maudsley Hospital, London. He had also worked at the Crichton Royal with Willy Mayer-Gross, who left Heidelberg in 1933 and whose pioneer contributions to phenomenology in the field of psychiatry have had profound and lasting effects on British psychiatry. His appointment saw the beginning of a new era of psychiatry in the RVI in which clinical research flourished and, not surprisingly, therefore attracted an unusual number of gifted psychiatrists, many from a background of general medicine and neurology, who would later occupy Chairs both in this country and overseas: R. Ball (Melbourne), S. Brandon (Leicester), T. Fahy (Galway) J. L. Gibbons (Southampton), I. M. Goodyer[II] (Cambridge), D. Kay (Tasmania), L. Kiloh (Sydney), I. Kolvin[III] (London), A. R. Nicol[IV] (Leicester), F. Oyebode (Birmingham), D. Savage (Psychology - Perth), J. Scott (Glasgow and later Maudsley) and A. Whitlock (Brisbane).

The way clinical research and clinical practice were inextricably linked was one of the major hallmarks of the department - a *modus vivendi* introduced and encouraged by 'the Prof' who expected every member of the Department to be involved in a research project. Although mood disorders (depressive illness and anxiety states) were the major area of research of the Department, numerous other investigations, such as the epidemiology of deliberate self-harm and suicide, and schizophrenia, in collaboration with colleagues at St. Nicholas, were pursued. All such projects had their origins in clinical work and received all the support they needed from colleagues with special expertise in such areas as epidemiology and statistics. The latter were handled by Dr Roger Garside, Senior Lecturer in Clinical Psychology, a gifted statistician who was equally at home with clinical problems as with the appropriate method with which they were best studied. Funds, as always, were in short supply, but the Medical Research Council, recognising the importance

[II] Chair in Child Psychiatry
[III] Chair in Child Psychiatry
[IV] Chair in Child Psychiatry

Fig 9.3: Claremont House.

of proposed projects and the high standards of the investigations, was generous in its support. The result was the publication of many seminal studies, mainly in relation to the classification of affective disorders and their treatment, which have become part of the classic psychiatric literature. The first description of the Phobic Anxiety Depersonalisation Syndrome was but one example of what could be achieved by meticulous clinical observation combined with rigorous statistical analysis of data.

Out-patient clinics which, until 'Sectorisation', a scheme of dubious merit which came into effect in the mid-eighties, served a large population and received referrals from all over the counties of Northumberland and Durham, and even further afield.

The reputation of the Department resulted in the referral of ever-increasing numbers of patients, many suffering from neuroses and requiring special facilities. To provide these, Claremont House, an elegant Victorian House adjacent to the Infirmary was acquired by the RVI and converted into a Neurosis Day Unit which also had limited in-patient facilities, with patients spending the weekends at home with their families. (*Fig 9.3*) This was a novel arrangement at the time and viewed by some of our non-psychiatric colleagues with some envy, reflected in the name they gave it - "The Psychiatric Summer Palace"! During the sixties many patients with severe agoraphobia, a condition which had been the subject of a number of seminal studies published by members of the Department, were successfully treated with new treatment regimens. Specialties such as Psychogeriatrics and Child Psychiatry blossomed and resulted in the provision of out-patient and in-patient facilities, the Brighton Clinic situated behind the Department of Psychological Medicine (DPM), at Newcastle General Hospital for the former and in a new Unit, the Nuffield Child Psychiatry Unit, adjacent to the Fleming Childrens' Hospital in Jesmond for the latter.

Within the RVI, close links with all other specialties grew during the next decades. This was largely due to the increasing contact achieved by an effective consultation service which led to a better understanding of how patient care may be improved when both physical and mental aspects of the patient's illness received recognition. Such collaboration was educational and enjoyable so that we kept up with the latest developments in other specialties and our colleagues received an important part of what is now called their 'Continuing Professional Development'.

My own special interest in anorexia nervosa resulted in sharing the treatment of these, often difficult, patients with a physician on a medical ward for which I was given two beds. This arrangement not only often proved very successful as regards the patient's response to treatment, but over the years provided excellent training for nursing staff in the understanding and management of these patients. Similarly, up to three beds were allocated on Ward 6 for patients who required both neurological and psychiatric assessment and management.

Collaboration with colleagues in other departments resulted in the establishment of a Pain Relief Clinic, in a study group looking at the relationship of thyroid over-activity to anxiety states, and also in the formation of a Gender Dysphoria Panel which assessed and advised on the management of patients with transsexualism, a condition in which Dr C. N. Armstrong, Senior Physician and Clinical Sub Dean, had established an international reputation. It was the first such panel in the country, comprising of two psychiatrists, a clinical psychologist, an endocrinologist, a social worker, a speech therapist, a plastic surgeon, a genito urinary surgeon, and a lawyer. The work of this panel, and that of the many other collaborative activities as well as the major psychiatric research projects that continued throughout this time, resulted in many important publications which made Newcastle a Centre of Excellence, with an international reputation.

1971 saw the foundation of the Royal College of Psychiatrists and the election of Professor (by then) Sir Martin Roth as its first President. The invitation to take up the Cambridge University Foundation Chair of Psychiatry in 1977 was one he could not refuse. Apart from the immensely important developments, Martin Roth left behind him, like his predecessor, a truly remarkable fund of stories, albeit of a very different kind; the two men were as different from one another as chalk from cheese. His love of music (he was a fine pianist), and his immense knowledge of literature were often evident in his professional life and more than compensated for the difficulties he had with mechanical problems as, for instance, with his motor car. Help in these matters was readily available from his colleagues. Martin Roth is remembered for his perceptive clinical acumen and his gift as a teacher who taught and expected from his students the most rigorous standards of clinical practice. His clinical notes were literary masterpieces and his turn of phrase often drew admiration and occasionally smiles from his colleagues, as when in the case notes of one of his patients the following sentence appeared under the section on 'Family History': *"Mother a lapsed Catholic, Father an unlapsed psychopath."* Punctuality was not one of his virtues, but equally he was always worth waiting for…

His successor, Donald Eccleston, arrived from Edinburgh where he had been Deputy Director of the MRC Unit. His special interest in animal laboratory work stimulated the development of this aspect of the academic activity in the department. The special interest and expertise in affective (mood) disorders which had developed over the years inevitably led to the referral of a number of patients with chronic depressive illness who were included in a number of therapeutic trials. Another important development was the establishment of a region-wide rotational postgraduate training programme.

The eighties saw great changes, both within the organisation of the National Health Service and, more particularly, in the treatment of the mentally ill. The move to close the large mental hospitals and the care of patients in the community was reflected in the closure of a large part of St. Nicholas Hospital. 'Beds' were no longer given the priority they once had. However, a new and larger In-patient Unit, The Hadrian Clinic at Newcastle General Hospital, replaced the old DPM on site.

The growth of psychotherapy as an integral part of clinical practice resulted in the conversion of Claremont House into a Department of Psychotherapy.

The major change within the Department in the late eighties and early nineties was the creation by the Trust and the University of new academic posts, with the creation of a number of 'Chairs', such as that in Old Age Psychiatry, with each new professor pursuing and developing his own particular special interest. This development was accompanied by what in many ways must be considered a major step in the history of psychiatry in the RVI, the opening of the new Leazes Wing. This significant expansion came into being when psychiatrist Gerard Vaughan was Minister of Health and it was he who was a strong proponent of a new Psychiatric Department with an in-patient unit. The in-patient unit comprised an adult acute ward of 21 beds and a smaller ward of ten beds dedicated to the treatment of patients with affective disorders, (in particular those with bipolar illness) and those suffering from eating disorders. Improved out-patient facilities and ample space for the Academic Department with its research and teaching commitments, resulted in a psychiatric facility of which any teaching hospital could be proud. A formalised liaison service was created so that all patients with deliberate self harm and patients in medical and surgical clinics in need of psychiatric assessment would be seen promptly. A small but active Occupational Therapy Department completed the range of therapeutic facilities the new development offered.

The new unit was officially opened by Professor Andrew Sims, then President of the Royal College of Psychiatrists, on 11 May 1993. The Department flourished both in terms of its clinical contribution to the National Health Service and its research activities which were greatly enhanced by a remarkable growth of its academic staff. (*Fig 9.4*) However, changes in the practice of psychiatry with emphasis on care in the community and crisis intervention teams has reduced the need for hospital admissions. More recently, equally radical changes have occurred within the University with the fusion of departments into 'Schools', changes which are not merely administrative, but affect, more importantly, the functioning of what at one time was a fairly independent department with its own style and charisma. At the time of writing, Professor I. N. Ferrier, who was Head of the department, is now Head of the School of Neurology, Neurobiology and Psychiatry. The practice of Medicine both in hospitals and in the community has undergone changes which no one could have predicted, and continues to do so. In times of rapid change, anxieties and rumours tend to abound and it is to be hoped that with regard to psychiatry in the RVI, which during the last century has grown to play such a valuable and vital role in the treatment of its patients and in the training of students, a rumoured proposal to move the psychiatry out of the RVI will be strongly resisted. Such a retrograde move ignores the development of psychiatry during the last century and more specifically the increasing role over the years that the department has played in the work of a hospital beloved by its staff, students and not least of all by its patients.

Fig 9.4: Members of staff (past & present), 9th July 1982.

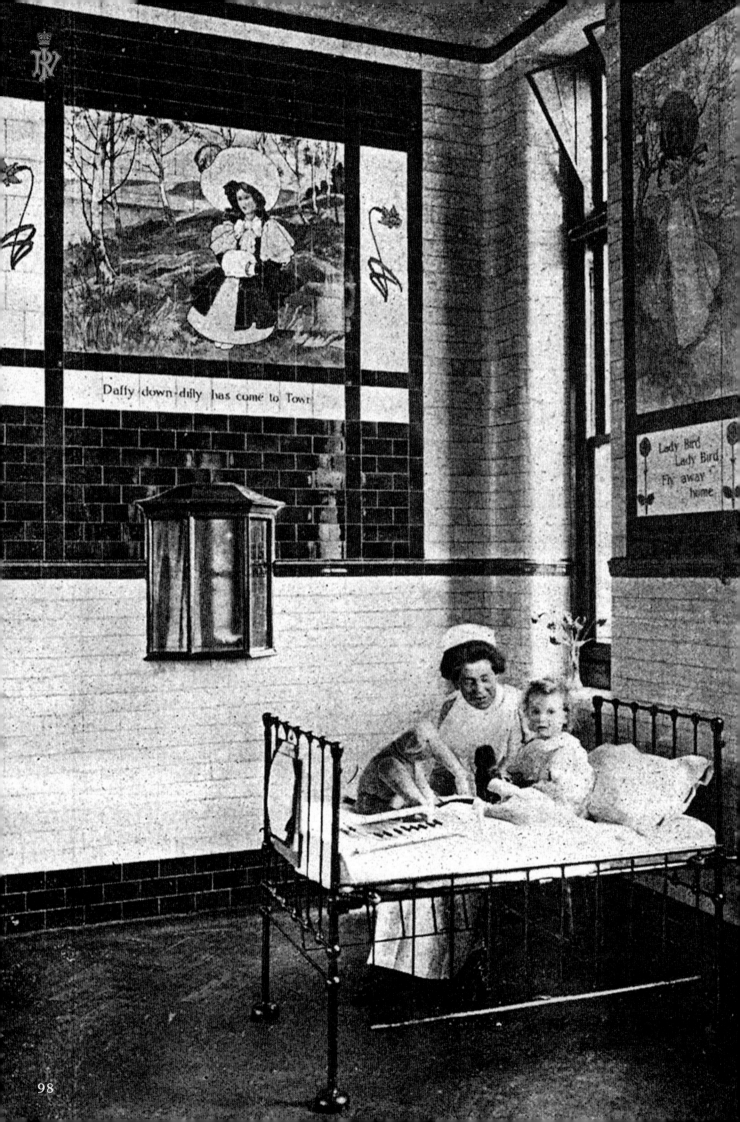

Daffy-down-dilly has come to Town

Lady Bird
Lady Bird,
Fly away
home

Chapter 10: *Children at the RVI*

Investing in our future Alan Craft

The development of dedicated services for children was slow in the UK compared to other parts of Europe. The Hôpital Charité in Berlin and the Hôpital Enfants Malades in Paris both date from the late 18th century. The first children's hospital in England was Great Ormond Street in London which opened its doors on Valentine's Day 1852. Similarly children's doctors were much slower to evolve. The reasons for this are complex and debatable. A trade dispute in the early part of the 19th century between the Physicians and the Apothecaries led to the development of general practice and they took responsibility for the care of children at home. There was little that could be done in the way of curative treatment.

There were children's wards in the old Infirmary on Forth Banks but by the time it closed they were described as being in a grimy old hospital with a declining reputation. However, close by in 18 Hanover Square in Newcastle, a hospital specifically providing for children had been established again on Valentine's Day in 1863. This was eventually to become the Fleming Memorial Hospital for Sick Children situated on the North Road, which was ultimately amalgamated into the RVI in 1987. (See chapter 13).

The opening of the RVI in 1906 provided a brand-new start for children. Purpose-built wards were provided, which continued to serve children for over 80 years. Amongst the most remarkable features of the children's wards were the Royal Doulton nursery rhyme tiles which are described in detail elsewhere. (*Fig 10.1*) (See also chapter 17).

Ward 8 comprising Ochiltree Ward (female) and Victoria Ward (male), were primarily for surgical cases. The children's medical ward was Ward 16, Percy Ward (male) and Newcastle Ward (female). From the outset these wards were open to the Infirmary's physicians and surgeons with Dr Horsley Drummond being nominally in charge of medicine and Mr Rutherford Morison of surgery. But it was recognised that the sisters of these two wards were really in charge. (See Annual Report 1910.) They lived in rooms just above Ward 16. There were no physicians or surgeons dealing only with children. They all had an adult practice and in addition looked after children. Although children had their own wards they received little attention in the annual report of the hospital. Numbers of children admitted were not recorded separately until 1931. It was noted in 1910 that there had been a big increase in out-patients and that this was mainly due to implementation of the *"Act for the medical inspection of school children."* Children were brought to the Infirmary in large numbers on the advice of the Medical Officers of the surrounding Education Authorities. The increasing demands on Infirmary staff led to a call for the School Authorities to pay for the services provided. It was also thought in 1910 that there was *"abuse of the hospital facilities by poor people who really needed nourishing food rather than medical treatment."*

Visiting by parents was always limited but on several occasions all visiting was stopped for considerable periods because of outbreaks of infection. The public were kept informed of the condition of patients by the issue of bulletins three times a week to the press. Each parent was given a number for their child and they had to look in the Evening Chronicle to see the state of their child's illness.

In 1919 the question of prevention of disease was beginning to be addressed. The annual report contains this paragraph:

"As an indication of the lack of sympathy shown to preventive methods as compared with curative, no better instance can be given than that of the way in which infants, suffering from Ophthalmia have been treated in the past. It is said on sound authority that fifty per cent of the blind are blind because of this disease, curable in almost every instance if treated skilfully at an early date. The establishment of a sufficient number of beds in the area for the early treatment of these children, accompanied, if necessary, by the mothers, is a sufficiently obvious preventive step, a step that would relieve the Blind Asylums throughout the country of a great deal of their work and confer incalculable benefits upon a large number of individuals."

From the early days of the Infirmary a bed could be named in memory of someone for £1000 and a cot for £500. (*Fig 10.2*) In December 1920 a ceremony took place in the Children's Wards to endow a cot by members of the Cinema Profession. Miss Daisy Dormer presented a cheque to Lord Armstrong and afterwards members of the Hospital Committee attended an "entertainment" at the Pavilion Theatre where a film illustrating the work of the Infirmary was shown.

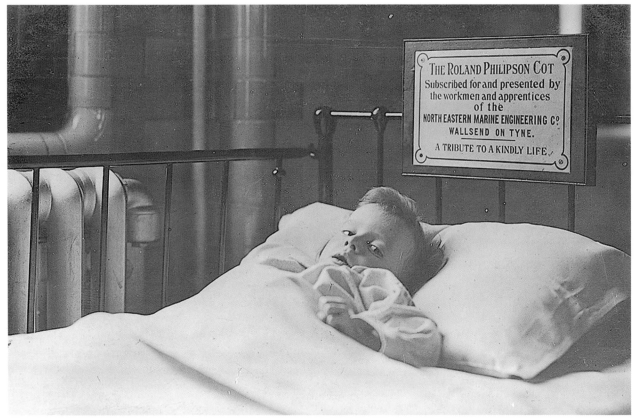

Fig 10.2: An endowed bed in the children's ward.

In 1924 the House Committee recognised the increasing overcrowding in the children's wards. On January 12th, 1928, James Spence, a Durham graduate, was appointed as an honorary assistant physician to the Infirmary. He was to go on to become Newcastle's first full time paediatrician and a leader of paediatrics worldwide.

The overcrowding in the hospital was at least partially addressed by the building of the new "paybed hospital" - later to be known as the Leazes Hospital in 1930. Children were treated privately, for those families who could afford it, in the Shipley Wing, later Pavilion 2, and in the William Watson Ward. For the first time in 1931 the annual report included details of numbers of children admitted. A total of 1571 admissions took place (908 surgical, 400 medical, 67 eyes, 179 ENT and 17 skin) as well as 56 to the pay beds. The new orthopaedic block opened in 1932 with a dedicated children's ward which had its own sun balcony.

Medical knowledge continued to progress and an example of the use of laboratory investigation was given in the 1932 Annual Report relating to an outbreak of scarlet fever.

"Towards the end of the year, an epidemic of Scarlet Fever, and the appearance of cases in the Hospital, led to the institution by Dr J. Cottrell, the Resident Medical Officer, of routine tests of children admitted to the Children's Wards of the Hospital. Between December 25th and January 15th, 79 children were admitted. Of these 19 were found to be susceptible to Scarlet Fever, and these were given a protective dose of serum. No cases occurred, and it was thus found possible to avoid closing the Wards because of infection and also to avoid spread of the infection."

In 1934 an application was made by the Princess Mary Maternity Hospital (PMMH) and the Babies' Hospital (see chapter 13) for a new dedicated Children's Hospital on the RVI site. This will eventually come to fruition when the new ward block opens in 2009! In 1944 both the PMMH and the Babies' Hospital came under the administrative wing of the RVI.

A partial solution to overcrowding and the problem of long-stay patients was found in 1936. There had long been a convalescent home for adult patients at Castle Hill, Wylam but in this year Mr Norman Newall, Chairman of the RVI Finance Committee, very generously donated Greycourt, near Riding Mill, as a convalescent home for children. 25 children could be accommodated and this provided a very valuable service until the building was destroyed by fire in 1940. Whitton Tower at Rothbury also offered beds to children in 1937. Children stayed for prolonged periods, the average being 60 days and the Hospital Committee of the day decided that children needed time to "settle in". Visiting was, therefore, not allowed for the first month and then mothers were allowed to visit on a Saturday.

In 1939 Spence was appointed an honorary physician and by this time was dedicating virtually all of his time to the care of children. He was also very involved in education, and by 1942 he had persuaded the Nuffield Provincial Hospitals Trust to endow the first full time Chair of Child Health in the UK. There had previously been part-time chairs in Edinburgh and Birmingham. The RVI co-operated in this development by providing clinical facilities. Spence was put in charge of the children's wards. Up until this time child out-patients had been seen in the adult department but the recently vacated House Governor's House at the entrance to the RVI grounds from Queen Victoria Road was given to the "Department of Child Medicine", along with a newly built waiting room extension. This continues to serve children in 2005. The annual report for 1942 reported -

"The first aim of the department will be to raise the hospital treatment of children to a higher standard. It will also undertake research into the fundamental problems of child health and disease, which must be understood if a satisfactory policy for the health of children and for their satisfactory care and treatment in hospitals and institutions is to be formulated. It is hoped that the new department will thus become the regional centre both for the teaching of nurses and doctors and for the study of children's diseases."

Fig 10.3: Lady Ridley, Dr Spence and Miss Cummings.

The Babies' Hospital, which had been in West Parade, was evacuated to Blagdon Hall during the war. It too suffered a serious fire, again with no loss of life. Blagdon was the home of the Ridley family and Lady Ursula Ridley (*Fig 10.3*) became a firm supporter of the Children's Department. Spence and Lady Ridley worked together to develop services and she would often spend afternoons in the Children's Clinic looking after mothers. In the 1970s an extension, named the "Ursula Ridley Wing" to Wards 8 and 16 provided mother and baby rooms and teaching space.

The Children's Clinic was used for consultations where GPs could send up any child, without an appointment, to be seen by a member of the medical staff. In 1944, at the request of the Health Committee of Newcastle Corporation, a child welfare clinic was established, one session each week. This was important for teaching purposes as well as for the benefit of parents and children.

For almost 30 years up to 1976 Sister Hylda Hope was in charge of the Children's Clinic. She became a fount of knowledge and inspiration for both mothers and paediatricians alike.

Spence was a prolific writer and his most thoughtful and important contributions were brought together into a book after he died - The Purpose and Practice of Medicine. Shortly after Spence's death, a GP in Heaton discovered a letter in a patient's notes relating to someone who had been referred for circumcision. It said:

"My Dear C...,

Your patient C. D., ætat 7 months, has the prepuce with which he was born. You ask me, with a note of persuasion in your question, if it should be excised. Am I to make this decision on scientific grounds, or am I to acquiesce in a ritual which took its origin at the behest of that arch-sanitarian Moses.?

If you can show good reason why a ritual designed to ease the penalties of concupiscence amidst the sand and flies of the Syrian deserts should be continued in this England of clean bed-linen and lesser opportunity, I shall listen to your argument; but if you base your argument on anatomical faults, then I must refute it. The anatomists have never studied the form and evolution of the preputial orifice. They do not understand that Nature does not intend it to be stretched and retracted in the Temples of the Welfare Centres or ritually removed in the precincts of the operating theatres. Retract the prepuce and you see a pin point opening, but draw it forward and you see a channel wide enough for all the purposes for which the infant needs the organ at that early age. What looks like a pin point opening at 7 months will become a wide channel of communication at 17.

Nature is a possessive mistress, and whatever mistakes she makes about the Structure of the less essential organs such as the brain and stomach, in which she is not much interested, you can be sure that she knows best about the genital organs...."

Dr Douglas Gairdner, who had worked with Spence and later went to Cambridge, wrote a paper entitled "The Fate of the Foreskin" which received much national publicity.

At last with the appointment of Spence as a Children's Physician, paediatrics began to develop and a series of honorary assistant physicians were appointed who went on to develop the specialty, both in the RVI and elsewhere. Dr George Davison went off to take charge at the Newcastle General Hospital and Dr George Brewis at the Walkergate Infectious Disease Hospital.

Spence became a real leader of paediatrics and attracted visitors from all over the world. He became very important at a national level, was knighted in 1951 for services to medicine and was an influential member of the Medical Research Council. He had been much involved in the setting up of the NHS in 1948. Unfortunately he died prematurely in 1954 from lung cancer, having been a lifelong smoker. Fred Miller, a local graduate, and Donald Court, an "incomer" from Birmingham, had been assistants to Spence and both expected to succeed him. Court was appointed and took over the Department and Ward 8. Miller was given the consolation of a readership and control of Ward 16. Although on the surface they had a civil relationship, Miller would always refer to Dr Court, never acknowledging his Chair. Spence had taken a particular interest in the social aspects of paediatrics. Prior to the Second World War the City Council had become concerned about the high levels of infant mortality. An investigation showed that the majority of deaths were due to infection. After the War, in 1946, Spence said to Fred Miller - "Well Freddie, what are we to do about these infections?" This led to the Newcastle One Thousand Families Study. All babies born in the City in May and June 1947 were enrolled into a study designed to last for one year. It showed quite clearly that the excess mortality was due to infection and that this was related to social factors, especially poverty and poor mothering. This one year study is still continuing and a 60 year follow up is being planned for 2007.

In the 1960s there was an explicit view not to develop subspecialisation. However, the progress of medicine with the need for research and teaching inevitably meant that there would be developments in this way. Willie Walker (Fig 10.4) had qualified during the war and had been attracted to paediatrics. He also became very interested in haematology and blood transfusion. He was very involved in the unravelling of the mystery surrounding rhesus incompatibility and it was always claimed that he and George Knox had the idea about prevention with antiD immunoglobulin. However, it was Cyril Clarke (later Sir Cyril) in Liverpool who took most of the credit. Walker developed the "Attic Laboratory" which was University space above Ward 16 and which took in the old ward sisters' accommodation. He did hundreds of exchange transfusions at both the Princess Mary Hospital and Newcastle General.

Fig 10.4: Professor Willie Walker and Sister Hylda Hope.

He is also well remembered as the organiser of social activities. Car rallies and picnics were frequent but most notable of all were the "Walker-Twitchett" mystery tours. A bus would leave from the RVI gates for an undisclosed itinerary which would invariably end at a pub. On one famous occasion Spence was reported marching into the Lord Crewe Arms at Blanchland "crowned" with a toilet seat! Walker became Reader, then Professor, and was the inspiration behind much of this subspecialisation. Peter Jones developed a world recognised haemophilia service which emphasised the need to address the social issues surrounding this disease. In the 1960s leukaemia was invariably fatal but Walker had the vision to develop a service which has grown into a major Oncology Unit treating all forms of malignant disease in children. Donald Court set up a malignant disease registry in 1968, being only the second of its kind in the world. His statement that it was a *"pre-requisite for the planning and evaluation of treatment"* has been borne out. Now almost 80% of leukaemias can be cured.

Hugh Jackson, who worked with Spence, developed interests in gastroenterology and nephrology, both of which have now grown into separate sub-departments with several consultants each, as well as being an international leader in injury prevention. Mike Parkin (*Figs 10.5 & 10.6*) worked mainly on Ward 8 and was involved in much of the evolution of teaching as well as developing a special expertise in growth and endocrinology.

John Webb succeeded Donald Court in the James Spence Chair of Child Health. Webb had been a registrar with Spence but then went off to India as a missionary and became Dean of the Christian Medical College of Vellore. Al Aynsley-Green then took over the chair before he too went off to Great Ormond Street and recently became the first National Children's Commissioner for England.

Fig 10.5: Professor Mike Parkin circa 1989 - a wonderful man devoted to children.

Fig 10.6: Professor Mike Parkin as he is remembered.

103

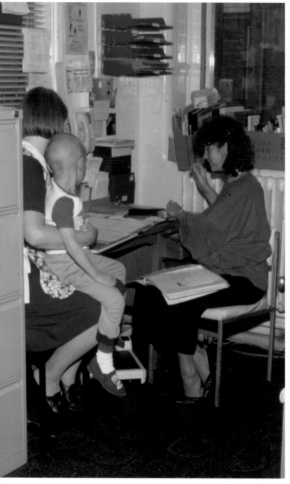

Marian Farmer (wife of Frank Farmer, Professor of Medical Physics) developed a paediatric cardiology service at the RVI, which later moved to Freeman Hospital when all cardiothoracic services for the region were centralised there.

The Children's Clinic was extended in 1972 to house the new Child Development Centre. Court and Errington Ellis had recognised the importance of early recognition and intervention in childhood disability. After a visit to centres in the US they raised funds to develop a model centre for the RVI and a close relationship was established with the Percy Hedley Centre for Cerebral Palsy in Forest Hall.

In 1986 the Fleming Children's Hospital, which had already subsumed the Babies' Hospital, moved into the RVI. (*Figs 10.7 & 10.8*) Around the same time, maternity and neonatal services for the City were amalgamated in the new Leazes Wing with the closure of PMMH.

Hospital maternity and neonatal care in the City was divided between the PMMH and NGH with Gerald Neligan, and later Edmund Hey and Mike Parkin developing largely minimal intervention care at PMMH, and Fred Miller and Cyril Noble, followed by Philip Kenna taking a much more active approach across the City. (*Fig 10.9*) These two contrasting philosophies created a considerable challenge when the two units amalgamated.

Fig 10.7: Sister in Nurse station circa 1980 - showing cramped conditions.

Fig 10.8: Paediatric ward circa 1980.

Fig 10.9: Stained glass window in the children's clinic in memory of Mike Parkin.

Child Psychiatry had also developed at the Fleming Hospital initially under Philip Connell and later Professor Issy Kolvin.

In the nineties children moved out of Wards 8 and 16 to make way for geriatrics. Now much of the original hospital is given over to the care of children.

In 1984 the University Department moved into the new Medical School but it rapidly outgrew its accommodation. Following a major fundraising appeal, co-ordinated by a new charity, the Children's Foundation, a new Institute of Child Health, named after Spence, was opened in 1994. The foundation stone was laid by Viscount Ridley, son of Ursula, who had done so much with Spence to establish the Department. (*Fig 10.10*)

So in 2006 most children's services for the area are on the RVI site and very soon the vision of 1934 will be realised - a Children's Hospital embedded at the heart of the RVI. Spence was the first and only paediatrician in 1942. In 2005 there are 49 paediatricians working in the RVI and NGH.

Fig 10.10: Yellow Brick Road building, August 1998.

Editor's Note:

Sir Alan Craft, author of this chapter achieved an international reputation for his work on childhood cancer and was elected President of the Royal College of Paediatrics and Child Health in 2003.

Chapter 11: *The Service Departments*

Informing Patient Care Ian Lavelle, Andrew Skillen, John Burn, Alastair Burt,
Steve Proctor, Len Constable, Charles Madeley

Introduction

Hospitals vary both in the number and type of clinical units they have, but whatever their make-up they are all dependent on the presence of a full complement of service departments. The RVI is no exception to this rule. For many years they were to be found along the long corridor which stretches from Peacock Hall towards the relatively new multi-storey car park. For the purposes of this book, I was commissioned to survey all of these departments but, lacking intimate knowledge of those apart from my own, I invited others to write about their particular disciplines. Their names are included at the head of the respective sections, which are presented in alphabetical order.

I Lavelle.

Biochemistry

Andrew Skillen

The medical knowledge gained during the First World War and the years which immediately followed, had a great impact on the hospital. In 1922 insulin was discovered and in 1926 pernicious anaemia was treated with liver extracts. These new fields of biochemical investigation and clinical treatment necessitated the appointment of a biochemist. The assistance of a well equipped biochemical department became essential and in 1941, appropriate extensions were made to the Department of Pathology to fill this need.

In the period following the second World War, the Director of the Department, which was then called Chemical Pathology, was the notable Freda Herbert, a non-medically qualified biochemist with an interest in porphyrin metabolism. She was reader in Chemical Pathology and an able scientist, but had the unfortunate habit of confronting any colleague who happened to be near her, on the long corridor, and giving them a 15-20 minute talk on porphyrin metabolism or relevant issues. Many of her colleagues were obliged to go out of their way to avoid her. She was also frequently seen smoking in the laboratory and, whilst this was fairly dangerous, it was a common occurrence in those days.

Herbert was succeeded, in the late 1950s, by Albert Louis Latner, Reader in Medical Biochemistry, who changed the name of the department, first to Clinical Biochemistry and then later, to Clinical Chemistry. He was an able and thrusting personality, who did a lot of the fundamental work on Vitamin B12 and the intrinsic factor, in conjunction with our own R. B. Thompson and also Charles Ungley and Lester Smith of Glaxo. Latner also worked on steroid assays and gel electrophoresis of proteins and enzymes. In 1962, together with Gordon Dale, he developed the first 2D technique for isoelectric focussing and electrophoresis of proteins, the precursor of the techniques used in modern proteomics. In 1962, the University created the department of Clinical Biochemistry, awarding Latner a personal chair, thus further strengthening the bond between hospital and University departments.

The sixties were a time of change and significant developments in Clinical Biochemistry. Automation of laboratory tests began with the purchase of an auto-analyser for blood glucose, foreshadowing the plethora of equipment required to meet the demands on today's laboratory. Two training courses were instituted; one was for Registrars in Clinical Biochemistry, two of whom, T.R.C. Boyd and P. Vadgama, were subsequently appointed to Chairs in their subject. The other course was for the MSc. in Clinical Biochemistry which, although it was set up to train staff for the northern region, consistently attracted students from across the world until the University withdrew the course in 2003. The need for facilities to accommodate trainees, coupled with increasing research activity, led to the building of new laboratories above the RVI corridor, adjacent to Wards 9 and 15. Prior to this, a large amount of hospital-based research had been carried out in the J.H. Burn research laboratory, situated next to the hospital kitchens. The new development served both the Department of Medicine and that of Clinical Biochemistry. Incorporated in the latter was the Cancer Research Unit, funded by the British Empire Cancer Campaign, with Professor Latner as the first Director.

Other contemporaneous developments were the Paediatric Biochemistry section, in the attic laboratory above the children's wards, and the erection in the car park, next to the nurses' home, of prefabricated laboratories needed for steroid assays and the Supraregional Assay (SAS) Unit. This was one of two laboratories in the UK which were set up for the assay of peptide hormones such as PTH and ACTH; the first directors were Professor Latner and Professor Reginald Hall with a remit to assay other peptide hormones. Latner retired in 1978 and was succeeded by K.G.M.M. (George) Alberti, whose interest in diabetes led to research being more clinically orientated and the appointment of a number of clinical research fellows. Their work included the use of an 'artificial pancreas', which enabled a patient's blood glucose to be maintained at different levels. The effect of these varying levels on the blood concentration of a range of other metabolites, could then be determined. The influx of clinical research workers led to the department being renamed yet again, this time as the Department of Clinical Biochemistry and Metabolic Medicine. This persisted until 1985, when Alberti moved to the Chair of Medicine. By this time, Clinical Biochemistry, which for a number of years had been dispersed over several sites, was re-housed in new laboratories in the Medical School. This was the first time since the 1960s that the department was fully integrated. There followed a four-year period, during which the University reviewed the teaching of biochemistry and research within the subject. Hospital and University functions gradually became less integrated until 1989 when Colin Self was appointed to both the Chair and to lead the hospital service. His research was primarily focussed on the development of ultra-sensitive immunological techniques, which proved valuable for example, in the assay of peptide hormones and cancer markers in blood. The work attracted significant industrial funding.

In the mid 1990s, the University and the RVI Trust decided to unravel the joint account system, whereby costs of the separate functions had been shared on a 'knock-for-knock' basis. There is now separate funding and the hospital section is headed by a Consultant in Administrative Charge. In the light of the past history, further changes would seem highly likely.

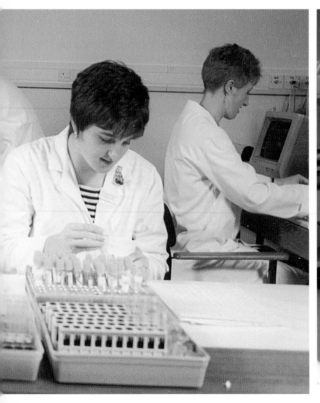
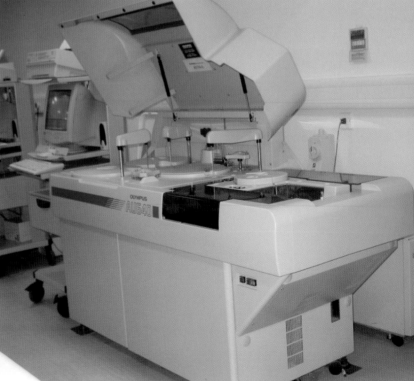

Fig 11.2: Biochemistry: from test tubes to computerised robot driven biochemical analysis - all in 20 years!

Clinical Genetics

John Burn

Genetics is a newcomer amongst medical specialties. The first appointment in the subject was in 1966 when Derek Roberts was made Lecturer in the Department of Child Health. He assembled a small research team and in 1971 the Regional Health Authority adopted two part-time nurse posts, a part-time clinical assistant and three scientific staff, to develop genetic marker tests and chromosome analysis. One of those appointed has been a technician in the department ever since. Chromosome studies were also performed in the Department of Anatomy and laboratories were subsequently developed on Teesside, in West Cumbria and at Dryburn Hospital; all were eventually united into a single laboratory at the RVI.

In 1972 Human Genetics became a full department in the University of Newcastle and was recognised by the Lord Chancellor's office as a centre for paternity testing. This work has continued uninterrupted, now under the banner of Northgene Ltd. In that same year the current Professor of Clinical genetics (and author of this account) joined the department as its third B.Med.Sci student, returning 11 years later as the first Consultant Clinical Geneticist. At that stage the service was still housed in 19 Claremont Place, a Victorian terraced house, which served earlier as a medical residence for the hospital, whilst the University office had migrated to 25 Claremont Place. (*Fig 11.3*) The late 80s saw the rapid expansion of the clinical service and the construction of the region's first DNA laboratory in what had been the first floor bedroom of 20 Claremont Place, using flat pack kitchen units. The acquisition of 20 Claremont Place allowed further expansion of the clinical service. The difficulty of finding anyone to pay for building modifications to allow the dangerously overcrowded cytogenetics laboratory on the top floor of 19 Claremont Place to expand into the available top floors of number 20, resulted in an example of what the French call *action direct*. It was some years before a puzzled university plumber triggered an investigation of an unrecorded doorway.

Fig 11.3: 19 and 20 Claremont Place. Home to the Northern Genetics Service, prior to the move in 2001, to the new Institute of Human Genetics, part of the Centre for Life.

With no room at the RVI inn for the infant specialty, genetics continued to grow into all available space, beginning with portacabins a quarter of a mile up Claremont Road. The site had previously been used by plant geneticists who had moved into the new Medical School building! Intermittent unpleasant smells were tracked to rats who were fatally attracted to the insulation on the electricity cables under the building. By the time attempts were made to move Human Genetics into the Medical School the combined clinical and research group was too big to be accommodated. They spread instead to the University Ridley Building on the corner of Claremont Road and Queen Victoria Road, whilst still occupying 19, 20 and 25 Claremont Place. In 1989 to 1999 a unified regional NHS contract was established to provide a clinical genetics and laboratory service to what was then the Northern Region. The department was awarded Professorial Chairs in Clinical Genetics and Human Molecular Genetics.

Fig 11.4: Institute of Human Genetics, International Centre for Life.

In 1995 a speculative suggestion that Human Genetics and the Northern Genetics Service might move alongside a business science park and education centre led to the successful creation of the Millennium landmark International Centre for Life (*Fig 11.4*) next to the Central Station. The new Institute of Human Genetics was built over the area that had once been the garden of the old Infirmary at Forth Banks. Before building could commence it was necessary to relocate the remains of 1000 former patients whose unclaimed bodies had been buried in the grounds. The Centre for Life was officially opened in 2000 by the Queen and Duke of Edinburgh. In April 2001 the then Secretary for State for Health, The Rt Hon Alan Milburn, combined an invitation to officially open the new genetics clinic with a seminal speech on the importance of genetics in future healthcare.

He announced the creation of Genetics Knowledge Parks with funding from the Department of Health and the Department of Trade and Industry. In September 2001 the staff of the whole NHS genetics service, now more than 100 strong, transferred into the new Institute. In 2002 Newcastle was made one of the six Knowledge Parks in the UK and Human Genetics became one of three independent research institutes in Newcastle University, in recognition of having been awarded the highest grading in the 2001 Research Assessment Exercise. In 2003 a satellite unit opened in the James Cook University Hospital in Middlesbrough and the post of Harold Macmillan Professor of Medicine at North Tees was filled by a specialist in muscle genetics with affiliation to the new Institute of Human Genetics. This brought to five the number of clinical professors in the team of 12 full-or part-time consultants, plus 12 genetic nurse specialists and counsellors with 20 administrators and over 70 genetic scientists.

Genetics is now a fully-grown specialty, with Royal College recognition of its extensive training programme, Clinical Directorate status in the Trust, and outreach clinics in almost all other Trusts in the region. Diagnostic services are provided by four laboratories. The Northern Genetics Service has achieved a national and international reputation, illustrated by being made one of the four referral services in a national service for rare genetic muscle diseases.

Cellular Pathology

Alastair Burt

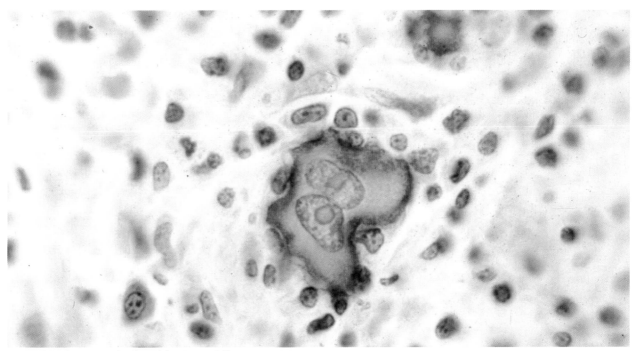

Fig 11.5: Special staining to identify Hodgkins Disease Cells.

There has been a close liaison between the University and Clinical Departments, since the appointment of Stuart McDonald as Professor in 1909. At that time, autopsies were the predominant activity in the department. The postmortem room was a cold and eerie place, where it would be difficult not to acquire enthusiasm for morbid anatomy, from two Honorary Physicians who also acted as pathologists, Drummond and Beattie. McDonald became the first President of the RVI's exclusive and successful scientific society, known as the Pathological Club; it was not solely the domain of histopathologists and morbid anatomists; distinguished guests such as Professor George Grey Turner and other dignitaries were welcomed. In 1938, McDonald was succeeded by Professor Arthur Frederick Bernard Shaw, *(Fig 19.8, p.209)* whose diverse interests ranged from encephalitis lethargica to the Mummy of Har-mose, a singer of the 18th Dynasty, 1490 BC. Shaw was frequently irritated by the question, *"are you the Bernard Shaw?"* to which his reply was usually *"I am equally important as any other by that name."* (GBS was in fact his uncle!) Shaw's lectures were full of pomp and circumstance, his entry was preceded by Young, a senior technician, who would march through the gallery of students carrying a mace.

During the Second World War, a section of the Medical Research Council headed by Dr Grant studied war wounds. His group included Wittgenstein, *(Fig 11.6)* one of the most influential figures in British philosophy this century, who had interrupted his period as Professor of Philosophy at Cambridge to do war service. He worked as a technician at the RVI from April 1943 to February 1944 and established a reputation for his meticulous and conscientious approach to frozen sections of lung and other organs. A commemorative plaque has been placed in the Peacock Hall of the hospital. *(Fig 11.7)*

Fig 11.6: Ludwig Wittgenstein.

Fig 11.7: Plaque in Peacock Hall recording that the philosopher Wittgenstein worked at the RVI.

111

John Bright Duguid took over the Department in 1948. He is best known for early innovative work on atheroma and pneumoconiosis. This latter work was continued by his successor, (Alfred) Gordon Heppleston, a tall austere individual. His father had been Rector of Manchester Grammar School and Heppleston had a fairly strict upbringing. His younger brother, known for his "carrot locks" was also in the medical profession and the two brothers were known as Grey Hep (Gordon was already sporting silver locks) and Red Hep. For those who have forgotten, or never knew, in basic pathology grey and red hepatisation, are part of the classical process of pneumonia!

During Heppleston's reign, a number of rising stars joined the department, most notably Nicholas Wright and Ian Lauder. Wright went on to become an international leader in the field of cancer registration and is currently Dean of the London Medical School, whilst Lauder is Dean of Medicine at Leicester/Warwick. Trainees were not well paid in those days and there was a tradition of moonlighting in general practice. Heppleston believed this would 'corrupt' the young pathologists and outlawed their involvement. The practice, however, did not cease until one day the young Lauder was carrying out a clandestine GP surgery, when in walked Gordon Heppleston for an immunisation!

A greater division within pathology led to clinical biochemistry being established in its own right, although fierce rivalry existed between Heppleston and Latner, the departmental heads. The importance of cytology was becoming recognised and Rolf Schade pioneered gastric cytology in Newcastle. His method involved shaking the patient vigorously to obtain the gastric sample. Heppleston retired in 1977 and Alex Watson ran the department for a year. He was the first to document the important relationship between dermatitis herpetiformis and coeliac disease, work undertaken in conjunction with dermatologist Sam Shuster.

Angus Stuart was appointed to the Chair of Pathology in 1978. His start was rather inauspicious. Just prior to moving from Edinburgh he fell in his bath and was transferred to Newcastle by ambulance and spent his first six weeks at the helm, tending his injured back, at home. His wife, concerned for his health, insisted that he walked home every evening but Stuart was frequently found hanging around the car park for lifts from his colleagues, thus avoiding the long trek over the Town Moor. In 1983, he retired to Skye and became an expert on midges. Indeed, he was even called to give advice to the House of Lords on the subject. Wilson Horne succeeded Stuart and brought Brian Angus with him. Between them, they developed a particular skill in raising antibodies for diagnostic purposes and, in many respects, revolutionised routine immunohistochemistry. Horne quickly appreciated the substantial commercial opportunities in this and established a spin-out company, Novocastra, one of the most successful ventures of its type from universities and hospitals in the UK. For his work in this field, he received the Queen's award for industry and the MBE.

Horne retired in 1997 to concentrate on the company. There have since been substantial changes to the structure of cellular pathology at the RVI. In 1998, the Department of Oral Pathology and its professor, originally in the Dental School, moved to the pathology building. In 2000, all the departments of cellular pathology in the Newcastle upon Tyne Hospitals NHS Trust, were brought under a single administrative umbrella.

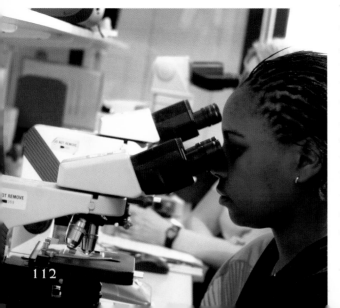

The combined department is one of the largest of its type in the United Kingdom and has established a strong national and international reputation in a number of specialist areas including liver, lymphoreticular and gynaecological pathologies. There is little doubt that the environment in Cellular Pathology, is very different from that of McDonald almost a century before. Technologies have moved on considerably and there is a different skills mix and approach to the subject, with much greater emphasis on team working, both in the Department and as part of clinical management teams. The strong association with the University, however, continues and Newcastle remains a very attractive place to study and practice Cellular Pathology.

Fig 11.8: The microscope remains the most useful tool in pathological diagnosis.

Diagnostic Radiology
Ian Lavelle

Fig 11.9: The collection of old X-ray tubes in the Radiology department. When in use they glowed red in an alarming fashion.

The first diagnostic radiograph in Newcastle showed a gun pellet in a man's hand. It was made on the 21st April, 1896 by Dr (later Professor) Stroud, at the Newcastle upon Tyne College of Science, less than six months after the discovery of X-rays, by Roentgen, on the 8th November, 1895. Two years later, a diagnostic service was being provided to the old Infirmary, surprisingly by two pharmacists, Brady and Martin, and Proctor Son and Claque. The following year, the hospital bought its own equipment and placed it under the clinical charge of a surgeon, Mr H. Brunton-Angus. The first member of the X-ray staff, Mr Thomas Dodd, the brother of the Head Porter, was also appointed. His duties were to act as a technician and keep a record of the procedures; the book in which he kept them is still in existence. He served the old and then the new Infirmary for 20 years, during which time he sustained severe radiation burns, from which he ultimately succumbed. He died in 1929 and his name was placed on the International Memorial for Radiation Martyrs, in Hamburg. In contrast to many other hospitals across the country, the demand for X-ray services remained small, possibly due to the poor results. Looking back some years later, Dr Muirhead, a houseman at that time, remembers how screening for fractures of the hands worked well but *"when you came to the knee, shoulder and hip, the results were like a foggy night at the coast!"* (Warrick, 1977)[1]

This changed in 1906, when the new Royal Victoria Infirmary opened. There was an Electrical Department, containing equipment for X-ray and electrotherapeutic work, situated in the basement underneath Ward 1, probably because it had been overlooked in the planning process. However the House Committee made some amends, firstly by ruling

[1] Warrick, C. K.
  Note on the history of the Department of Radiology of the Royal Victoria Infirmary, Newcastle upon Tyne. Radiography, 43, 190-194. 1977

[2] Burrows E. H. Pioneers and Early Years. A history of British Radiology. Colophon Ltd. St Anne. Alderney. 7 136 –139, 1968

Fig 11.10: *The first record book of patients radiographed. One had an exposure time of 20 minutes for a fractured femur.*

that all suspected fractures should be radiographed and secondly, by appointing Dr W. D. Arnison as Medical Officer in charge. He was a colourful character who always wore a black bowler hat, even around the hospital. The department comprised an X-ray room, a darkroom and two rooms for electrical and massage treatment. Equipment was a primitive gas tube held in a wooden stand and powered by a coil and interrupter. There was no protection against radiation and the tube glowed red, to the justifiable alarm of the patient. Radiographs were taken on glass plates, which were viewed against the windows facing Ward 8. Slotted wooden bars, fixed across these windows to hold the plates, were still in place when the basement was refurbished in 1960. It seems that the habit clinicians have, of viewing radiographs against windows, has a long history.

For 13 years, this small department provided the only hospital X-ray service in Newcastle. The workload increased steadily until the time of the First World War when there was an explosion of work, due mainly to war wounds, but in a smaller part the advent of screening with bismuth - a forerunner of barium studies. (Burrows, 1968) [11]

1906	1,135 plates	983 screenings
1909	2,974 plates	474 screenings
1911	4,196 plates	
1915	7,603 plates	960 screenings
1918	12,905 plates	1,061 screenings

The Department, like the rest of the hospital, was severely stretched by this influx of patients with war wounds and in 1918 a public appeal was launched, resulting in the construction of the Military Orthopaedic Hospital (later called the Leazes Hospital) which included new accommodation for X-ray equipment. Part of the Radiology Department is still on this site today. Staffing problems were particularly acute, although in 1916, some senior medical students serving in the RAMC were sent back to Newcastle to qualify. One of them, Harold Graham Hodgson, later became an eminent radiologist and was made K.C.V.O. for his services to King George V.

After the war, Thomas Dodd acquired two assistants, Joseph Ridley and Cornelius McMeekin. The famous American neurosurgeon Harvey Cushing had worked at a hospital in France during hostilities, and McMeekin had been fortunate in working under him. Dodds and his two assistants performed all the fluoroscopy examinations themselves, including the barium studies which had now superseded bismuth. After each examination, they drew a diagram on the patient's

Fig 11.11: The 'new technology' in action - X-ray Department of the Royal
Victoria Infirmary, circa 1920.

X-ray form to show what they had seen. Their workload was continually increasing and in his Annual Reports, Dr Arnison referred to the difficulties in keeping up. In 1922, he said, "We are now one of the great spending departments of the Royal Victoria Infirmary and I do not see any prospect of it changing." Time has proved him correct.

Dr Arnison retired in 1925, his place being taken by Harold Ernest Gamelen, who had practised Radiology since 1896, the year he had bought his first X-ray set. During the war years, he was a major in the RAMC and developed a device for localising foreign bodies, known as "Gamelen's Frying Pan". Although he also had several years' experience in radiotherapy, and had visited the Finsen Institute in Copenhagen, he expressed total ignorance of the correct handling of radium. He stored his supply in a thermometer case kept in his waistcoat pocket, it was then easily available to be taken out and held against the patient's lesion. When appointed, he was already suffering from the effects of radiation and by 1930 was severely disabled by dermatitis. After his death, his name also was added to the Martyrs Memorial. Radiation was not the only danger; much of the equipment was still primitive, for instance a mercury 'make and break' switch was incorporated into the fluoroscopy unit and required filling with coal gas, to expel any air. On one occasion in 1925, the connections had been incorrectly made, resulting in some air remaining and the whole unit blew up when switched on. Although large pieces of cast iron embedded themselves in the ceiling and walls, the radiographer, Joseph Ridley, escaped injury.

When Dr Gamelen retired from hospital practice in 1930, his place was taken by Dr S. Whately Davison, who had been appointed Assistant Physician to the Electrical Department in 1925. He had the vision and drive to take Radiology at the RVI into its modern state. From 1948 onwards, he supervised the planning and building of an extensive new department, taking advantage of the great improvements in the design and performance of X-ray equipment. The glass plates were superseded by films in cassettes containing intensifying screens and fluoroscopy was aided by the development of the image intensifier. These advances, coupled with stringent methods of protection, considerably reduced the radiation dose to both staff and patients and his work influenced the design of many departments in the North of England. Outside of his department Whately Davison was active both locally and nationally, helping to unite the College of Medicine and the Armstrong College as part of the University of Durham and which later became the University of Newcastle upon Tyne. From 1955-58 he was President of the Faculty of Radiologists - later the Royal College of Radiologists - an honour only equalled from Newcastle, by Mr W. M. Ross, who was President from 1983-86. Davison was succeeded by Charles (C. K.) Warrick as Head of the Department. The year 1948 also saw the inception of the National Health Service and coincidentally, the separation of diagnostic and therapeutic radiology. In this context, it is worthy of note that in 1934 Mr C. J. L. Thurgar was appointed Radium Officer to the Radium Institute, which was contiguous to the X-ray Department (see chapter 4).

During the early 1960s there was further expansion of the department to accommodate nursing staff required to assist in the growing number and variety of 'special procedures', particularly angiography. Concomitant developments in television enabled closed circuit TV to be attached to an image intensifier. The Superintendent Radiographer, Mr J. Lazonby, was one of the first to acquire this equipment which enabled procedures to be performed in subdued light rather than the total darkness which was so unpleasant for staff and patients. However, even in 1966 radiologists wearing red goggles, could be found groping around the department as they 'dark adapted' for the old fluoroscopy screens.

The 1970s saw the beginning of an exponential growth of imaging services. Perhaps to the horror of some clinicians, radiologists emerged from their department to take a more active and clinical role in patient management. Vascular procedures, masterminded by Peter Hacking, became increasingly complex and able to show important vessels such as the coronary arteries. Narrowed vessels could be dilated and those supplying tumours blocked. Radiology was an essential adjunct to some of the new clinical procedures involving endoscopy. The arrival of ultrasound, which carried no radiation risk, had an obvious application in Obstetrics but rapidly developed a valuable role in other areas.

In 1975 Peter Rose was appointed Consultant to develop and maintain the ultrasound services which, apart from those for obstetrics, were non-existent. There followed the usual uphill struggle typical of any new modality, to acquire appropriate equipment and convince clinicians of its value. This was completed by about 1979. One of the many major outcomes was the Northern Regional Foetal Anomaly Survey, which gave the largest data base in the world for pregnancy outcome versus antenatal assessment. With the establishment of clinical neurological services at the RVI, Dr Gordon Gryspeerdt, based mainly at the Newcastle General Hospital, together with Dr Arnold Appleby, introduced neuroradiology. On the radiographic side, a significant development was the introduction by Martin Yorke of a 'daylight loading' system for cassettes, obviating the need for a darkroom. There was a national shortage of Radiologists and more trainees were appointed. In the early 1960s two were appointed in alternate years. Now three were appointed annually to join the training scheme approved by the newly formed Royal College of Radiologists.

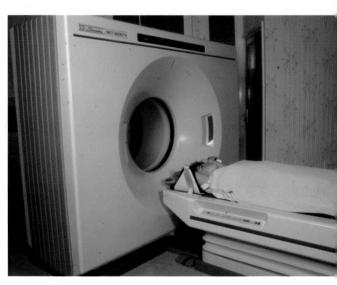

Fig 11.12: *The hospital's first CT scanner made by Shimadzu and opened by the Japan Minister Plenipotentiary.*

1983 saw the installation of digital imaging equipment, which enabled, for instance, clearer images of blood vessels to be obtained by 'subtracting' them from the adjacent bones. Whereas this machine had been one of the first of its type, the RVI was late in acquiring computed tomography. In 1988, a united drive by radiologists, clinicians and management secured a new Japanese scanner which was opened officially on the 17th. February, 1989 by Mr T. Sezaki, the Minister Plenipotentiary from the Japanese Embassy. At this time, the new wing of the hospital which contained the first part of a completely new department, was taking shape. This resulted in a 'split department' offset to some extent by being linked with a Picture Archiving and Communication System (PACS). This proved of great interest to HRH Princess Anne when she opened the new wing. The Princess was well versed in IT matters and asked many questions. Later that year, the department was featured by Joan Thirkettle on the ITN national news. The Trust Board agreed to the installation of Magnetic Resonance Imaging on the 25th. February, 1993. Again, the hospital secured a first, by renting the machine from that manufacturer. The pundits doubted that we would make the first year's rental but such was the demand, it was achieved within six months.

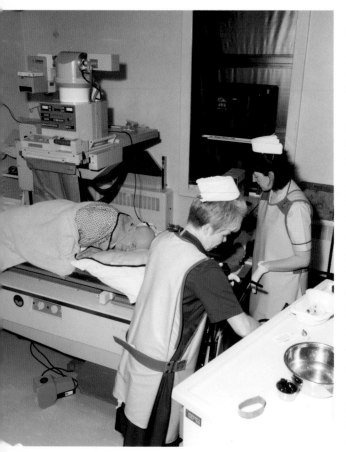

Fig 11.13: *Radiographic room prepared for endoscopy. X-ray screening is essential for procedures such as ERCP.*

Fig 11.14: *An expensive ball. The first MRI scanner is lifted out of the carrying vehicle.*

The early years of the 21st Century have seen the continuing development of the department. The original CT was replaced in 2001 by a much faster multislice machine, capable of dealing with a greater number of patients. Likewise the MRI was updated the same year. Both CT and MRI are forms of digital imaging. In addition, banks of detectors can be used to record a radiographic image, dispensing with the need for films. By 2004, the department was well down the road to a filmless department and linked by development of IT and PACS to all departments in the RVI and also to all departments in the other hospitals and the Newcastle Centre for Life.

With MRI and similar equipment costing around £1,000,000 to install, Dr Arnison was indeed correct in his 1922 prognosis but if he could return, he would be amazed to see how his infant department has grown. (*Figs 11.14 & 11.15*)

Fig 11.15: *The MRI scanner is eased through a hole in the wall of the Radiology Department.*

117

Haematology, the laboratory aspects

Steve Proctor

In the early days, hematology essentially involved blood counts and cross-matching. This was often carried out in small rooms either on, or near to the wards. Hewan Dewar, who was House Physician (HP) in 1937, remembers the procedure followed when a blood transfusion became necessary. The HP rang the House Governor's office where the names of two people were selected from a panel of volunteers donors, usually at one of the larger works, such as Vickers. They were summoned to the RVI, taken to the ward 'secretions room' where ward investigations were performed. Here the donors' blood was grouped and if it was apparently compatible, the donor was bled into a glass flask containing citrate. The blood was stirred continuously with a glass rod to defibrinate it before being transferred to a bottle attached to the patient's drip. When the blood was needed out of hours, the key to the laboratory had to be collected from the Head Porter's office in Peacock Hall, then the blood had to be delivered to the ward before returning the key. The distances were not inconsiderable and House Physicians of the era solved the problem by the judicious use of a bicycle along the hospital corridors!

By the late 1940s, two technicians (Harry Newman and Jim Shaw) did all the blood counts and cell counts from other body fluids in a tiny laboratory situated on the medical corridor of the hospital. R. B. Thompson, a prominent physician with an interest in the field, kept a watching brief over the fledgling specialty. Later still, haematology joined the other pathology services departments along the long corridor and was long regarded as part of pathology. Tom Boon played an important role as a founding director of the Regional Blood Transfusion Service which co-ordinated donation, storage, grouping and distribution of blood to the various hospitals. (*Fig 11.16*) Tom also cared for many haemophiliac men, often young teenagers, with awful clinical problems. William Walker (universally known as 'Willie') worked after the war with Tom and also Sheilagh Murray. He subsequently obtained a Luccock research fellowship and worked on the Rhesus factor with James Spence. Later, he held research and personal University posts and had his base in the 'Attic Lab' situated on top of the east end of the hospital.

Fig 11.16: Cross matched blood ready for transfusion.

In 1972, laboratory haematology became a separate entity, when a new Department of Haematology was established combining University and service elements and also facilities for haemophilia. Walker was asked by Henry Miller to lead the whole department, which by then included both adult and paediatric work. Walker had one of the brightest minds around, a tremendous sense of fun and many non-medical interests including rally driving. He was awarded a personal Chair in the late seventies and, with Steve Proctor, went on to establish a flourishing clinical and laboratory research department of Haematology. He retired in 1984 to continue in a part-time role in the Blood Transfusion Service until he became 70 years of age.

The early 1980s saw an expansion of work due to the introduction of marrow transplants for adult patients in the Northern Region. There were major interests in lymphoma and Hodgkin's Disease developing and the advent of Factor VIII treatment had considerably improved the treatment of haemophiliacs. The management of large groups of these patients from the NE was centred on the RVI, under Peter Jones. Many were treated on an out-patient basis in the Department of Haematology. Finally, between 1982 and 2002 a full Academic Department of Haematology was created.

Bacteriology
Len Constable

Fig 11.17: The bacteriology laboratory with culture plates.

The emergence of bacteriology as a specialty was roughly coincidental with the foundation of the RVI and it developed rapidly under the influence of the War of 1914-1918.

No record seems to exist of the location of a bacteriology laboratory at that time but there is reason to believe that it was in the temporary hutted accommodation erected during the War at the extreme end of the main corridor. Part of these huts was still used by the department as late as 1960.

In 1947 the first appointment of a Clinical Bacteriologist was made, Dr C. A. Green filling the position. The department at the time was housed on two floors with access from the main corridor; offices on the ground floor, laboratories upstairs. The main laboratory comprised two large rooms, one for specimen reception and culture medium preparation, the other for routine investigations. In addition there were three staff rooms and an animal house for guinea pigs and mice.

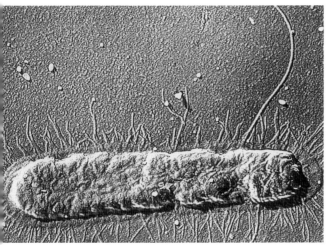

The workload included routine bacteriology and serology for the RVI, the Princess Mary Maternity Hospital and the Fleming Memorial Hospital for Sick Children. The staff included a Consultant, a Senior Registrar, Registrar and House Physician, supported by a team of Medical Laboratory Technicians led by the Chief Technician Mr Mark Thompson, together with secretarial and clerical staff. (*Fig 11.17*)

In addition to bacteriology the department undertook blood grouping and cross-matching for the RVI and this service was provided at night by the resident House Physician who was also committed to working in the Accident Room one night a week. At this time the laboratory

Fig 11.18: An electron micrograph of Salmonella paratyphi with its fringe of fimbriae, x 25,000.

was independent of the Medical School Bacteriology Department, led by Professor E. M. Dunlop, and was wholly financed by the hospital.

In 1953 preliminary work on virology began with the cultivation of suitable viruses on fertile hen egg membranes. This progressed slowly into the provision of human and animal tissue cultures for virus propagation. It became clear that a separate virology laboratory would have to be created.

In 1959 Professor Dunlop retired and C. A. Green was appointed in his place while retaining his consultancy at the RVI. Staff exchanges now took place on a part-time basis with routine hospital work for certain university lecturers, notably Dr M. Williamson, and teaching commitments for NHS consultants. The two departments were never fully integrated however, remaining financially independent. Nevertheless university funds were obtained for the purchase of an electron microscope which was installed in the RVI in an offshoot of the virology laboratory and operated by Dr L. Constable.

When Professor Green retired in 1974 the Chair was filled by Professor Max Sussman, non-medical bacteriologist, but the university/hospital relationship was maintained and even reinforced. Administrative charge of the hospital department fell to Dr J. Kennedy.

A cordial relationship was established between the Public Health Laboratory at Newcastle General Hospital, the RVI and the new Freeman Hospital. Selected staff from all of these laboratories assumed the role of Control of Infection Officers and Control of Infection Sisters were recruited from the respective nursing strengths. At the RVI two scientific officers joined the staff and undertook diagnostic mycology and parasitology.

The retirement of Dr J. Kennedy left Dr L. Constable in administrative charge and soon afterwards Dr A. J. Bint was appointed and later Dr S. Pedler joined the team.

The Royal College of Pathologists began increasingly to exert its influence and application was successfully made for the department to be recognised for the training of medical staff for admission to Membership of the College. Also at this time, the rapid development of automation and computerisation required significant changes in laboratory procedures.

A great deal of work was undertaken when planning began for a new ward block, and after that, for the building of a new medical school that was to incorporate the RVI microbiology department. Since these changes would not take place during his tenure of office Dr Constable, who was due to retire in 1985, handed over to Dr Bint who currently remains in charge.

Virology
C. R. Madeley

The Virology Department began as an offshoot of the University Department of Microbiology when Philip Gardner was appointed as Consultant Virologist in 1958. It was located over what was then the animal house, not an ideal situation but one which ensured the introduction of meticulous techniques to counter the ever-present risk of contamination.

The classical diagnostic methods of serology and culture were too slow to form a basis for treatment. This led Gardner's team to redevelop the older technique of immunoflourescence (IF) to provide a 'same day' diagnosis which resulted in placing the department on the world diagnostic map. Gardner and his principal collaborators, Joyce McQuillin and Rosemary McGuckin produced a book 'Virus Diagnosis, Application of Immunoflourescence' which became the standard work on the subject.

The original department rapidly became too small and, in 1976, it was rehoused in a purpose-built structure across the road from the old fracture clinic. Unfortunately, the air-conditioning and heating system never worked properly, it was programmed only for the hours of 8am to 5pm, leaks were frequent and the heat failed to arrive at the outer reaches of the accommodation. During winter epidemics, the diagnostic team, often working late, could be dimly seen in the darkness, welded to their microscopes wearing overcoats, scarves and mittens with a one bar electric heater for comfort. Captain Scott would have been proud of them!

Their dedication resulted in the establishment of a centre of world-wide excellence which attracted many visitors, although few were prepared to be as rigorous about getting the sera and specimens right. Gardner founded the European Group for Rapid Viral Diagnosis, later merging with other societies to form the European Society for Clinical Virology.

The technique of IF was later complemented by electron microscopy and in 1979 a high quality second-hand machine was purchased from the Atomic Energy Research Establishment. It did not appear to be radioactive but there was always a nagging doubt. However the arrival of this equipment meant that an immediate diagnosis could be offered on most common viral illnesses, backed by serology and culture for epidemiological purposes. It is not an idle claim that for some 15 years, it was one of the best diagnostic laboratories in the world. A 24-hour, 7-day-a-week service was offered through the generosity of senior staff, who did out-of-hours work for nothing, totally within the spirit of the old NHS.

The new Medical School opened in the mid-1980s and space had been allocated to virology but it was insufficient for the needs of the whole department. Only the University component was transferred, resulting in a split department. Further problems arose when the concept of the internal market within the NHS was introduced. The difficulties with the high class service that Virology offered, were that it was labour-intensive, there were few effective antiviral drugs and the chief value was to the community as a whole, in providing accurate information on which viruses were circulating at any one time. These aspects were not good for fund raising and in 1995 the unit was moved to the General Hospital into the Public Health Laboratory.

It is a far cry from long dusty corridors to the landmark International Centre for Life, yet this is where the Institute of Human Genetics is now based. It is electronically linked by PAS (Patient Administration System) and PACS (Picture Archiving and Communication System) to all other Clinical and Service departments at the RVI. It is probably true to say that nowhere has the impact of technological advances been greater than in the Service Departments.

Chapter 12: *The Ancillary Departments*
Underpinning the clinical services   Leonard Barron

Part 1
Professions Allied to Medicine

Introduction

When the new RVI building was opened in 1906, the staffing was dominated by the Honorary medical staff, the Matron and a House Governor. There was a housekeeper to look after the domestic services and a small number of artisans responsible for service and maintenance of the buildings. Apart from the nursing staff there was also a small number of professional staff who were linked to the treatment and care of patients. A dispenser made up and dispensed a limited number of medicines, and the Lady Almoner was responsible for matters of patient welfare and the collection of funds which were needed to supplement the subscriptions and donations on which the hospital depended for its running costs.

The application of science to the practice of medicine, which started during the end of the 19th century, rapidly increased over the following decades. The use of X-rays was already established in 1906 within the electrical department, which also included the use of electrotherapy and massage. This explains why the departments of Radiology and Physiotherapy had a common origin. The School of Massage and Medical Gymnastics separated from radiography in 1918.

In the years that followed there was increasing specialisation and an exponential rise in the importance of technical and professional staff. With the introduction of the National Health Service, the status and nature of the non-medical staff changed and in 1960, a register was established for Professions Allied to Medicine (PAMs) which regulated the standards of training.

The discovery of X-rays and radioactivity created a whole new sphere of diagnosis and treatment. At first, nurses took the X-rays but as their use increased it was necessary to have specially trained radiographers and the school of radiography was founded in the 1940s. Radiographers were also involved in managing treatment which used radium and high frequency X-radiation and in 1948 the profession separated into diagnostic and therapeutic sections.

As radioactive materials were increasingly used for diagnosis and treatment, the dangerous side-effects of radiation caused concern and this led to the employment of a physicist to measure and control the use of radium. It was not long before other forms of diagnosis and treatment needed to be monitored by physicists and as a result a medical physics department was set up in 1945.

Speech therapists, occupational therapists, social workers, chiropodists and optometrists have increased their contribution to the work of the RVI, and no modern hospital could function without them.

Sources: The Annotated Annual Report of the Board of Govenors for 1906 is in Tyne and Wear archives ref HO/RVI/72/91 as are many of the House Committee and various other Committee Minutes.

Physiotherapy

The Department of Electrical Treatments, which transferred into the new building in 1906, housed both the early X-ray department and the masseuses who provided electrotherapy, such as ultraviolet light and long wave treatment. They were members of the Incorporated Society of Trained Masseuses but there does not appear to have been any formal training.

The School of Massage and Medical Gymnastics was founded in October 1918 by Major Whately-Davidson (later head of the X-ray Department) and Major Arnison, an Orthopaedic Surgeon, with Miss Margaret G. Nicholson as Principal of both the School and the Department of Massage. (*Fig 12.2*) She had three qualified masseuses who were responsible for teaching students and providing treatments for patients. The first intake comprised five students and the course, which lasted from six to twelve months, involved massage, medical gymnastics and electrical treatments as well as studies of anatomy, pathology and physiology. Students completed the examinations set by the Society of Trained Masseuses, which became the Chartered Society of Trained Masseuses and Medical Gymnastics in 1920.

In 1933, when the new orthopaedic buildings were opened, they included a new massage department and a school for 48 students with Miss M G Nicholson continuing as Principal. The length of the training course was extended to two years and much of the students' training involved treating patients on the wards and out-patient therapy rooms. There was a gymnasium, and separate rooms for massage, exercise, sunlight and electrical treatment and there was a small hydrotherapy pool located near the exercise room.

By 1943 the total number of students had increased to 53 and the length of the course to two years. When the Chartered Society of Trained Masseuses and Medical Gymnastics became the Chartered Society of Physiotherapy the names were changed to the Physiotherapy Department and School, and the qualified staff were now known as Chartered Physiotherapists.

Miss Nicholson retired in 1947 and was succeeded by Miss Phyllis Lyttleton, followed by Miss Margaret Roper. In 1955 a new Department of Physical Medicine was formed and the School of Physiotherapy came under the direction of Dr Malcolm Thompson, Consultant in Physical Medicine. The annual student intake was increased in 1959 to 28 women.

Fig 12.2: Staff of the School of Physiotherapy, 1926. In the front row are Miss Margaret Nicholson (sister of Grace), (unknown), Dr Whately Davison (right), and Miss Kaplin.

Miss Nancy Bolam, who was the Principal from 1960 until 1984, was responsible for setting up a library and audio-visual learning room in the School. The number of new students was increased to 30 per annum including, in 1973, the first male student.

During the 1960s the Chartered Society of Physiotherapy considered that the future education of student physiotherapists should be of degree standard and the School of Physiotherapy as well as a new Occupational Therapy Course were established at Newcastle Polytechnic in 1976, as the first stage in the development of degree courses. The RVI continued to provide clinical placements where students assessed and treated patients under the supervision of qualified Occupational Therapists and Physiotherapists.

Post 1976

After 1976, the government delayed degree developments for therapists so that the lecturers too could obtain degrees, undertake research and gain valuable experiences in higher education. In 1990 the BSc Hons Occupational Therapy and BSc Hons Physiotherapy were validated at University of Northumbria.

Physiotherapy students now study for a minimum of three years before gaining an honours degree in physiotherapy, with license to practice as a Chartered Physiotherapist. The subjects covered during the training have also broadened, to include research methodology. Physiotherapy, with Occupational Therapy, is now part of the Department of Rehabilitation. There are currently 67 whole-time equivalent physiotherapy staff working across the RVI and the acute services at Newcastle General Hospital. There are also physiotherapy assistants and technical instructors to support physiotherapists in their work.

As with all hospital staff, physiotherapists have had to adapt to changes in medical care and technology. In 1944 the most common treatment was long wave therapy. The equipment was housed in a metal cage because it could interfere with the outside world - including, it seems, the instruments of planes flying overhead! This has been replaced by short wave diathermy, which is much more versatile and safer to use.

Whilst rehabilitation following trauma and surgery continues to be very important, physiotherapists are now much involved in the management of medical conditions, such as heart disease and stroke. There is also increased specialisation. In the care of the elderly, physiotherapists work closely with the Falls and Syncope Service and occupational therapists. In Women's Health a service is provided for antenatal and post natal care and for the management of incontinence.

Physiotherapists also play an important part in the Occupational Health Service where they can advise on the prevention and treatment of work-related strains and injuries among hospital staff.

Occupational Therapy (OT)

The benefits from providing useful occupations to long-stay patients were recognised in the 19th Century and were used particularly in orthopaedic hospitals and mental institutions but until the 1980s, occupational therapy at the RVI existed only to provide craft work to elderly patients recovering from stroke or awaiting discharge.

The expansion of the service followed changes in the concept of occupational therapy which has been described as *"the treatment of people with physical illness or disability through specific selected occupation for the purpose of enabling individuals to reach their maximum level of function and independence in all aspects of life..."* Training is through a three-year degree course, which is offered locally by the Universities of Northumbria and Teesside with clinical experience within the RVI occupational therapy service. The emphasis is towards rehabilitation and, like physiotherapy, there is increasing specialisation.

In about 1990, new OT posts were created in the care of the elderly, general medicine, orthopaedics, general surgery, ophthalmology, and paediatrics and there are currently (2005) 21 occupational therapy staff working across the RVI and in acute services at NGH. This includes qualified occupational therapists and unqualified support staff.

Sources: Professor Jean Potts, Northumbria University, allowed me to quote from her history of radiography at the RVI and provided some of the illustrations. Many thanks also to Sheila Bull and Andrea Hepburn, Rehabilitation Services Manager at the RVI.

The OT staff assess the needs of the individual patient and the majority of services are delivered to in-patients, much of them directed towards ensuring that on leaving hospital they have the necessary skills and equipment to deal with the ordinary tasks of daily living. There are also services for out-patients. Occupational therapists also provide a service to patients who have lost their sight, to help them adjust, physically and psychologically.

Radiography

The first radiographs in the RVI were taken in 1898 and in the year following the opening of the new building in 1906, 1135 radiographs were taken and 983 screen examinations were carried out. The first radiographer was Thomas Dodd assisted by Cornelius McMeekin. The equipment for radiography was very primitive. It is small wonder that Thomas Dodd was severely burnt and ultimately lost his life as the result of X-radiation.

Dodd and McMeekin did most of the X-rays themselves but Dr Davidson, the director, recruited two Red Cross nurses to help them. As the demand for X-rays, and radiographers increased, the Society of Radiographers was started in 1920. In 1921, examinations were introduced for entry to membership, and a syllabus developed. The staff were trained informally but during the 1940s Drs Warrick, Middlemiss and Farmer, (who was the first medical physicist at the RVI) set up a School of Radiography. During the day the radiographers worked in the department and the formal lectures were given in the evening. Until the 1950s qualified radiographers could chose to work in either the diagnostic or therapeutic departments, but after 1948, students had to make the choice at the beginning of their course.

Newcastle became a recognised examination centre and hosted the examinations for the Society of Radiographers twice a year. This meant that all radiography students in the Northern Region had only to travel Newcastle to take their examinations, instead of going to the next nearest centre in Wakefield.

In 1976 a purpose-built Radiography School was opened at a cost of £105,000; the space was created by adding a third storey to the existing diagnostic X-ray department at the RVI. This provided three classrooms, a demonstration room, library, darkroom, office space and rest room facilities for the students. By this time the school boasted three full-time radiographic teaching staff and one full-time secretary. The additional teaching posts in both therapeutic and diagnostic radiography were slowly filled over the next ten years, a major difficulty being a national shortage of qualified teachers.

Whilst the school flourished, the number of students was reduced because there were thought to be too many. Like similar perceptions in the training of medical students, this was to cause serious shortages of radiographers later on. During the eighties the courses were transferred into Centres of Higher Education. However at the beginning of the next decade two centres of radiographic education in the Northern Region (Newcastle and Teesside) were invited, along with others, to tender for the contract to train Diagnostic and Therapeutic students. Sadly Newcastle lost and training for Diagnostic students moved to Teesside, whilst training for Therapeutic students went to Liverpool and the Newcastle School of Radiography closed its doors in 1994.

The use of ultrasound to produce simple images of the fetus, during the 1970s, was rapidly developed into the sophisticated ultrasound imaging which is now used in all branches of diagnosis. It was followed by the invention of computerised tomography (CT), magnetic resonance imaging (MRI) and positron emission tomography (PET). There is now less projection radiography, because of guidelines on the use of ionising radiation.

As a result of this, and changes in diagnostic techniques, radiographers with specialist training now play an increasing role in providing a diagnostic service and there is a new grade of consultant radiographer; such individuals are now taking over some of the reporting of axial skeleton radiographs and CT head scans from the radiologists.

There are now 38 radiographer posts at the RVI. Obstetric ultrasound is now a sonographer run service with little medical input and the majority of non-obstetric ultrasound is now performed and reported by sonographers Radiographers also carry out the majority of the barium examinations and take a increasing role in managing the scanning lists.

126 Sources: Warrick C. K. (1977) Notes on the history of the Department of Radiology RVI Radiology, 63, 190-4.
Sheila Bull and Dick Whitlock provided information about the past and Phil Wilson allowed access to the departmental archives.

Medical Physics at the RVI

It did not take long to realise that the use of X-rays for diagnosis and of radium for treating tumours was potentially dangerous. Newcastle upon Tyne became a nominated National Radium Centre in 1930 and the Radium Commission subsequently recommended that a physicist with an adequately equipped laboratory and workshop should be an integral part of each Radium Centre. The North of England Council of the British Empire Cancer Campaign contributed generously, including to the salaries of staff and the overhead expenses of the accommodation at the RVI.

In 1945 Dr F. T. Farmer (*Fig 12.3*) was appointed physicist to the Radium Centre and was housed in the Radiotherapy Department of the RVI. He was the first medical physicist appointed in Newcastle, or indeed the Northern Region. In 1952 he was appointed Honorary Principal Physicist at the RVI but still was in the employ of the Regional Hospital Board. By then the embryonic Medical Physics Department, apart from its role in radiation protection, radiotherapy and its pioneering work on radiation dosimetry, was collaborating with other departments, especially in exploring the use of the artificial radioisotopes that were becoming available from the nuclear reactors developed during the War. In 1967, Dr Farmer was appointed Honorary Professor of Medical Physics and continued as head of the Regional Unit until his retirement in 1978 when he was succeeded by Professor Keith Boddy. Frank Farmer continued to serve the NHS for many years as chairman of the Newcastle Ethics Committee and he died in 2004 at the age of 91.

The medical physics unit always had a regional role and in 1964 much of the physics staff and equipment decamped into the relatively spacious accommodation provided in the extension of the Radiotherapy building at Newcastle General Hospital.

Dr Farmer was joined by Michael Day in 1947 and J. F. Fowler from 1950 to 1956. John Haggith came in 1957, and in 1962 Barry Clayton moved to the RVI to head the Medical Physics Unit. The Unit consisted of two physicists and seven workshop, electronics, radium and radioisotope technical staff.

Professor K. Boddy, who succeeded Frank Farmer in 1978 retired in 1997 and was replaced in 1997 by Professor Brian Diffey. When Barry Clayton retired in 1997 Dr M. J. Keir became Head of the RVI Unit.

The role of Medical Physics has expanded to provide clinical services in nuclear medicine, photobiology, ophthalmology and laser physics (total number of patient studies in 2003 was 5224), provides support from its clinical instrumentation, electronic and mechanical engineering sections, and provides radiation protection advice to the hospital. It remains a unit of the Regional Medical Physics Department and as such has access to the array of services and expertise offered in the component units in the other Newcastle Hospitals.

Fig 12.3: Frank Farmer.

Sources: *John Haggith provided notes of the history of the department.*

Pharmacy

The first recorded reference to the house apothecary (a Henry Gibson) comes in 1753 with the opening of the Infirmary at Forth Banks. The Apothecary was recognised as a skilled practitioner who was able to prescribe medicines but not offer medical advice. By the time of the opening of the new building in 1906, the pharmacy at the RVI was well established. By this time the role of the Apothecary was changing to that of a general practitioner and drugs and other medicines were dispensed by druggists and chemists. The Pharmaceutical Society, founded in 1841, set down the training for qualified pharmacists and the term 'dispenser' is now reserved for an unqualified person.

Within the Infirmary, the apothecary was still engaged in preparing medicines from natural sources by means of solution, distillation or grinding powders. Each pill had to be made by hand and the medication was incorporated into an excipient (a base) which could be treacle, wax or even glycerin. (*Fig 12.4*)

Since the 1700s, digitalis was prepared directly from the percolation of foxglove leaves and was used indiscriminately for a variety of disorders, often at toxic doses. It is now available in tablet, solution and injection form, has a standard potency and the dose of drug can be measured exactly by chemical analysis. Other new drugs, such as insulin, revolutionised the treatment of diabetes and a new class of drugs, such as aspirin and salvarsan were being produced in the chemical laboratory. The dispensing of liquid extracts and hand-made pills began to disappear in favour of mass-produced tablets and this was the time when many famous pharmaceutical companies began.

In Newcastle there were a number of factories associated with commercial pharmacies which produced medicines to order. In 1920, Professor Pybus, then a young surgeon, was providing an aerated and flavoured citric drink containing glucose, for his patients recovering from surgery. (*Fig 12.5*) The drink was being made at the nearby Owen Pharmacy and the chief assistant, Mr Hunter, realising the potential of this formulation began the manufacture of LUCOZADE from the Owens factory. Today the position of the Owen pharmacy is marked by an air-shaft on the Metro system and the Lucozade factory is now a University car park.

Fig 12.4: *Storage vats for lotions in the pharmacy department in the early days of the RVI.*

Fig 12.5: *Machine for producing soda water and lemonade.*

When the NHS started in 1948 there were only five staff in the dispensary. Over the years there have a number of memorable Chief pharmacists. Dossie (Doswell) Foggan, who died in 1954, is still remembered as a fine teacher and as the inventor of a disinfectant called 'Dossol' which was still in use at the infirmary in 1978.

Fig 12.6: Modern robot controlled drug storage and dispensing.

There are now a huge number of very potent drugs with duplications, interactions and numerous side-effects. Pharmacists have had to rise to the challenge by changing their role from mere dispensers of prescriptions, to playing an active role in the purchasing, prescribing and management of drugs and other related substances such as infusion fluids. Thus, when Miss Dryden was appointed deputy head pharmacist in 1955, it was on condition that she obtained a diploma in biochemistry. Membership of the Pharmaceutical Society, which alone confers the ability to practice as a pharmacist, has increased the length of training and now requires a four-year degree followed by one year pre-registration pratice under supervision. When the additional year was introduced in 2000, there was a hiatus for a "fallow" year which caused great difficulties for the RVI service.

The RVI pharmacy serves not only the RVI but also the acute sector of Newcastle General Hospital; and the cost of drugs which was about £28 million in 2003 rose to £33 million in 2004. (*Fig 12.6*)

The establishment is for 39 qualified pharmacists, 42 technicians and 39 support staff, including nine secretaries. To cope with the new manufacturing facilities for producing specialised infusion fluid, there are four quality control scientists.

There has always been a problem in retention of pharmacists in the hospital service where, despite great job satisfaction, pay was often allowed to fall well behind that of colleagues in the private sector. The advent of pharmacies in supermarkets, which offer better pay and more flexible hours than the hospitals, are serious competitors to recruitment, added to which changes in the NHS are creating new roles for pharmacists in primary care centres.

Sources: Mike Hannon allowed me to use the material he had prepared for an exhibition at the RVI and Rodney Lonsghaw, the current Chief Pharmacist brought me up to date.

Speech and Language Therapy

Although the idea of Speech Therapy as a discipline seems to have started in the USA and took a long time to become established in Britain, it was Dr Morley at the RVI who was the pioneer in this country.

In 1932, Dr Muriel Morley responded to an unusual advertisement. A Newcastle Plastic Surgeon had devised a new type of pharyngoplasty for cleft palate and was seeking an "educated woman" who could assess the children's speech before and after surgery. The lessons she learned with Mr Fenton Braithwaite at the Fleming Memorial Hospital over the next five years were set down in her first book "Cleft Palate and Speech".

Dr Morley qualified as a speech and language therapist in 1938, and by 1945 was working full time in Newcastle's three hospitals - NGH, RVI and the Fleming - with a varied caseload that included a number of men who had become aphasic from war-time head injuries, to children with various voice disorders including stammering, articulation and delayed language.

One of Dr Morley's major research studies at the RVI was in collaboration with Dr Donald Court in Child Health and Dr Henry Miller, neurologist (and later Vice Chancellor of Newcastle University). Speech and language samples of 847 children in Newcastle were recorded at ages 3, 4, 6 and 15 years. The results of these assessments were published in 1957 as *"Development and Disorders of Speech in Childhood"*. In 1959 Dr Morley founded the UK's first University Department of Speech in Newcastle.

Between 1949-89, Dr Morley was joined by Miss Ann Irwin who became internationally known for her work with stammerers. They would assess up to 200 regional patients a week by seeing them in groups of 10 for an hour's assessment. The children attended with a parent, who was responsible for ongoing therapy at home. Dr Morley's niece, Mrs Elisabeth Scanlon was appointment Speech and Language Therapist at the RVI in the late 1950s and continued working in Newcastle until 2000.

The Speech and Language Therapy Service has grown and the skills of speech therapists are used well beyond the problems of speech defects in children. The treatment of patients recovering following stroke may involve problems of swallowing as well as speech. On the RVI site the Regional Cleft Palate Service continues to flourish, as does the Child Development Centre. The adult department focuses on neurologically impaired in-and out-patients.

The district service has grown from one therapist serving the whole of Newcastle and beyond, to a team of 70 full-time and part-time therapists working over seven sites!

Social Work

The original office of Almoner dates back to the time of the monasteries but the office of Lady Almoner seems to date from a 1862 parliamentary committee of enquiry into overcrowding in hospital clinics, which recommended that Lady Almoners should be appointed in Voluntary Hospitals to assess which patients were entitled to free treatment. With the nationalisation of the voluntary hospitals in 1948, the title of almoner changed to that of Medical Social Worker and the duties now included the provision of the newly available medical appliances.

In 1948, the head almoner was Miss Grace Nicholson (*Fig* 12.7) who was one of six distinguished children of Canon Ralph and Mrs Margaret Nicholson - one of Grace's sisters, Margaret, founded the School of Physiotherapy at the RVI. (*Fig* 12.2) She soon ran into difficulty over funding for the provision of appliances and applied to the Board of Governors for increased funds. This unexpected demand for spectacles, dentures and other appliances led to a national financial and political crisis and in 1952 charges were imposed for appliances and prescriptions and Aneurin Bevan, the architect of the NHS, resigned as Health Secretary in protest. Grace Nicholson was secretary of the Training Committee for the Institute of Almoners and was awarded a MBE on her retirement in 1956.

Fig 12.7: Miss Grace Nicholson after receiving the MBE.

Medical Social Workers were then employed by the NHS but in 1968 the Seebohm Committee recommended that all social workers should have a generic training and be employed by the Local Authority. The advantages claimed for such a system were the improved links with social services in the community and with those in other Health Authorities. The Local Authorities Social Services Act (1970) instituted the integration of social workers, and a small working party was convened in 1972 to discuss how to retain an effective medical social work service in the RVI, under the new system. As a result, Brian Roycroft, the charismatic Director of Social Services, organised a very effective service for the Newcastle hospitals which worked very well for about six years.

In July 1978, during the Summer of Discontent, social workers in Newcastle went on strike over pay and conditions. There were wide variations between local authorities and they wanted national pay agreements. The effect on Newcastle hospitals varied but it was most strongly felt by the ward sisters who had to do the best they could to sort out welfare problems which were becoming increasingly common. In particular, ward sisters at the Princess Mary Maternity Hospital had to cope with the everyday problems of single parents, illegitimate infants and adoption, all of which had a very different connotation in 1978 compared with today. Relations between the clinical staff and social workers became strained and took some time to recover once the strike was over in 1979.

During the early 1980s the RVI team expanded, but could not meet the needs of specialist regional units. It was necessary to find additional funding and the Malcolm Sargent Foundation agreed to fund two posts for paediatric oncology. By about 1990 there were several such funded posts in the Renal, Haemophilia and Sensory Support Units. Accountability remained with Newcastle Social Services Department who liaised through a Senior Social Worker.

With the advent of the NHS & Community Care Act (1990) there were new pressures on the social services. These were due to the now familiar phenomenon of bed blocking. There was insufficient accommodation at home or in the community for the elderly and disabled who were ready to be discharged from hospital. With limited resources, the City Council felt that their main priority had to be to the people of Newcastle and it could not continue funding social work to neighbouring regions. This problem is a very familiar one in any hospital receiving referrals from a wide area.

In 1994 the decision was made to restructure, and Hospital Social Work was badly hit with the abolition of many management posts. This changed the face of hospital social work and was a very difficult time for those involved.

Nowadays, the Social Service department at the RVI is part of the team within the Newcastle Acute Hospital Trust. There is a Team Manager, 11 Social Workers, and two Social Care Assessment Officers. The busier wards have a Social Worker or SCAO attached to them and they attend ward rounds and case discussions, sharing information and experience in order to improve the speed and efficiency of response.

An important innovation is the provision of a full time Duty Social Worker who deals with all cases referred from wards which do not have an attached social worker, as well as work when social workers may be unavailable.

Sources: Rodney Nicholson provided family memorabilia and the photographs of his aunts Grace Nicholson MBE and Margaret Nicholson.
Moira Woodford was a great help with the recent history and the obituary of Brian Roycroft by T. Philpott appeared in the Guardian on 31 May 2002.

Part 2
Support Staff

Introduction

This section is devoted to an account of the hidden army of workers who run what are now called the support services and who receive scant mention in official reports. In 1906, The RVI was a Voluntary Hospital, run by a Board of Governors, and was a closely knit community. After the introduction of the National Health Service in 1948, the Board of Governors remained for a number of years but with successive reforms of the NHS the management changed several times and the records have become dispersed, resulting in a confused record of events. The size of the workforce increased in the early years with the building of the Leazes Hospital in 1918 and inclusion of the Princess Mary Maternity, Dental and Babies' Hospitals into the United Newcastle Hospitals.

One of the few available documents which record the numbers of the support staff is a handwritten note in the Annual Report of the RVI for 1906. The domestic workers in hospital were equivalent to domestic servants and many lived in the hospital. There were 25 ward maids who worked under the supervision of the ward sisters and were expected to keep high standards of cleanliness at a time when the prevention of infection was recognised to be vital. There were six kitchen maids, four maids in the dining rooms, seven in the Nurses' Home and five house maids. There were also nine charwomen who presumably did the hard scrubbing of the corridors and public areas.

To cope with the large amount of linen used every day, there were 19 laundry workers, including a superintendent and one 'laundry man'. (*Fig 12.8*)

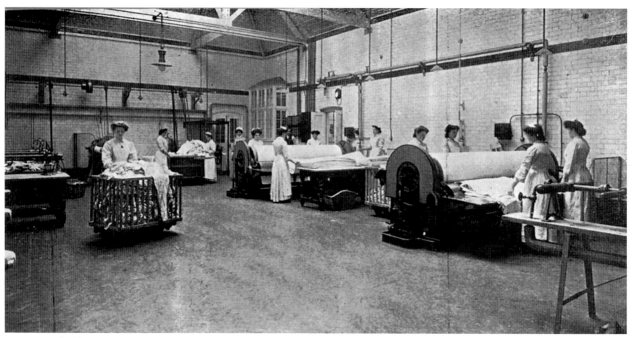

Fig 12.8: RVI laundry at the beginning of the 20th Century.

The committee which planned the new building in Queen Victoria Road received a letter from Mr Watson-Armstrong (son of Lord Armstrong) about the need for electric lighting and there was much discussion about the number of electric sockets to be installed in the wards. A contract was agreed with the District Electric Lighting Company to supply mains electricity, and coal-burning boilers provided hot water. Heating in the wards was dependent on open fires. The RVI employed four firemen, one plumber, two engineers, two carpenters, as well as a storekeeper and an instrument clerk. We also know that one of the duties of the porter was to light the gas mantles so lighting was not exclusively electric.

The introduction of the National Health Service in 1948 provides the second insight into the staffing of the RVI. The Finance and Establishment committee recorded 309 domestic staff, 125 porters, 39 artisans, a catering supervisor, two cooks, one housekeeper and her assistant and one laundry forewoman. With the NHS came new grades and a large bureaucracy. In particular, engineering services had grown to cope with the need for electrical power. Plumbing had also become more complex, with central heating replacing the need for fireplaces in the centre of the wards. It was not long before the unexpected increase in the costs of the NHS became a political issue.

Catering Services (*Fig 12.9*)

Florence Nightingale regarded the preparation of invalid food as an important part of the nurse's duty. That probably explains why in 1906 there were only two cook-housekeepers and six kitchen maids, because some cooking was done in each ward kitchen.

During the 1960s the Catering Officer was the legendary Miss Esther Clapham who provided meals of high quality and whose buffet suppers on special occasions are still remembered. When she retired, her successor Bill Brain found himself under attack by the management, egged on by the Ministry of Health, for the excessive spending on provisions. A series of minutes record how he had to limit his spending to 38/- (190p) per patient per week, reduce portion sizes, close the Registrars' Dining Room, and increase the cost of lunch in the Consultants' Dining Room to 1/- (5p). Bill Brain also complained that some patients were having porridge *as well as* fruit juice. More was to follow with the introduction of a tray system and advance ordering of meals.

Pressure on costs eventually led to industrialised catering with a central kitchen based at St.Nicholas Hospital. The food was then frozen and then transported for reheating in the various hospitals. It was not long before there were newspaper reports that the unit was working at 40 per cent of capacity and there were warnings of privatisation.

The hospital kitchens were not suited for the production of the special diets needed by patients with diseases like diabetes or for patients following major surgery. In 1953 a Diet Kitchen was established but it proved difficult to recruit the requisite number of trained dieticians.

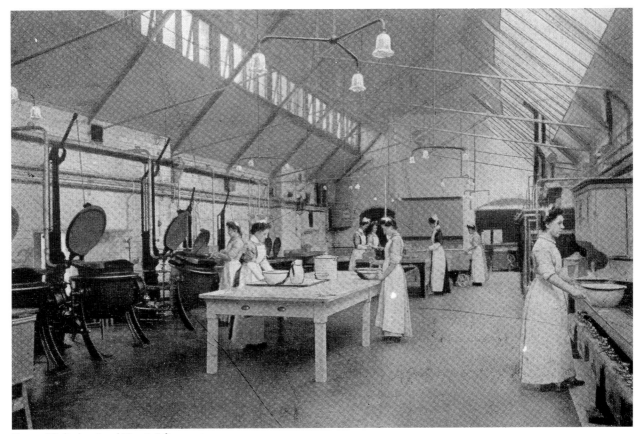

Fig 12.9: The kitchen, Royal Victoria Infirmary, circa 1910.

Fig 12.10: *If there is a thankless task in a public institution it is supervising car parks. Raymond Winpenny undertook his job with tact, firmness and a willingness to solve problems.*

Porters

Porters are often the first point of contact for patients and visitors and the Head Porter has always been a person of some importance. In the early days he wore a frock coat and had his Porter's Lodge near the gates of the RVI, later a flower shop but now demolished. In 1956, Mr Stanley retired after 15 years as Head Porter and was succeeded by Mr Vince, who is still remembered as looking 'sepulchral', wearing a frock coat and carrying, discretely, in the pocket of his pin-striped trousers the book of death certificates, which he took to the wards for the doctors to sign.

There were 18 porters in 1906 and their work consisted mainly of transporting patients and materials around the hospital. The role of the hospital porter has slowly changed over the years. They still look after the deceased and one is now a trained mortician. But now, 15 are employed solely on security and car parking duties, which include patrolling the hospital and scrutinising the CCTV images. (Fig 12.10) The other 75 still transport patients, look after the supply of medical gases, distribute the mail and, with four drivers, provide a courier service between hospitals.

Hospital rubbish is now strictly segregated into ordinary, infected, clinical and radioactive waste and is transported, now with the aid of a tug, to designated disposal areas from which it is taken away and processed by specialist outside companies.

Industrial Action

In 1972 a wave of strikes over pay disrupted the NHS, with the ancillary staff in the forefront, although there was also unrest among doctors and nurses.

It was the strike in 1982, however, which did the most damage. The wave of unrest started with resentment over government policy in 1976 intended to make the service more efficient by going out to tender for domestic, catering and laundry services. In March 1976, 34 out of a total of 300 porters and domestic staff stopped work over a bonus scheme and by June they were joined by 40 laundry workers. Patients were asked to bring in their own bed linen. The unrest smouldered on with protests against government cuts in spending.

In 1979 industrial action flared up and in February supplies of linen and sterilisation services were stopped and the **Newcastle Evening Chronicle** reported how *"health chiefs acted as porters"* and *"hospital porters dump rubbish on RVI lawn"*. (Fig 12.11) The catering staff also stopped work and, as a result, other staff began to bring in their own lunch and the use of the hospital canteens declined.

The best account we have of the work and attitudes of the ancillary staff came in an article in the **Newcastle Journal** in June 1980. In it, the reporter Sue Hercome described a typical day at the RVI, starting with Bill Brain, then catering manager:

"There is also the matter of last-minute plans for Mr. Jones's retirement dinner this Friday - smoked rainbow trout, asparagus soup, sirloin steak with Bernaise sauce, sherry trifle... As Bill Brain does the rounds of the two kitchens, two canteens and one dining room under his care, the staff who eat his grub have their say. Nine pence for a boiled egg - that is too much. But it would cost you five to buy one in the shops and you've got to have it cooked, served and your plate washed up afterwards".

The most revealing comments concern the strikes:

"And talking of strikes, on this industrious Wednesday morning, steam rising busily in the kitchens, dust being energetically laid on the corridors, laundry machines churning out their daily load of cleaned sheets, what about the status and value of these people uniformly called, for all their variety of activity, "hospital workers?" They manage the lowly mechanics of hospital life yet last winter they proved that the service would collapse without them. Now a new pay struggle looms against a background of health service cuts. Where should priorities lie? it is not a popular subject - not in the kitchens, anyway...

Fig 12.11: Rubbish dumped on front lawn of RVI in 1979 strike.

Down in the laundry, it's a slightly different matter. The laundry has a reputation - *"it's all those noisy machines, makes them very militant"* - and in the last resort, it's the laundry workers who have the power of ward closure. Relatives, after all, can supply food for patients and nurses can clean up the wards. No one else, however, can deal with a "foul wash" - heavily stained or infected linen, and no one else can manipulate the fearsome machines that churn and grind their way through the entire process of washing, drying, airing, pressing.

Linen Services Manager Andrew Campbell, said *"The wards need clean linen every day, and a failure in the supply can close a hospital. We get through 1600 lb. of linen an hour, but during the industrial dispute the staff decided they would only handle a certain amount ..."*

The laundry goes into action at 8 a.m. but by that time the domestic maids, *"that's our title, we're not cleaners"* - have already been rubbing and scrubbing for an hour. It's hard work, they say, because a hospital demands a far higher standard of cleanliness - *"clinically clean"* is the term - than any other institution. Carpets get vacuumed every day, polish is regularly stripped and replaced and there are the special treatments like spray-cleaning, damp dusting and suction drying. There's an art to hospital cleaning, too - it all has to be done with a minimum of disturbance. So there are regular training sessions, and talks about new products; and because everything has to be cleaned every day, good attendance and time-keeping are vital. This is the reason, says Jackie Thompson, Domestic Services Manager, that turnover on domestic staff is so high, 42 per cent, last year, and in the period 1973 to 1974 - a frightening 73 per cent. The hospital hit a bad patch with its domestic staff then.

Mrs Thompson doesn't pretend that hospital cleaning is a particularly rewarding task - not at floor level, anyway - but she does think that cleaning a hospital is as vital a task as any cleaner might be called upon to do. But the domestic maids - *"that's our title, we're not cleaners"* - who are taking their half-hour lunch time at mid-day in the Leazes canteen are less sure. Hospital work is all right, they say, and yes, it does have an atmosphere all of its own. But so does any place, any big office - and often the bosses are not so fussy elsewhere, and the money is better, too. They don't want to go on strike, however. *"We can't afford it,"* says one lady, who keeps her name to herself. All right for the consultants, of whom there are quite a few at this moment in the Leazes canteen; they never miss the odd pound or two.

Much has changed since then. In 1981 government said that services must go out to competitive tendering and the in-house bid from RVI won in 1981 and again in 1985/6. Many staff took voluntary redundancy but since then the numbers fell, but then rose to compensate for opening of the new Leazes Wing in 1993, the transfer of the Princess Mary Maternity Hospital into the RVI and the re-incorporation of the Dental Hospital.

The laundry was too small to justify the use of expensive modern machinery, and laundry is now sent to a large unit at Queen Elizabeth Hospital, Gateshead. Food comes from a commercial cook-chill unit and is heated up in the hospital. The only real cooks are the dieticians who prepare special meals for patients.

Domestic staff are now managed by the Head of Domestic services and include 410 domestic assistants. The only staff on the wards answerable to the ward sister are the ward orderlies who help look after patients.

Engineering services (*Fig 12.12*)

The engineering services had grown to cope with the need for electrical power and the huge increase in electrical equipment. In 1906, the public power supply was used for lighting and for power sockets between the beds. It is almost certain that in order to provide the high current needed for X-ray machines, DC was also generated within the hospital. Every ward had a central fireplace with coal brought round by the porters. Central heating was introduced in the 1920s and the fireplaces were removed over time. One of the porters' duties was to light the gas lamps but there is no record of where they were; it is possible that gas lights were thought, along with open fires, to improve ventilation.

Although mains generated AC became available, the hospital still needed standby generators but they were not always reliable. Eventually there were nine of them and power supply was split into essential and non-essential users. Now power is essential to every facet of the hospital and they were replaced by three units producing 1.5 megawatts, enough for the whole hospital.

Fig 12.12: Engineers working in the depths of the RVI ensure continuity of heat, light and water.

The original boiler house was underneath the laundry and in 1959 it was moved to the NW corner of the RVI site. It remained coal-fired until 1973 when it was converted to use heavy fuel oil, which required a very tall chimney. It then went over to dual fuel with the ability to use natural gas. In 2001 a CHP (combined heat and power) unit was installed in a new Energy Centre built and maintained by Dalkia Ltd. This generates electricity from a gas driven engine and the waste heat is fed into the hot water system; surplus electricity, e.g. at night, is fed into the National Grid.

Plumbing also became more complex. In 1906, there was a direct water supply via a large pipe from the Leazes Park lake, mainly to provide emergency supplies in case of fire. Within the hospital, narrow bore central heating is now standard, but public health has become a major influence. In order to reduce the risk of Legionella, the hot water must be kept at 60°C but this is dangerously hot and all basins used for hand washing are fitted with thermostatic taps.

Many services are now shared across the Trust but the RVI has its own Chief Engineer, an Engineer Manager (his deputy), two workshop Managers (one for engineering and one for building), four maintenance Technicians, an Energy and Environment Manager and 40 maintenance staff. Their responsibilities are wide-ranging and cover air-conditioning, refrigeration, sterilisation equipment, fire alarms, forty lifts, the air tube system and waste management.

The Chief Building Officer is based in the Trust Headquarters at the Freeman Hospital and the RVI has its own senior building officer on site. Regular wall-washing, which used to be carried out by hospital staff, is done by outside contractors. Building work is mainly confined to maintenance but an increasing amount of small-scale work is carried out in-house.

Fig 12.13: The technology may have changed, but telephonists remain the vital first point of contact for those phoning the hospital.

Telephones and communications *(Fig 12.13)*

As far as is known, the RVI had telephones in 1906, but it would have been a simple plug and hand-rung system. A small hand-operated exchange was located behind the reception area of Peacock Hall and this was replaced by a larger automatic exchange near St. Luke's Chapel. In the 1980s, when the volume of telephone traffic became overwhelming, a new electronic switchboard was installed and this provided a tandem dialling system which made it easy to reach other Newcastle hospitals without using an outside line. Now, there is a single Newcastle Hospitals switchboard physically based at Freeman Hospital. It is entirely computerised and it is possible to dial directly into an extension. The switchboard is also the centre for the various electronic paging devices now so essential for rapid communication.

Communications within the RVI and between hospitals are now dominated by computer driven systems and it is hard to remember how we functioned without them.

Library

The doctor of the early 1900s would find a very different RVI Library Service today, almost one hundred years on. In 1907 textbooks such as Cunningham's Anatomy, Brodie's Dissections, Handley's Cancer of the Breast, Diseases of Children and Diseases of the Eye were provided and the Library Sub-Committee reported how staff *'have found it of great service to have the latest publications to hand for reference'*. In 1911 a Standing Library Committee was established which ensured that an expert was appointed *'to catalogue, arrange and place the books in order on the wall shelves'*.

The RVI Library has recently moved back to its original home near Peacock Hall. Today's Librarian still organises and manages textbooks on shelves but is also responsible for a much wider range of services including pc's, internet access and electronic resources such as databases, e-journals and e-books. Today's Library is multi-disciplinary, providing services for all staff groups working in the hospital, instead of the two separate libraries for medical and nursing staff that existed previously. In addition, literature searches and accessing information from a network of libraries throughout the country is now a normal part of the service. To deal with the increase in users and the huge amount of information available there are now three members of Library staff instead of the sole Librarian of the past. Library staff have proved to be essential in spite of the numerous changes in services and technology.

The Library Service has been through many changes but a doctor from 1907 would still be able to visit the Library today and pick up a textbook to update himself. With a little help from Library staff he would also be able to gather valuable information from electronic sources. What will the clinician of today find in 100 years' time?

Sources: Ian Ward and John Swinhoe were particularly helpful with the section on engineering, maintenance and building and Mick Brennan told me about the portering and security services. The article by Sue Hercombe appeared in the Newcastle Journal on 9 May 1980.

Acknowledgments:

Wherever possible I have acknowledged the source of my information but I am very grateful to the many other current and past members of staff who helped to steer me in the right direction.

Chapter 13: *The Associated Hospitals* John Scott

A number of hospitals were associated with the RVI. Many provided specialist services such as opthalmology and ear, nose and throat surgery. Other hospitals such as the Newcastle General and Hexham Hospitals became associated for what may be described as political reasons. In the space available it is not possible to give a detailed account of what happened to each of these institutions. This detailed account of how specialist children's services developed and ultimately were absorbed into the RVI explains how this process occurred in a similar fashion in another associated hospital. The author's career was concentrated in a relatively small specialty, namely paediatric surgery, which was part of the children's service. However, the development of the paediatric surgical services represented, on a small scale, the developments that accompanied the progress of other departments and specialties in the separated hospitals.

How it began

The background is important. There were, in England outside London, recognised departments of paediatric surgery only in Liverpool, Manchester and Sheffield. These were based in established children's hospitals, which had a substantial reputation. Newcastle child health services were becoming concentrated and developed as a separate specialty under the leadership of Sir James Spence, who was appointed to the first University Chair of Child Health in England. Opinion was forming that a paediatric surgical service should also be developed, so as to expand the health care of children to cover both medical and surgical disorders. The concept that sick children were not simply miniature versions of sick adults was at last being accepted. Newcastle did have a children's hospital in the form of the Fleming Memorial Hospital, but it had unfortunately become side-lined and neglected academically and was not considered a viable institution. It was administratively part of the Newcastle upon Tyne Hospital Management Committee group based at the Newcastle General Hospital, and therefore not part of the university teaching hospital (Board of Governors) group based at the RVI. However, there was a second factor, which cannot be ignored. There was serious disagreement and friction between the staff at the Fleming and the professor of Child Health as to how children's medical services should be run. The surgeons took the view that a child requiring surgery was their responsibility and they would request the assistance of the paediatricians when and where necessary. The paediatricians felt that surgical intervention for a sick child was a decision which they should make, even to the point of indicating what operation was required and how it should be done. Not surprisingly, professional relationships between physicians and surgeons at the Fleming deteriorated and the professor withdrew. Considering that at that time medical services for children in Newcastle were fragmented between some seven or eight different institutions, this was a disastrous state of affairs. The opportunity to unite children's medical services for the city on one site in a purpose-built hospital, around which there was plenty of room for expansion, was lost. Such an institution would, furthermore, have been located in close proximity to one of Newcastle's main maternity units, the Princess Mary Maternity Hospital.

Although there was general agreement that a specialist service in paediatric surgery run by a consultant trained in the specialty was an urgent necessity, disagreements between paediatricians and surgeons about how it should be run and who should be in clinical and administrative control continued. A general surgical trainee, (Mr Harold H. Nixon) who had gone to London to train in paediatric surgery with a view to returning to Newcastle, could wait no longer and obtained a consultant position at the Hospital for Sick Children, Great Ormond Street.

Given this background, the development of a paediatric surgical service in Newcastle was never likely to be easy. To join an established department as a new recruit, most usually as a replacement for a departing member, does not, as a rule, create serious difficulties. But to initiate a department that had never previously existed involved professional encounters that, if they had been foreseen, would have dissuaded the most enthusiastic applicant.

---

[1] Ridley, W. The Babies' Hospital, Newcastle upon Tyne: Newcastle upon Tyne: Andrew Reid 1955.

The Babies' Hospital (*Fig 13.2*)

There were, initially, two sites within which paediatric surgery was to take place: the Babies' Hospital and the two children's wards at the RVI. The former comprised three adjoining houses in a Victorian terrace. The fascinating history of the Babies Hospital was described by Lady Ursula Ridley in 1956.[1] The service it provided dated back to 1917 when a day nursery was started by Miss Greta Rowell to care for children who were roaming the streets while their mothers were working in factories making munitions for the War. The predominant feature of the hospital, which was promoted by James Spence, was the revolutionary belief that infants and very young children should not be separated from their mothers when admitted to hospital. This ran counter to the strict orthodox belief that visits by parents to children in hospital served only to upset the children.

It was clear that certain structural developments were needed in the Babies' Hospital in order to provide a paediatric surgical service with an emphasis on neonatal surgery. The RVI Board of Governors agreed and in 1961 the necessary alterations went ahead. Thus surgery for the newborn, infant and young child commenced in an institution that had a somewhat improbable external appearance but functioned extremely well. Most of the credit for this must go to the nursing staff and particularly to the anaesthetic service developed by Dr John Inkster. The neonatal surgical recovery room was well equipped with the type of incubators that were employed at that time, together with other ancillary devices. A year or so subsequently another small area of the hospital was developed to create an intensive care room where babies requiring long-term ventilation could be treated. This was pioneer work by Dr Inkster, assisted by Sister Linda Maybee, and it is noteworthy that it is now a standard method of treatment in most neonatal intensive care units.

At the RVI a small number of beds in the professorial children's ward were allocated for surgery, together with a one day per week operating session in one of the general surgical operating theatres. These had been negotiated by Professors Lowdon and Court who were very supportive and helpful in solving clinical and administrative problems as and when they arose.

At this point it seems worth mentioning the "new children's hospital" that was being planned. As indicated previously, there was already a children's hospital in Newcastle, namely the Fleming. The fact that it could have been expanded and developed at a substantially lower cost did not seem to occur to those in authority. Eventually, the architects reached the point of producing outline drawings for the new hospital. The new building was to have nine floors; five lower floors for a new Princess Mary Maternity Hospital and four upper floors for the new children's hospital.

Optimism was rising. By this time government and civil service must have realised that the threat of actually having to fulfil an undertaking made by politicians was becoming too realistic. A decree was therefore issued by the then Minister for Health (one Enoch Powell) that no further children's hospitals were to be built in the UK. Newcastle, a city in the midst of an area of degenerating industry, high unemployment and serious socio-economic deprivation, was not to be provided with the kind of children's medical centre which was necessary to cater for the needs of its sick children.

The Fleming Memorial Hospital

The Fleming Memorial Hospital for Sick Children started life in 1863 as the Children's Hospital, Hanover Square. In 1886, John Fleming, (*Fig 13.1*) a Newcastle solicitor, gave £25,000 to build a new hospital for sick children in memory of his wife who had died in 1882. The hospital was officially opened by Lord Armstrong in 1888. Unfortunately, as mentioned previously, at the inception of the NHS in 1948 the hospital did not become a member of the university teaching hospital group. Surgery at the hospital was performed by Mr Stewart Feggetter, a general surgeon on the staff at the Newcastle General Hospital. He had great experience in the "general surgery" of children. He had performed somewhere in the region of 2,000 Ramstedt's operations for pyloric stenosis in small babies. (Indeed he performed such an operation on the three-week old son of this writer.) Plastic surgery for cleft lip and palate was another major undertaking in the hospital. The anaesthesia for these operations was usually given by Dr Philip Ayre who had designed a simple, but invaluable piece of apparatus known as the "T-piece", which served to reduce dead

Fig 13.2: *The Babies' Hospital at 33-34 Leazes Terrace.*

Fig 13.3: *The Fleming Memorial Hospital for Sick Children.*

space in the anaesthetic breathing circuit. This simple device is still being employed widely throughout the world. So the paediatric service at the Fleming had a high reputation, even though it went largely unrecognised. Furthermore, it received little support from the administration and was seriously underfunded.

When appointed to the hospital as a member of the surgical staff this writer visited the place in order to meet other members of the staff and see the facilities. With some pride, a room set aside for intensive care was demonstrated. It was a sizeable room standing in the centre of which was an infant incubator. When in use this incubator would at times have had oxygen fed into it in large quantities. However, there was the terrifying spectacle of a large naked electric radiant heater hanging from the ceiling. The consequences of an explosion caused by the heater were too awful to contemplate. But this was an example of the standard of administrative care from which the hospital had suffered.

Eventually, the administration of the Fleming was transferred to the RVI group. Money was spent on upgrading the building and services and RVI staff transferred their commitments to the Fleming. A small ward was divided into cubicles to create a neonatal surgical unit and one of the larger wards was similarly converted to expand the mother and baby accommodation. A room was set aside for the anaesthetic department to store its equipment and install a blood gas analysis machine. Perhaps the most important improvement was to the radiology department, where an image intensifier was installed, enabling more effective contrast radiology to be performed. Radiographers came from the RVI to operate the equipment and enjoyed working with the children. One in particular, Miss Liz Hunter, decided to specialise in paediatric radiography: as a result the X-ray department provided a skilled radiography service and became a place that children could enjoy, even though they were being subjected to potentially frightening procedures. Paediatric surgical services were thus effectively transferred from the Babies' Hospital to the Fleming, although some minor surgery continued there for a time. In 1980, the first consultant paediatric radiologist, Dr Richard Lee was appointed with the result that all paediatric services in the Fleming commenced operating at a higher level. The hospital was extremely popular with the children who were admitted to it and in particular with their parents and the staff who worked in it. It had a "family" atmosphere, and was dedicated to one single purpose, namely making children admitted to it, often with distressing and difficult problems, as happy and as secure as possible. A detailed description of the history of the Fleming Hospital was published in a special booklet.[II] Some illustrations of life at the Fleming are shown in Figures 13.4 to 13.11.

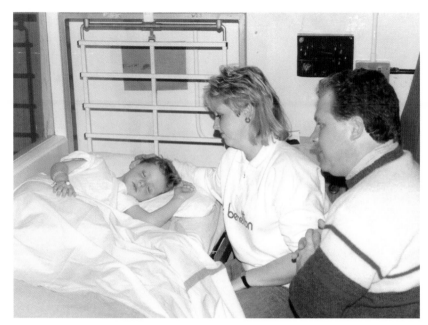

Fig 13.4: After the operation. Peaceful sleep.

Fig 13.5: Where's my supper?

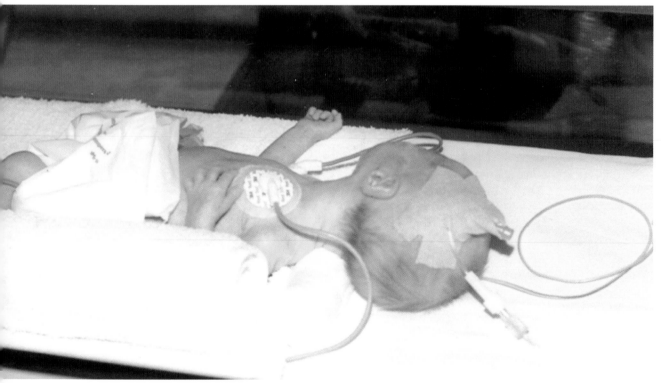

Fig 13.6: Small, but doing well.

II Dale G, Donald J, Wagget J. The Fleming Memorial Hospital for Sick Children, Newcastle upon Tyne 1887-1987, J. & P. Bealls Ltd., Newcastle upon Tyne.

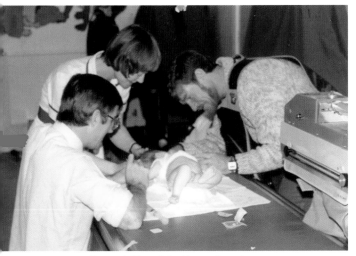

Fig 13.7: *In X-ray, dad, with a routine patient.*

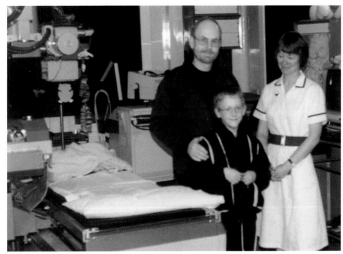

Fig 13.8: *All finished and no tears in X-ray.*

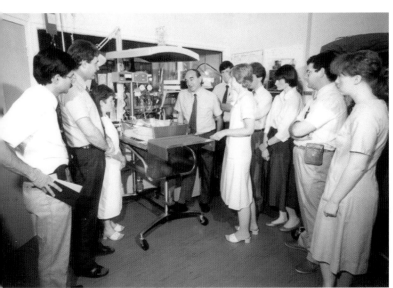

Fig 13.9: *A ward round.*

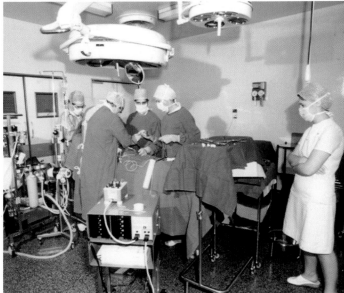

Fig 13.10: *The operating theatre.*

Fig 13.11: *The out-patient department.*

The Princess Mary Maternity Hospital (Fig 6.17, p.71)

Next door to the Fleming, separated only by a low wall, was the Princess Mary Maternity Hospital. The maternity service in Newcastle had originated in 1820 in the Lying-In Hospital. This was located in a building in New Bridge Street designed by John Dobson. This building was subsequently occupied by the BBC. The maternity hospital was later moved to Jubilee Road but in 1939, at the outbreak of war, the site was thought to be too close to the river and at risk from enemy air raids, so it was transferred to the orphanage building facing the Great North Road, just north of the city. So here was a children's hospital with a major neonatal surgical service sitting next door to a hospital where newborns were appearing in large numbers. The possibility of expanding the children's hospital and linking it physically and administratively to the maternity hospital to create a unified paediatric service was apparently never seriously considered. Further details of the Princess Mary Maternity Hospital are given in chapter 6.

Further progress

Paediatric surgery continued as a single-handed practice for four years until a registrar post in paediatric surgery was created. This man held the appointment for two years and was replaced by Mr John Wagget, a Newcastle trainee in general surgery who had expressed an interest in paediatric surgery. It also soon became obvious that he would be a welcome permanent partner and colleague in the department. Arrangements were made for him to spend some time training in the United States. On his return he was eventually appointed as a second consultant paediatric surgeon in Newcastle. It had taken ten years to get that far.

As well as the surgery, there was a sizeable paediatric medical commitment at the Fleming under Dr Hans Steiner. There was a brief moment when it seemed possible that an expansion could occur because the administration had agreed to provide a structural enlargement of the neonatal surgical unit. It was then discovered that the money was needed for something else.

Other hospitals that were involved in the medical care of children and which, though not administratively attached to the RVI, played an important role in the services it provided, were the Stannington Children's Hospital and the Sanderson Orthopaedic Hospital. The former was, in 1907, known as Philipson's Colony and was the first tuberculosis sanatorium for children in the country. The Sanderson, in Gosforth, was in existence in 1910 when it was known as the Home for Crippled Children. Both hospitals provided long-term care for children with tuberculosis and other chronic diseases such as osteomyelitis and poliomyelitis. The hospitals also had thriving schools so that the children received an education during the many months that they were confined. In later years, the chronic infective diseases for which these hospitals were founded disappeared and were replaced by the long-term sequelae of spina bifida. This congenital anomaly of the spine was prevalent in the '60's and '70's and many were treated surgically.

In 1987 the Fleming Hospital was closed, ironically, in the same year as it achieved its centenary. Notwithstanding the reputation of the hospital amongst the families of the children who were treated there, or of the opinions of the medical and nursing staff who worked there, the administration concluded that it was too expensive to run a separate children's hospital. Perhaps the future holds out some hope. There is yet another plan for a children's medical centre on the RVI site. It will have taken only fifty years.

The above account gives a clear insight into the life and tensions in the associated voluntary hospitals as they emerged in response to medical progress, and the associated specialisation and subsequently had to confront the management and financial problems associated with isolation from nearby major institutions such as the Royal Victoria Infirmary. One can appreciate the conflicts and sadness associated with the sequential closure of such institutions to which so many had given so much of their lifetime endeavours. Space does not allow a detailed account of these hospitals but they are mentioned because their association with RVI was close and productive. In addition, following their closure, the memory of their existence and contribution lies within the present RVI where the work they initiated continues to be undertaken to this day.

Fig 13.12: Ryton Convalescent Hospital.

Fig 13.13: Wylam Convalescent Hospital.

Thus the Eye Hospital and the Throat, Nose and Ear Hospital, after helping pioneer the delivery of developments in these specialties, were absorbed into the Infirmary. Similarly the convalescent homes at Ryton on Tyne, donated to the Infirmary in 1923, (*Fig 13.12*) and the Castle Hill Convalescent Home in Wylam on Tyne donated in 1934, by the Newall family (*Fig 13.13*) did sterling work in providing support to the Infirmary by allowing the early discharge of patients to convalescence, thus relieving pressure on in-patient beds. The demand for managerial efficiency also led to the incorporation of even bigger hospitals under the umbrella of the RVI's responsibilities. In 1925 the acute services of Newcastle General Hospital were absorbed by the RVI management, as for a short period were the services of Hexham Hospital prior to their incorporation into the newly formed Northumbria Heathcare NHS Trust.

Chapter 14: *The Universities and the RVI*

A story of joint endeavour   David Shaw

Let us begin by borrowing the words of an historian of another great university and hospital on another centennial occasion: 'one and indivisible', he wrote,[I] adverting to our sister institutions in Edinburgh - words that may as fittingly be applied to our own. Is it not remarkable that organisations with different primary objectives, different forms of governance, different sources of funding and different allegiances to departments of government can so often enjoy conspicuously harmonious and effective collaborations? The answer must lie in the unquantifiable yet all pervading cross benefits of the partnerships. The teaching hospital affords students the opportunity to learn at the bedside and it allows, indeed expects, its staff members to devote time and effort to their instruction. It provides amenities for a wide range of other educational activities. It facilitates and supports the conduct of research and, in the case of the RVI, it has accepted a proliferation of University departments, first in its own buildings, later in extensions to its own buildings; and finally, it has accommodated an entire medical and dental school within its precinct. In return, it benefits from the services of clinical academic staff, access to specialised laboratories, the expertise of research scientists and the stimulus and prestige of a teaching and research environment. Newman[II] in his famous book on medical education got quite carried away: *'To have medical students about a hospital completely transforms the character of the institution: it means that there are so many pairs of eyes watching everything that goes on, eyes that understand, moreover, and are young, idealistic and critical, that the whole conduct of the place is stimulated to improve itself'*. Readers may recall one or two students who lacked quite such inspirational qualities.

It would be unrealistic to pretend that there have never been any frictions or disagreements in the relationship between the RVI and the Medical School. NHS staff may occasionally have resented the intrusion of the academics. University staff may have cast an envious eye at the opportunities for private practice at one time denied them. But common goals, shared activities, cross-representation on governing and advisory bodies and lack of discrimination in any particular have made for consistently easy relationships. Such disruptions as have occurred have usually been internal to, rather than between, the parties and history tells us that the best rows have involved the Medical School rather than the Infirmary.

of quarrels

Before the start of the century with which we are concerned, indeed, only seventeen years after its founding in 1834, the Newcastle-upon-Tyne[*] School of Medicine and Surgery contrived a most spectacular row. An irreconcilable dispute within its membership led to its formal dissolution and the establishment of two separate institutions - a College of Medicine and Practical Science and a new Newcastle School of Medicine and Surgery.[#]

The 1851 'disruption', by which misleadingly genteel term the schism has subsequently been known, was acrimonious and was debased by some extraordinary

---

* The hyphens in Newcastle-upon-Tyne were dropped in official City documents from 1914 onwards.

\# This is the name by which Grey Turner[III] and other authorities refer to the new establishment. Embleton[4], on whose historical text Grey Turner drew heavily, states clearly that it was named the Newcastle-upon-Tyne College of Medicine; yet in its first prospectus, which he reproduces, his name appears as Secretary over the title Newcastle-upon-Tyne School of Medicine and Surgery. Embleton was later to become the first Professor of Medicine in the University of Durham.

[I] Turner, A. Logan. Story of a Great Hospital - The Royal Infirmary of Edinburgh 1729-1929 Edinburgh: Oliver and Boyd, 1937

[II] Newman, C. The Evolution of Medical Education in the Nineteenth Century London: Oxford University Press, 1957

Left: Fig 14.5: Opening of King's College Medical School by H.M. King George VI accompanied by H.M. Queen Elizabeth on 21st February, 1939.   **147**

skulduggery on the part of the College of Medicine and Practical Science to deprive its adversary of the existing stock of museum specimens. There was to be a lapse of six years before the rift was healed, and then it was largely because the School of Medicine and Surgery had conducted successful negotiations with the University of Durham and had reconstituted itself as 'The Newcastle upon Tyne College of Medicine in connection with the University of Durham'. This afforded privileges denied its rival which sued for peace. The separate establishments were reunited in time for the 1857-58 Session. In the ensuing years the links with Durham were increasingly strengthened and in 1870 the School became known as 'The Durham University College of Medicine, Newcastle upon Tyne'. It then occupied premises in Orchard Street near the Central Station (*Fig 14.1*) but these became overcrowded and in 1888 it moved to its fine new building in Bath Road, now Northumberland Road, which was later to become the home of the Dental School and Hospital pictured in chapter 9. Although in the early days the College had no formal connection with the Infirmary it was customary for its annual prospectus to refer to the fees charged for hospital practice and for clinical lectures.

The next bewildering exhibition of internal strife cannot go unremarked although it was glossed over in Grey Turner's [III] history of the Medical School. What was to become known as the 'Hutchens Affair' arose largely through conflict between an energetic, effective, but domineering President, Sir Robert Bolam, and a recalcitrant, disenchanted Head of the Bacteriological Department, Professor H. J. Hutchens.

In the aftermath of the 1914-18 War, there was an increased demand for medical student places and a general requirement to expand many of the departments in the College resulting in a pressing need for new accommodation. The site on Queen Victoria Road close to Armstrong College and directly opposite the RVI became available. Its

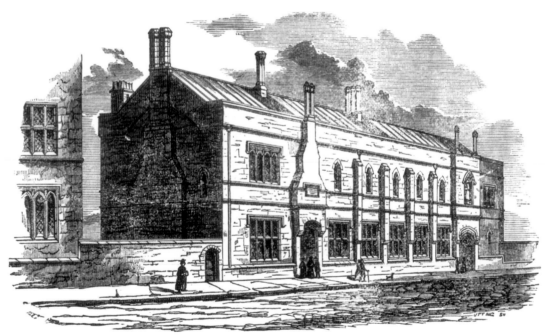

NEWCASTLE-UPON-TYNE COLLEGE OF MEDICINE,
IN CONNECTION WITH THE UNIVERSITY OF DURHAM.
John Dobson, architect.

Fig 14.1: The College of Medicine in Orchard Street.

[III] Grey Turner, G. assisted by Arnison, W.D. The Newcastle upon Tyne School of Medicine 1834-1934 Newcastle upon Tyne: Andrew Reid and Company Limited, 1934

[IV] Embleton, D. The History of the Medical School, Afterwards The Durham College of Medicine at Newcastle upon Tyne, For Forty Years, From 1832 to 1872 Newcastle upon Tyne: Andrew Reid, Sons and Co., 1890

acquisition stretched the resources of the College and money would have to be raised for a new building. 'Efficiency savings', as they are now known, were instituted and Professor Hutchens took exception to what he regarded as personal persecution and victimisation of his Department by Bolam. Once again the College was split into two rival factions. Members of its Council, of the City Council, and others with no obvious interest in College affairs, aligned themselves with one side or the other. According to Bettenson,[V, VI] former Registrar of Newcastle University, the 'Hutchens Affair' raged with varying degrees of intensity for about eight years. 'Personalities', he wrote, 'figured largely in the dispute. There were a good many unedifying episodes; two meetings of the College Academic Board broke up in disarray, there were allegations, often justified, of bullying, double-dealing, favouritism and chicanery of every kind'.

The College Council eventually dismissed Hutchens, locked him out of his Department and sent his personal belongings to his home which, surprisingly, was in Guildford. His wife declined to accept them and he refused his superannuation payments. Some extraordinarily devious, but unsuccessful, machinations on the part of the Bolam faction brought matters to crisis point and the Chancellor of Durham University, Lord Londonderry, on the advice of the Chairman of the University Grants Committee, pressed for and secured the establishment of a Royal Commission. Although several of the leading players in the Hutchens story were on the staff of the RVI and in opposing camps, there is no record of the hospital as such taking one side or the other.

The Report of the Royal Commission was published in 1934. It found against Bolam except in respect of the right of a governing body to dismiss a non-cooperative member of academic staff. But in the course of its deliberations the Commission recognised how unsatisfactory were the constitutional arrangements that linked Durham and Newcastle. Its recommendations, incorporated in the University of Durham Act, 1935, resulted in the College of Medicine and Armstrong College combining to form King's College as a separate Newcastle Division of Durham University. The new arrangement worked well. The two divisions became largely self-governing institutions loosely bound within the University of Durham which did retain authority for the award of degrees. It was not until 1963 that full recognition was given to the existing *de facto* arrangement and the University of Newcastle upon Tyne was established by Act of Parliament.

of buildings

The foregoing account of the unruly behaviour of members of staff of the Medical School has included reference to some of its not infrequent relocations. An admirable lecture on the nine sites associated with the teaching of medicine in Newcastle was delivered by Gordon Dale[VII] at the Sesquicentennial Celebration of the School in 1984. He observed that although need for expansion had occasioned some of the moves, the extension of the railway system had played a major part in forcing the migrations. He also lamented the frequency with which these noble

V Bettenson, E.M. The University of Newcastle upon Tyne, A Historical Introduction, 1834-1971 University of Newcastle upon Tyne, 1971

VI History of the Medical School, in Newcastle School of Medicine 1834-1984 Sesquicentennial Celebrations, ed. Dale, G., Miller, F.J.W., Bramley, K., University of Newcastle upon Tyne, 1984

VII Dale, G. The Newcastle Medical School Buildings, in Newcastle School of Medicine 1834-1984 Sesquicentennial Celebrations, ed. Dale, G., Miller, F.J.W., Bramley, K., University of Newcastle upon Tyne, 1984

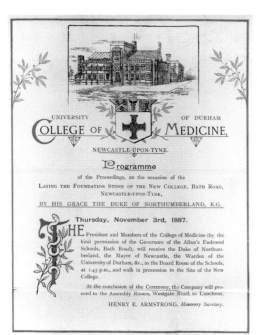

UNIVERSITY · OF DURHAM
COLLEGE OF · MEDICINE,
NEWCASTLE-UPON-TYNE.

Programme

of the Proceedings, on the occasion of the

LAYING THE FOUNDATION STONE OF THE NEW COLLEGE, BATH ROAD,
NEWCASTLE-UPON-TYNE,

BY HIS GRACE THE DUKE OF NORTHUMBERLAND, K.G.

Thursday, November 3rd, 1887.

THE President and Members of the College of Medicine (by the
kind permission of the Governors of the Allan's Endowed
Schools, Bath Road), will receive the Duke of Northumberland, the Mayor of Newcastle, the Warden of the
University of Durham, &c., in the Board Room of the Schools,
at 1.45 p.m., and walk in procession to the Site of the New
College.

At the conclusion of the Ceremony, the Company will proceed to the Assembly Rooms, Westgate Road, to Luncheon.

HENRY E. ARMSTRONG, Honorary Secretary.

Fig 14.2: Laying The Foundation Stone of The New College, Bath Road, by His Grace The Duke of Northumberland K.G. - Programme of Proceedings.

sites had ended up as car parks. When Algernon George, sixth Duke of Northumberland, laid the foundation stone of the Northumberland Road building, he remarked that: *'Our patron saint St. Cuthbert, carried about from place to place before he found his place of repose in the magnificent Cathedral of Durham, hardly went through more vicissitudes, apparently than this College of ours, which has been transferred from place to place. I hope that the tyranny of the iron rail will disturb it no more'.* (Fig 14.2)

By contrast, the Infirmary has restricted itself to but one dignified removal from Forth Banks to its present site. The opening of the RVI in 1906 had considerable significance for the College of Medicine. Although the College was still in Northumberland Road, the move brought the two institutions closer together. Two articles appeared in the University of Durham College of Medicine Gazette. One betrays the refreshing irreverence of the student pen; the other, the more patriotic dignity of the mature reporter. The former, having told us that *'the King and Queen visited our city on Wednesday last, and amongst other gracious acts, performed the opening ceremony of the New Infirmary'*, went on to say that *'the most noteworthy and striking phenomenon of the day was the rain'*, which clearly dampened the appeal of some of the more exuberant millinery. Of the procession, it observed that *'It was at this moment also that our patriotic bosoms heaved, a subjective symptom which it would ill become us to omit to mention'*; and of the unveiling of the statue of Queen Victoria *'the veil caught on a projection on the statue, and had to be freed by a man on a ladder'*.

The other, more sedate, report of the Royal Visit contains a paragraph which illumines the growing bond between the RVI and the University: for on the same day, 11th July 1906, King Edward VII with Queen Alexandra also opened the Armstrong Building, housing the College of Physical Science. *'Two great educational establishments'*, the report read, *'were on that day declared open by His Majesty the King. One having for its object the cultivation of the mind, the other more particularly connected with the ailments and injuries to which this frail human body, made in God's image, is liable'*. It went on to say that *'No one has shown a more practical appreciation of the medical profession, in which is included students and nurses, than our King and Queen'*. There was, however, a discordant note. The official hosts for the occasion were the Mayor and Corporation and whilst the report gives them due credit for the entertainment provided, the street decorations and the crowd control, it was offended by what it saw as their belittlement of the hospital staff to the furtherance of their own aggrandisement. After detailing the highly discriminatory seating plan for the opening ceremony, it ended *'Those who made and are maintaining the reputation of the Royal Infirmary have been slighted and treated most inconsiderately'*.

Thus affiliated by that day of ceremony and by a common thoroughfare, the RVI and the Armstrong Building were later to be joined in a less happy enterprise. On the outbreak of War in 1914 Armstrong College was evacuated at short notice and converted into a military hospital, the First Northern General Hospital (Territorial

Fig 14.3: Ward C1, First Northern General Hospital - now the Hatton Gallery.

Force), with a capacity of 1524 beds. (Fig 14.3) A building was also erected on the RVI site as a hospital for the rehabilitation of war wounded. Many members of the Honorary Staff of the RVI were already on the Reserve or joined up in 1914 and it was they who manned the First Northern General Hospital. A reminder of those days is to be found in St. Andrew's Cemetery in Jesmond where stands a memorial to five hundred and eighty-eight servicemen and women who are buried in Newcastle cemeteries. One hundred and seventy-nine of them lie in St. Andrew's Cemetery itself beneath headstones familiar to the eye of those who have paid homage to the casualties of war in so many corners of the world. (Figs 14.4 & 19.2, p.205)

From its earliest days the RVI was to find room in its precinct for University buildings. The Department of Pathology, which had a critical role in teaching as well as in the hospital service, was amongst the first. As recorded in chapter 8, a new Dental School and Hospital Building was erected in 1932. It was later to become the Department of Psychiatry and is now the Estates Department of the Newcastle upon Tyne Hospitals. On one of the early occasions when the College of Medicine was required to seek new accommodation it applied to the City Corporation to purchase what it regarded as an ideal site close to the old Infirmary. All went well until the proposed scheme was referred to the Infirmary authorities who objected on the grounds that such proximity would be insalubrious. The current distaste for anatomical dissection and the lingering shades of the resurrectionists no doubt influenced the decision. Fortunately, when some seventy years later the College was again on the move

Fig 14.4: Memorial and War Graves, St. Andrew's Cemetery, Jesmond.

and negotiating purchase of the site opposite the RVI, no such objections were raised. Contemporary accounts of the building that was to rise on the site were, not untypically, lacking in appreciation. An editorial in the College of Medicine Gazette opined that '*Of beauty of design it has little*', and likened it to '*a large warehouse or barracks*'. Another critic insisted on its resemblance to a jam factory. Like it or not, the opening of the building by King George VI took place on 21st February 1939, having been postponed from the previous year because of the Munich crisis. The Queen was reported as wearing a coat of a deep palatinate colour in honour of the University and the King's College O.T.C. formed the Guard of Honour. (*Fig 14.5*) Notwithstanding its supposed architectural shortcomings, the building, now named the King George VI Building and largely occupied by the Schools of Agriculture and Education, is held in great affection by many former students and teachers. (*Figs 14.6 & 14.7*) It provided vastly improved accommodation for teaching and research, mainly in the basic science departments, better facilities for students and more

Fig 14.5: Opening of King's College Medical School by H.M. King George VI accompanied by H.M. Queen Elizabeth on 21st February, 1939.

Fig 14.6: King's College Medical School in Queen Victoria Road.

Fig 14.7: Entrance to the Medical School - from a painting by Dr R.A.L. Brewis.

spacious administrative offices. But during the nineteen-forties and fifties there was a general move towards the development of clinical academic departments and the creation of whole-time university posts in the clinical specialties. In 1957, less than twenty years after the opening of the new Medical School and despite the addition of an extra floor, the Council of King's College approved a resolution that *'the University Grants Committee be asked for money for new buildings on the Royal Victoria Infirmary site'*. This was an endorsement of a recommendation of what was known as 'The Joint Committee of King's College and the Teaching Hospital', another illustration of the accord between the two institutions.

Thus started a long and frustrating story which is embedded in volumes of minutes of steering groups, planning committees and working parties, and in the memories of those who were involved in it. It was realised at an early stage of planning that the provision of adequate teaching and laboratory space for clinical academic departments could not wait for the building of the new school. In 1958 Council accepted a recommendation that short-term measures to provide accommodation for the Departments of Medicine, Dermatology and Psychiatry were urgently needed. In spite of the inevitable disruptions, and some would say disfigurement of its frontage, the Board of Governors of the RVI, with the support of their ever willing principal officers, accepted a series of new developments on their site. These included building extensions for the Departments of Dermatology, Surgery and Neurology, and the addition of two storeys to the main building to provide additional quarters for the Departments of Medicine and Clinical Biochemistry, generously funded by the Wellcome Trust. The developments needed to accommodate the Department of Child Health - the Children's Clinic, the Attic Laboratory and, more recently, the Sir James Spence Institute - are described in chapter 10.

Extending as it did over the best part of a quarter century, the planning of the new Medical School was beset by problems. At one stage there was opposition even within the Faculty of Medicine to its proceeding at all. A condition laid down by the University Grants Committee was that it must be designed to accommodate an intake of two hundred students *per annum* and there were those who argued that doubling the numbers would destroy the ethos and intimacy of the existing School. Three hundred and sixty-one medical students were enrolled for the academic year 2004/05 including ninety-five starting their training in Durham.

The oversight of the plan was complex because it was but one phase of a major development, jointly funded by the DES and the DHSS, including the new Dental School and Hospital described in chapter 8, two Medical School Blocks and the adjoining Hospital Ward Blocks, today's Leazes Wing. The very first phase was a new boiler house to service the whole complex. Its tall chimney is now a city landmark and ensures that our particulate exhalations land on Bergen rather than Benton. The ups and downs of the planning process could fill a chapter on their own. Most entailed reductions due to funding cuts and cost over-runs. One that caused confusion, if not disbelief, was the discovery that in making their dimensional calculations one of the government departments concerned took their measurements from the outside of the perimeter wall, the other from the inside. Although the new Medical School did not achieve quite the size or grandeur originally planned, it expanded considerably the University estate. (*Fig 14.8*) Taking a

Fig 14.8: Architect's model of the new Medical School on the RVI site.

Registrarial view of its dimensions, Bettenson[VIII] records that it increased the floor area which the University was required to clean by nearly 15%.

The new Medical School was opened by Queen Elizabeth the Queen Mother on the morning of 6th November, 1984; in the afternoon she was awarded an Honorary DCL by the University. (Fig 14.9) The individual blocks were later named after two generous benefactors of the University, William Leech and Catherine Cookson. The ever increasing requirements for departmental expansion have necessitated modifications and extensions but these are a welcome manifestation of the School's vigour and achievement. (Fig 14.10) Some time was to elapse before the completion of the hospital extension, now the Leazes Wing, which was the final phase of the joint project. The Medical School and the Leazes Wing are joined by a bridge which facilitates the integration of academic departments and hospital wards, so essential to modern clinical research, and which gracefully symbolises the union of the University with the RVI. The joint endeavour in pursuit of clinical research was further consolidated with the opening in 2005 of a new £4.5m Clinical Research Facility on the fourth floor of the Leazes Wing.

Fig 14.9: The Queen Mother receives an Honorary D.C.L. on the day of the opening of the new Medical School.

VIII Bettenson, E. M. The University of Newcastle upon Tyne, After 1970 - A Selective View University of Newcastle upon Tyne, 1987

Fig 14.10: Entrance to the Medical School as it is today.

of sundry reports and enactments

To take a step back in the annals of Newcastle's medical history, 1832 is a year to be remembered. It witnessed the foundation of Durham University by Act of Parliament. The Anatomy Act, passed in the same year, advanced the scope and propriety of medical education by licensing schools and teachers of anatomy as well as regulating the procurement of bodies for dissection. Hanged criminals ceased to qualify and the grave-robbers were put out of business. Six doctors practising in Newcastle, two of whom were subsequently appointed honorary surgeons to the Infirmary, started a course of lectures in a room in Bell's Court off Pilgrim Street. The room adjoined the consulting rooms of Mr (later Sir) John Fife, one of the six. The building, though somewhat derelict, still stands, but without its front door and portico which were preserved and now, despite resistance from the architects because of their height, guard the corridor between the Cookson and Leech Buildings. (*Figs 14.11 & 14.12*) This is the accepted wisdom and a plaque by the door states that it was acquired and presented by Norman D. Newall in 1939. The original suggestion for its acquisition can be traced to a letter from a Dr C. H. Milburn to the Editor of the College of Medicine Gazette and published in a special issue marking the centenary celebrations of the College in 1934. Pasted on to the opposite page is a letter to Dr Milburn from Sir Robert Bolam. In it he states that the doorway is '*in a very poor condition and it is quite impossible to restore it in any sense whatsoever.*' He goes on to say that '*what we have done however is to get an architect to make a drawing of it so that if the opportunity arises we might reproduce it in any new building that may be erected.*' There must, therefore, be some uncertainty as to whether or not the doorway is the original.

Although the lecture course was the prelude to the founding of the School of Medicine and Surgery, it is to Mr Thomas Greenhow, who in 1832 was appointed to the staff of the Infirmary, that the original idea of establishing a medical school in Newcastle is attributed. In April 1831 he read a paper to the Literary and Philosophical Society entitled '*The Expediency of Establishing in Newcastle an Academical Institution of the Nature of a College or University for the promotion of Literature and Science, more especially amongst the Middle Classes of the Community, briefly considered*'. A follow-up paper in June included the following: '*In the scheme proposed provision has been made for a School of Medicine, complete in all its departments, and I cannot but believe*

Fig 14.11: Bell's Court, Pilgrim Street in 1928.

that such a scheme is very much needed and would prove very successful'. There was a cholera epidemic in Newcastle in 1832, as there had been the previous year, and a young John Snow, who 'walked the wards' in the Infirmary and also attended the Bell's Court lectures, tended the victims in Killingworth. He was to become renowned for his work on 'The Mode of Communication of Cholera', for his insistence on the removal of the handle of the Broad Street pump in Soho, and for administering chloroform to Queen Victoria at the birth of two of her children by the method subsequently known as *à la reine*. Embleton [IV] records that Snow *'was a teetotaller when there were only few'*.

Fig 14.12: Bell's Court Doorway - now in the Medical School.

[IX] Atlay, J.B. Sir Henry Wentworth Acland London: 1903

The links between Newcastle's Infirmary and its academic institutions were thus established many years ago. They have remained strong ever since. Indeed, to a great extent their fortunes have been shaped together rather than separately. The Medical Act of 1858 was a significant event in their history. After years of dispute and seventeen aborted Bills, it finally brought some order to the hitherto capricious licensing of medical schools and it established the General Council of Medical Education and Registration, later abbreviated to its present title. Already the Durham University degree, along with those of Oxford, Cambridge and London, was recognised and shortly before the Act it had been given resounding acclaim by Sir Henry Acland, [IX] Regius Professor of Medicine in Oxford, who had been invited to act as an external examiner. Although initially hesitant about accepting the invitation because of other pressures, he thought that *my help would be of special value to meritorious persons*. He detailed the content of the examination, noting that *the ordeal was a severe one for the pupils*. Indeed, he did not *suppose there is so thorough a thing in the kingdom*. Unfortunately, Acland, for all he did to the benefit of medical education, bears some responsibility for the establishment of the rigid pre-clinical/clinical divide which stifled the development of the undergraduate curriculum for so many years and contributed significantly to its overload. Attention was drawn repeatedly to the excessive burden of information imposed on medical students but little changed. In 1938 a Sub-Committee of the Students' Representative Council in Newcastle voiced severe criticism of the curriculum and insisted that it was *in urgent need of reform*. The first ever inaugural lecture of a newly appointed professor in Newcastle was given by F.J. Nattrass in 1942, following his appointment as Professor of Medicine the previous year. In 1944 he was to become the first full-time Professor of Medicine. In his inaugural lecture, Nattrass analysed the weaknesses of the contemporary curriculum and suggested remedies. He urged that *everything possible should be done to link the common interests of the University and the Teaching Hospital* and quoted Osler's belief that more and more for the medical student *the Hospital became the College*. But the structure of the undergraduate course remained largely unchanged until a new style integrated curriculum was introduced in Newcastle in 1962 designed by a small group of far-sighted Faculty members. It triggered a gradual but unceasing process of educational reform in UK medical schools in which Newcastle continues to play a leading role. Nattrass's appointment was soon followed by that of James (later Sir James) Spence as full-time Professor of Child Health. It was the first such appointment in the country and he was to do much to influence the teaching and practice of paediatrics in the UK and beyond. Both men made considerable financial sacrifice in devoting their energies to the academic development of their specialties, the enhancement of the reputation of the Medical School and the promotion of the links between the University and the RVI.

The successful forging of these links is the reward of the efforts of many individuals. A few names from the past deserve special mention. R.B. Green, Professor of Anatomy and Dean of Medicine from 1937 until his retirement in 1960, although not a clinician, played a major role in the post-war development of the hospital services and their integration with the Medical School. He served on the Board of Governors of the United Newcastle upon Tyne Hospitals, which included the Princess Mary Maternity Hospital, the Babies' Hospital and the Dental Hospital as well as the RVI, and he was also Vice-Chairman of the Regional Hospital Board. He was thus deeply involved in the negotiations attending the transfer of the hospitals to state ownership in 1948. Andrew Lowdon, Professor of Surgery and Dean of Medicine from 1960 until his untimely death in 1965, was likewise dedicated to the joint development of the University and the Teaching Hospital and in his all too short period of service influenced enormously the activities of both. He master-minded the preparation of the original brief for the architects of today's Medical School and he chaired the Curriculum Committee which introduced the innovative New Curriculum in 1962. George (later Sir George) Smart, who succeeded Nattrass as Professor of Medicine and was Dean from 1968 until his appointment to the Directorship of the British Postgraduate Medical Federation in 1971, was closely associated with Lowdon in the design of the New Curriculum and was a major figure in the development of both undergraduate and postgraduate medical education in the UK. He initiated the creation of joint University/NHS consultant posts, the so-called A+B appointments which proved highly successful in Newcastle. As Dean he conducted crucial negotiations with the University Grants Committee over the scale and standard of the teaching, research and library facilities that were to be provided in the new Medical School. Two NHS Consultants, who had honorary academic titles and who made particular contributions to the University, were Dr C.N. Armstrong and Professor F.C. Pybus. The former was the first Clinical Sub-Dean and later the Regional Director of Postgraduate Studies. He also

campaigned successfully for the building in 1942 of the Lecture Theatre in the RVI which later bore his name. Pybus endowed the University with the magnificent and world-renowned collection of historic medical works, portraits and letters that is associated with his name. And two highly gifted lay persons, Sir Walter Drummond and Sir Edward Collingwood, chairmen respectively of the Board of Governors and the Regional Hospital Board, should be remembered also for their immense contributions to the governance of the University. The distinguished and highly influential career of Henry Miller (*Fig 14.13*) left few individuals or areas of activity unroused. His successive appointments - RVI Consultant, Clinical Sub-Dean, Professor of Neurology, Dean of Medicine, University Vice-Chancellor - wove a pattern that somehow enshrines the united enterprise.

Fig 14.13: Henry Miller.

Together, the RVI and the Medical School have been buffeted by countless Royal Commissions, Committees of Enquiry and Acts of Parliament embodying a variety of reorganisations and reforms. We have survived them all, strengthened by some, curtailed by others. Most of us give full marks to the National Health Service Act of 1946 although some of our predecessors were unenthusiastic. The Goodenough Report, which to some extent foreshadowed it, avowed that: *'Properly planned and carefully conducted medical education is the essential foundation of a comprehensive health service'*. It encouraged the growth of academic medicine and the enhancement of the status of the teaching hospital. It believed that the potential for teaching and research of neighbouring hospitals should be harnessed to that of the teaching hospital, something that Newcastle did conspicuously well. During the 1950s and 60s there were major academic developments at the Newcastle General Hospital and in the specialist hospitals. Undergraduate teaching extended into all of them and, indeed, into hospitals throughout the Northern Region. Postgraduate training flourished in all parts of the Region. It was against this background that the decision was taken in 1971 to bring all the hospitals in Newcastle under a single University Hospital Management Committee, the RVI thus foregoing the special privileges of Board of Governors status. This voluntary and amicably accomplished rearrangement was to anticipate the radical and disruptive changes that were to come with the 1974 reorganisation instituted by Keith Joseph.

In March 1981 the Government announced an overall cut of up to 15% in university funding over the ensuing three years. Redundancy schemes were developed. Many posts in the Medical School were lost, particularly in the lecturer, first assistant and technician grades. To their great credit, the Health Authorities agreed to fund some of the frozen posts. Alas, cuts in NHS funding were soon to follow, supposedly justified by some exceedingly misguided calculations of manpower need. At a private dinner, hosted by the Nuffield Provincial Hospitals Trust, the extent of the damage being done to medical and dental education and research by these bilateral assaults, totally lacking in coordination, was borne in with some vigour on the Permanent Secretaries of the two relevant government departments. Soon thereafter a Steering Group was set up under the Chairmanship of Christopher (later Sir Christopher) France, by then Permanent Secretary at the DHSS. It, and its successor organisation, have made honest and valued attempts to support and coordinate the common purpose of the NHS and the universities in maintaining and improving standards of education and research. One unhappy consequence of the cuts which the France Steering Group tried to tackle, but with limited success, was that the informal cost-sharing arrangement between NHS and universities known as 'knock-for-knock' came under close scrutiny by both parties. It has to be admitted that in Newcastle there were some vigorous exchanges but without bloodshed. Nor did the radical provisions of the NHS and Community Care Act of 1990 upset the relationship, which now also encompassed the Freeman Hospital, although the Faculty of Medicine did raise its collective voice in protest when the Bill was published.

of partnerships

Commonality of purpose, reciprocal support and mutual respect have secured the constacy of the links between the RVI and, first, Durham University and then Newcastle University. But it is not only with these academic institutions that the RVI has enjoyed fruitful collaboration. In recent times it has benefited from a close association with Northumbria and Sunderland Universities on which it now depends in large measure for the training of vital elements of its workforce. Northumbria University, (Fig 14.14) whose origins date back to the nineteenth century Colleges of Further Education, whilst still in the Polytechnic stage of its development, recognised the changes that were taking place in nurse education and established a degree course. The RVI and other hospitals of the North East continue to provide the opportunities for practical training, while the highly regarded academic courses in Nursing Studies are run by the University. Similar collaboration exists in the higher education of those entering the professions allied to medicine. There is a comparable and equally productive arrangement with Sunderland University in the training of pharmacists and radiographers. Recognition by all our institutions of the importance of inter-professional education has resulted in the establishment, with substantial government support, of what is known as the North East Centre for Excellence in Teaching and Learning for Health.

There is thus a long history which demonstrates both a desire and a capacity for secure and rewarding partnerships. It is a happy post script to this account to record that we have come full circle and that the ancient ties with Durham University in the teaching of medical students have recently been restored. In an age when great achievements so often stem from the merging of academic strengths, we can look back to these early days of the fragile link between Durham and the old Infirmary and hope that one day the RVI will clasp hands with a reunited University of Durham and Newcastle.

Fig 14.14: The College of Medicine Building, later Dental School, now the Sutherland Building of the University of Northumbria. (See also Fig 8.4)

Acknowledgments:

The willing contribution of Print Services, The Robinson Library, University of Newcastle upon Tyne in providing the illustrations is gratefully acknowledged.

The painting of the Entrance to the Medical School in Queen Victoria Road is reproduced by kind permission of the artist, Dr R. A. L. Brewis.

shall be new stuffed, and the blankets, bed-linen, and quilts shall be washed. 2dly, That the sheets of patients remaining for a length of time in the house shall be changed once a fortnight, or oftener, if necessary; the rest of the bed-clothes once in two m...ths; and whe... the patients have sores, on... ...dly, That th... shirts of the pa...

during the night on any account, on pain of ... and that no patient shall introduce, or admit ... into the house, without leave from the house-su... apothecary, and the matron, on any pretence ...

90. That no patients shall sit up after nine o... latest in the winter, nor after ten o'clock at late... summer; and that all patients, who are judged ... their respective physicians or surgeons, shall rise ... in the summer, and by eight in the winter.

91. That no men-patients shall go into the w... wards, nor women-patients into the men's wards ... that no patients shall go from their own to any ... ward or apartment without leave from the house-su... and apothecary, or the matron.

92. That the patients shall be decent and regula... ...their conduct; that they shall never curse, swear, ...e any improper language, on pain of being discharg... ...hey do n...

...at the patients shall not give any reward or ... f any kind to any nurse or other person belong- ...e Infirmary.

...That if any patient be taken ill in the night so ...eed the attendance of the house-surgeon and apo- ...ry, he shall desire any other patient, who is able, to ...up one of the nurses, who shall inform the house-sur- ...n and apothecary, without delay.

N. B. Such of the patients as do not exactly conform to these rules shall have the disgrace of being discharged for ir- regularity; and, being so discharged, shall never be admitted again by any recommendation whatever.

X. THAT he never be absent from the INFIR-MARY; on any Account, above two Hours toge-ther, or for any less Time, without acquainting the Matron where he is to be found, and be with-in Call: That he be always in the INFIRMAY at the Time when the Physicians or Surgeons attend there: That he be at home at Ten o'Clock at latest in the Evening, and do not lie out of the House, without special Leave from two Mem-bers of the Committee: That in such Case he ap-point another Apothecary, who shall be approved of by the Physicians to officiate in his Place; and that he observe all these Things on Pain of Dis-mission.

XI. THAT the Salary of the Apothecary do not exceed 30 *l. per Ann.* with his Diet, Washing, and Lodging.

December 28, 175

AT a General Quarterly Court of Governors of the INFIRMARY for ... SICK and LAME POOR of the Counties ... *Durham, Newcastle upon Tyne,* and *Northu...* ...berland, held this Day, the followi... STATUTES, RULES and ORDERS we... agreed to and confirmed; and the same we... ordered to be printed, and sold at 6 *d.* eac... for the Benefit of the CHARITY.

WM. BIGGE, *Chairman.*

R. BURDUS, *Secretary.*

ERRATUM.
Page 39. Line 7. for Monday, read *Tuesday.*

D   RULES

Chapter 15: *Governance of the RVI*

L. R. Fenwick

The governance story of the Royal Victoria Infirmary will reveal that in the one hundred years since the Infirmary opened on the Leazes site in 1906 and after repeated changes, what goes around comes around!

Fig 15.2: *The Right Hon. Lord Armstrong. Chairman of the House Committee, 1903/1904 and 1920/1941.*

As described in the first chapter, the Infirmary had its origins in the letter written in January 1751 that appeared in the Newcastle Courant suggesting an Infirmary be built in the city. There was an immediate and enthusiastic response and the proposal was soon to become reality. Those contemplating the proposal decided they could not wait for the erection of a new building and decided to hire a house in Gallowgate which was described as a *'very tolerable street and a very pleasant place having in it some good houses which are situated in gardens and fields'*. Here it was in May 1751 that the Newcastle Infirmary first opened its doors. It is noteworthy that just five months after the publication of the letter, records refer to the existence of Governors and before the Gallowgate house opened. The management of the RVI has evolved over the past 250 years out of that put in place for the house in Gallowgate in 1751 and subsequently in the purpose - built hospital at Forth Banks which opened in 1753. Even in Gallowgate, good management practice is evident and minutes were kept in a minute book. The earliest management of the Infirmary was undertaken by a secretary, an apothecary and a matron on behalf of the House Committee which consisted of 36 persons, 12 from each of Newcastle upon Tyne, Northumberland and Durham. Visiting physicians were employed by the Governors and were given strict instructions about when they should attend and services to be provided.

The Infirmary at Forth Banks prospered and was soon in such a good financial position that in January 1754 the quarterly Court of Governors ordered that £2000 should be advanced to the town at 3.5%. The power of the Governors, who met in a Boardroom remarkably similar to the present RVI Boardroom (*Fig 15.3*) appeared absolute. Thus, in 1773 at a special Court of the Governors it was decided by a majority vote that surgeons, who up to that time had not been allowed to prescribe medicines, should be allowed to do so for their own patients.

In those days, Annual Reports consisted of but a single sheet and gave little information about the professional work of the medical staff. However, such information was recorded in the minutes of the Philosophical and Medical Society, founded in 1786.

Fig 15.3: *Royal Victoria Infirmary Boardroom, circa 1951.*

Towards the end of the 18th Century, overcrowding of the Infirmary was of concern to the Governors and who were also faced with financial difficulties. In 1801, the foundation stone of a new extension was laid, the building of which was completed in 1803. Around this time, the Governors and the House Committee appeared to lose interest and on one occasion the minute book had the words *'no Governors'* written across one page. New statutes were introduced which ordained that the House Committee should consist of 12 ordinary and 36 extraordinary members, the 12 ordinary members being drawn from Governors who lived locally and were to form a Weekly Committee.

Fig 15.4: Mr Robert Robey Redmayne.

In 1853, one hundred years after the opening of the Infirmary, the Governors once again became aware of the inadequacy of the Infirmary but the single sheet Annual Reports did not inform the public of the problems. In 1850 the Annual Report was produced in the form of a booklet which drew the attention of the Governors and the public to the overcrowding of the hospital.

In 1855 a new wing was opened. In 1879, the first House Governor was appointed, one Mr Robert Robey Redmayne and who held this position for 21 years. (*Fig 15.4*)

In 1887 certain important changes were made in the administration of the hospital. The requirement for patients to have a letter of recommendation in order to receive treatment was abolished and the House Committee and Medical Board were amalgamated. At the same time, all was not well with the finances of the Infirmary. Thus at the quarterly Court of Governors meeting held on 4th November 1887 with Lord Ravensworth in the Chair, it was resolved on a motion proposed by the Reverend Dr Bruce and seconded by the Mayor, *"that a Special Committee of the Governors be appointed to confer with the House Committee as to the past management of the Infirmary, and the best mode of extricating itself from its present financial position and to report to a special court of the Governors what they recommend should be done under the circumstances"*. The Committee was set up under the Chairmanship of Lord Ravensworth.

The Infirmary was made a *'free hospital'* in the Jubilee year and in 1887, the title Royal was granted by Queen Victoria thereby re-designating the hospital as The Royal Infirmary for the Counties of Newcastle upon Tyne, Northumberland and Durham.

A "free" i.e. voluntary hospital can be defined as an institution having the legal status of a charity, being supported - partly at least - out of endowments and voluntary contributions.

In 1896, the approaching Diamond Jubilee of Queen Victoria suggested to the Mayor Mr (late Sir) Riley Lord that a fitting memorial of her reign would be the building of a new Infirmary. This was taken up with enthusiasm and at a meeting in the Council chamber on 7th October 1896 resolutions to this end were passed and a fund raising target of £100,000 was aimed at. Two large donations were received which enabled the Building Committee to enter into a contract for £203,527 to construct a new hospital on the Castle Leazes.

103, PILGRIM STREET,
NEWCASTLE-UPON-TYNE,
4th February, 1899.

SIR,

The Newcastle-upon-Tyne Corporation (New Infirmary Site) Act, 1898.

Referring to the Resolutions passed by the Body of Stewards at the Michaelmas Guild 1897, and at the Christmas Guild following, and pursuant to Section 3 of the above Act, to which Royal Assent was given on the 12th August 1898, I am instructed to and hereby give you Notice that a Meeting of the Stewards and Wardens of the Companies of Freemen of Newcastle-upon-Tyne will be held at the Guildhall on Monday the 6th day of March next at 12 o'clock Noon, when the Plan of the proposed Site upon the Castle Leazes for a New Infirmary for the sick and lame poor of Newcastle-upon-Tyne, and of the adjoining Counties of Northumberland, and Durham, (a copy of which Plan is hereto annexed) will be together with the following Resolution submitted for consideration and approval:—

RESOLUTION.

"That the Stewards and Wardens of the Companies of Freemen of Newcastle-upon-Tyne "assembled at this Meeting, having examined the annexed Plan of the proposed Site for "a New Infirmary, on the Castle Leazes, hereby approve thereof, and consent to the "appropriation and conveyance by the Mayor, Aldermen, and Citizens of the City and "County of Newcastle-upon-Tyne, to the Trustees of the Newcastle-upon-Tyne Royal "Infirmary (freed and discharged from all herbage right), of that portion of the Castle "Leazes, containing ten acres in extent, adjoining the road across the Castle Leazes, "leading from St. Thomas' Crescent to Spital Tongues, and lying between that road, "the footpath across the Castle Leazes, from the principal entrance of the Leazes "Park to Eldon Street, and the Eastern boundary of the Castle Leazes, and coloured "round with red upon the said Plan, as a site for a new Hospital or Infirmary for the "sick and lame poor of the said City and County, and of the adjoining Counties of "Northumberland and Durham."

I remain,
Your obedient Servant,
FRED. J. BROWN,
SECRETARY.

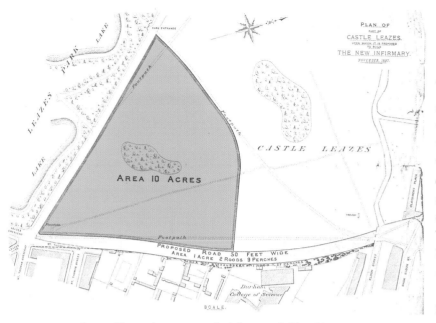

Fig 15.6: The initial 10 acre site at Castle Leazes on the Town Moor.

The Freemen of the City, who in effect act as guardians of the Town Moor and thereby the controlling interest of the vast 1200 acre city lung that is home to more than 700 cattle and over which the public enjoy traditional rights of 'air and exercise', were instrumental (Fig 15.5) in bringing about availability of the land at Castle Leazes to initially construct the RVI and subsequent developments. The Newcastle upon Tyne Corporation (New Infirmary site) Act 1898 provided the 10 acre site (Fig 15.6) that saw completion of construction in 1906. Then as a consequence of The Royal Victoria Infirmary Newcastle upon Tyne Act 1917 (Fig 15.7) the site was extended by an additional 14 3/4 acres and thereby enabled the provision of further facilities, much of which were a necessity to provide accommodation for the sick and injured returning from the war, as well as those in need of care because of increased industrialization. Of particular interest is the reverter clause which provides for reinstatement to Town Moor herbage if the site is no longer required as hospital premises!

Prior to 1888, each meeting of the House Committee appointed a Chairman for that meeting only. In 1888, the decision was made to make the position of Chairman to be recurrent. Thereafter the holders of the post included the names of some of the most distinguished people in the North, most notably Lord Armstrong (Fig 15.2) who held office for 21 years between 1920 and 1941.

Governors were appointed and nominated from a vast range of sources ie. by Firms, Companies, Associations, Social Clubs and Institutes, Friendly Societies as well by Workmen themselves (Fig 15.8) and in addition there were Honorary Life Governors.

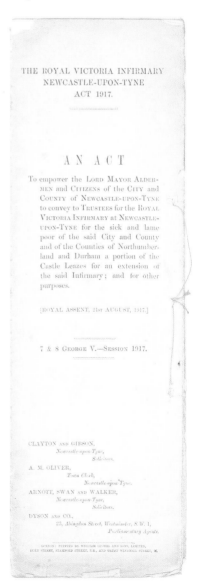

Fig 15.7: Act of Parliament to extend beyond the original site.

Fig 15.8: Workmen Governors.

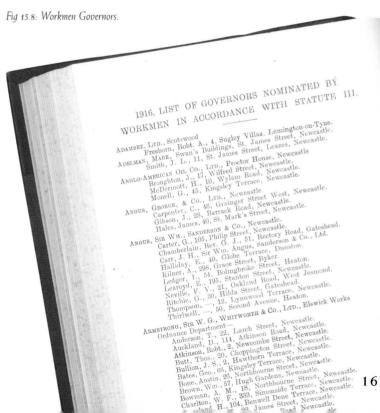

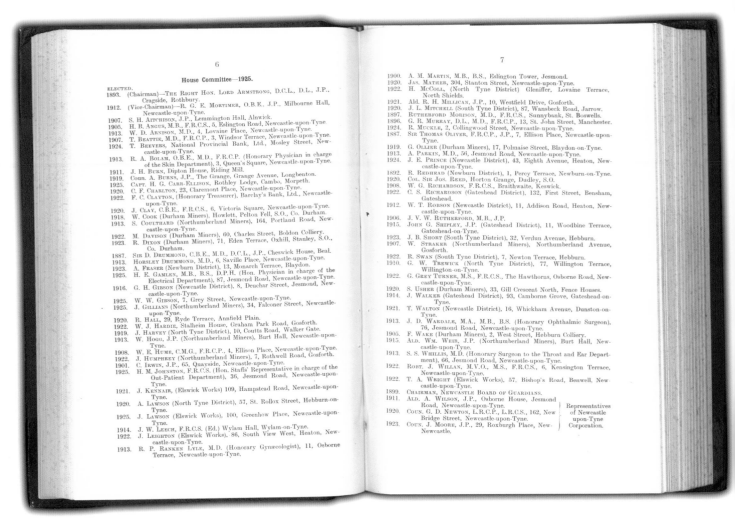

Fig 15.9: House Committee membership 1925.

Between 1906 and inception of the NHS in 1948, the House Committee (overall Governor membership of 51 rising ultimately to 95) was underpinned by a range of standing groups and in particular, throughout this period by a Weekly Committee as well as Finance; Subscriptions; Drugs & Instruments; Patient's Admission; Resident (Medical) Staff; Nursing Staff; and Building & Property sub-committees. The Governors by necessity were pivotal to the success or otherwise of the institution. (Fig 15.9)

Public involvement was enhanced considerably through the network of Governors. (Figs 15.8) It is of interest that today government strives to bring about a meaningful 'stakeholder' engagement in the delivery of public service. The Court of Governors was convened on a quarterly basis and addressed matters of significance in relation to the well being and future of the RVI.

Annual expenditure in the first year of the new RVI was £27,267 4s. 0d. with voluntary contributions amounting to £17,575 13s.1d. Management costs as such are described in the Accounts to be £849 3s. 9d.

Fig 15.10: Expenditure was strictly controlled.

Appeal for £150,000.

SEPTEMBER, 1927.

This Appeal is urgent and imperative.

The Infirmary has served this district since 1751, and after various extensions the present Royal Victoria Infirmary was opened by His Majesty King Edward VII, in 1906, and at that time was considered amply adequate for the needs of the district for many years to come.

The comparative figures of the work done respectively in the years 1906 and 1926 show the increased demand upon the present accommodation:—

	1906.	1926.	Increase.
In-Patients	4,899	13,942	9,043
Out-Patients	50,252	364,069	313,817
Operations	4,044	14,409	10,365

During 1926 over 2,000 extra beds have had to be placed in the Wards for urgent cases, and in spite of this overcrowding there remains a Waiting List of over 2,000 cases which cannot be overtaken.

The immediate necessity for this Appeal has been created by the fact that the Lease of the adjoining buildings of the Ministry of Pensions Hospital expires on March 31st, 1928, when they revert to the Infirmary.

The money is required to adapt these buildings for civil requirements in order to increase the number of In-Patient beds, to extend the Out-Patient Departments, and to provide the necessary increased accommodation for Nurses and Domestic Staff.

The Infirmary has a claim upon every household in the Counties of Northumberland, Durham and Newcastle-upon-Tyne. It not only tends the poor and needy and deals with cases outside the scope of the local Hospitals, but as one of the 22 great Teaching Hospitals of Britain (the only one of this character between Edinburgh and Leeds) it provides a Training School for doctors and nurses, which sets and maintains a high standard of Medical and Nursing skill, upon which every inhabitant within the area it serves is dependent.

To motorists and road users the needs of the Infirmary should specially appeal, for recently, motor accidents dealt with at the Hospital have amounted to an average of 20 per week, a sufficient number to occupy the greater part of a ward throughout the year.

It is estimated that at least £150,000 will be required to effect the necessary alterations and extensions, together with the equipment. This may appear to be an enormous amount to ask for in these times of financial strain, but the population of the two Counties, with Newcastle, totals over 2,225,000, and we feel confident that if every individual throughout the large area served by the Infirmary realises his or her personal obligation and affectionate interest in its beneficent work of healing, and will contribute the utmost he or she can afford, the sum required will be readily obtained and the splendid activities of the Institution continued.

Lord Mayor and Chairman of Appeals Committee.

Lord Lieutenant of the County of Northumberland.

Lord Lieutenant of the County of Durham.

Chairman of the House Committee.

Fig 15.11: The launch of an appeal in 1927 to finance much needed expansion.

Cost savings are perhaps considered to be something of a modern phenomena but in 1922 performance measure comparisons with similar institutions were beginning to emerge. The saving in annual expenditure of £12.286 1s. 5d. (*Fig 15.10*) was remarkable i.e. 11.7% because in the previous year, the spend was £104.704 14s. 2d.

In the year leading up to the NHS, expenditure had risen to £386,920 16s. 4d. with management then referred to as 'administration' incurring some £13,288 14s. 4d. Voluntary contributions were £176,314 18s. 10d. and of which £126,788 3s. 7d. were from workplace employees throughout the North East. Amazingly in 1946, the Kings College Students Rag, which had been in abeyance during the war, raised £8,005 1s. 11d. for the RVI.

Fig 15.12: Dr Alexander Watson Sanderson.

The Governors were influential, (*Fig 15.11*) well informed and primarily through the business conducted by the various committees gave direction and authority. In modern management parlance, the overriding consideration of balancing cost and quality focused upon ensuring the RVI remained a *'going concern'* in all that it did as a voluntary hospital. The House Governor and Secretary, being the forerunner to the Chief Executive of today, was charged with the task of facilitating informed decision making and ensuring effective action was taken in respect of policy and practice. The role of House Governor at the turn of the 20th Century demanded a gritty determination, steadfastness and continuity of purpose. When the plans to develop the RVI were coming into fruition, Mr Roden H. P. Orde was appointed and more than two decades later in 1922, he was replaced by Mr Sydney Dunstan, a proven stalwart, having first joined the staff of the Royal

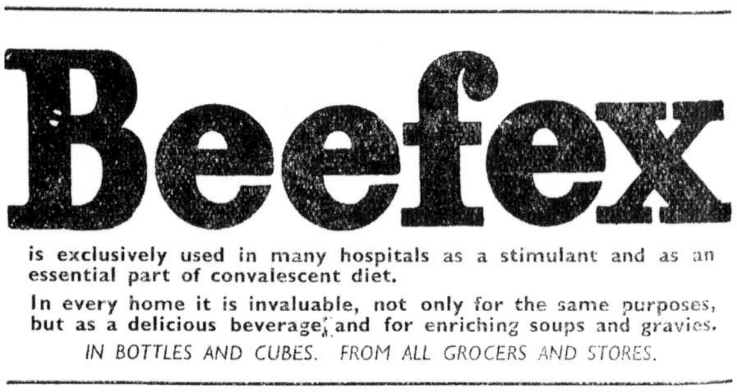

Beefex

is exclusively used in many hospitals as a stimulant and as an essential part of convalescent diet.

In every home it is invaluable, not only for the same purposes, but as a delicious beverage, and for enriching soups and gravies.

IN BOTTLES AND CUBES. FROM ALL GROCERS AND STORES.

Fig 15.13: Product endorsement (1934).

Infirmary as Head Dispenser in 1904. Mr Dunstan saw through the tradition of two decades of service and certainly did not shirk his responsibilities, participating for example during 1938 in no less than 189 out of a possible 194 meetings of the then 17 standing committees involved in administrative affairs. In 1941, Dr Alexander Watson Sanderson (*Fig 15.12*) joined the staff from Cadbury of Bourneville (the confectionery manufacturer) where he was Senior Medical Officer then Head of the Export Department. Dr Sanderson brought a fresh dimension to the administration and successfully steered through the transition from voluntary hospital to the NHS and then on into the new era that was so much heralded and with such great expectations. Held in high esteem, Dr Sanderson upheld tradition in terms of duration of service, retiring in 1959 and Mr Thomas Vaughan Roberts who had joined the staff from Oxford in 1951 as Deputy House Governor stepped up to be the last of a dynasty of House Governors. Mr Roberts was instrumental in the planning of the integrated NHS and University campus which became a reality in the late 70s and is so instrumental to the success of health related service, education and research in Newcastle upon Tyne. In 1974 Mr Roberts was appointed as the first Area Administrator of the Newcastle Area Health Authority (Teaching).

Proprietary product endorsements via advertising (*Figs 15.13 & 15.14*) featured as part of revenue raising. The sum of £2 10s. 0d. was paid for the privilege of featuring in the Annual Report. Such an action would in later years be frowned upon, although local suppliers and retailers could continue to advertise.

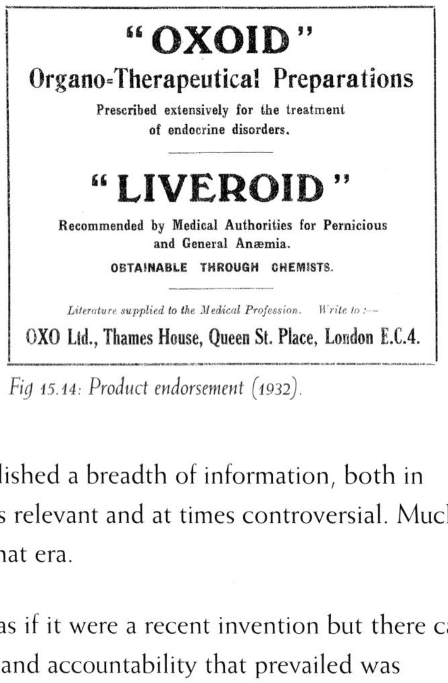

"OXOID"
Organo-Therapeutical Preparations
Prescribed extensively for the treatment of endocrine disorders.

"LIVEROID"
Recommended by Medical Authorities for Pernicious and General Anæmia.

OBTAINABLE THROUGH CHEMISTS.

Literature supplied to the Medical Profession. Write to :—

OXO Ltd., Thames House, Queen St. Place, London E.C.4.

Fig 15.14: Product endorsement (1932).

The voluntary hospitals pre 1948 published a breadth of information, both in quality and content (*Figs 15.15*) that was relevant and at times controversial. Much can still be learnt from the values of that era.

Good governance is spoken of today as if it were a recent invention but there can be no doubt the measure of openness and accountability that prevailed was exceptional and served to fortify the public confidence in the RVI as a much cherished institution.

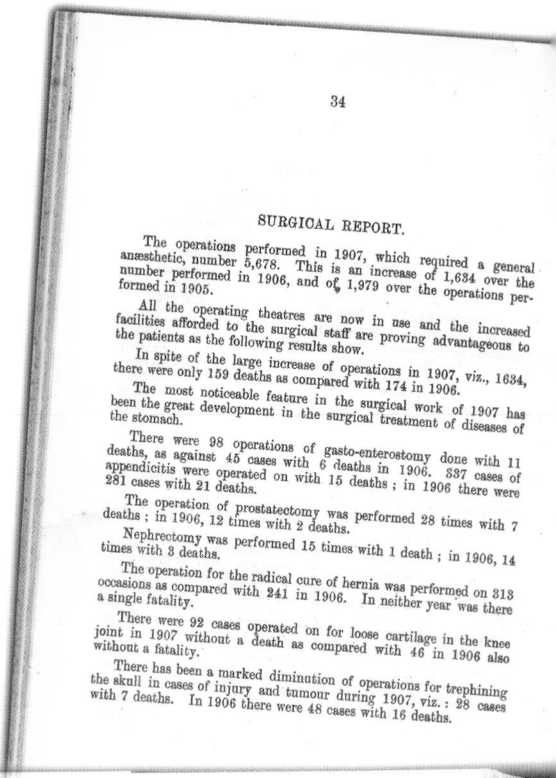

Fig 15.15: Surgical Reports.

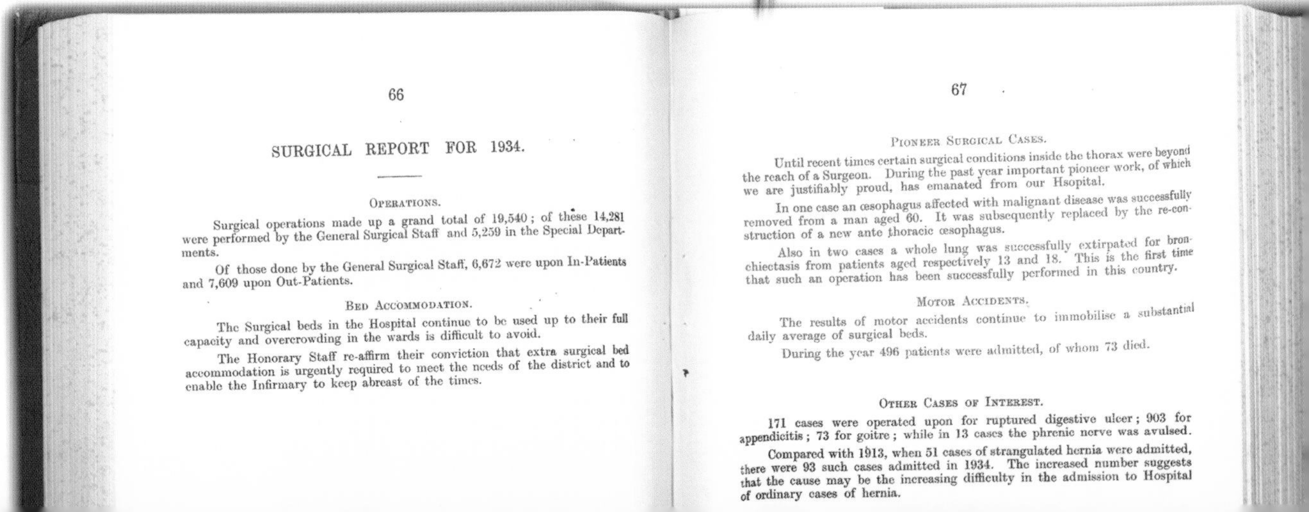

34

SURGICAL REPORT.

The operations performed in 1907, which required a general anæsthetic, number 5,678. This is an increase of 1,634 over the number performed in 1906, and of 1,979 over the operations performed in 1905.

All the operating theatres are now in use and the increased facilities afforded to the surgical staff are proving advantageous to the patients as the following results show.

In spite of the large increase of operations in 1907, viz., 1,634, there were only 159 deaths as compared with 174 in 1906.

The most noticeable feature in the surgical work of 1907 has been the great development in the surgical treatment of diseases of the stomach.

There were 98 operations of gasto-enterostomy done with 11 deaths, as against 45 cases with 6 deaths in 1906. 337 cases of appendicitis were operated on with 15 deaths ; in 1906 there were 281 cases with 21 deaths.

The operation of prostatectomy was performed 28 times with 7 deaths ; in 1906, 12 times with 2 deaths.

Nephrectomy was performed 15 times with 1 death ; in 1906, 14 times with 3 deaths.

The operation for the radical cure of hernia was performed on 313 occasions as compared with 241 in 1906. In neither year was there a single fatality.

There were 92 cases operated on for loose cartilage in the knee joint in 1907 without a death as compared with 46 in 1906 also without a fatality.

There has been a marked diminution of operations for trephining the skull in cases of injury and tumour during 1907, viz. : 28 cases with 7 deaths. In 1906 there were 48 cases with 16 deaths.

66

SURGICAL REPORT FOR 1934.

OPERATIONS.

Surgical operations made up a grand total of 19,540 ; of these 14,281 were performed by the General Surgical Staff and 5,259 in the Special Departments.

Of those done by the General Surgical Staff, 6,672 were upon In-Patients and 7,609 upon Out-Patients.

BED ACCOMMODATION.

The Surgical beds in the Hospital continue to be used up to their full capacity and overcrowding in the wards is difficult to avoid.

The Honorary Staff re-affirm their conviction that extra surgical bed accommodation is urgently required to meet the needs of the district and to enable the Infirmary to keep abreast of the times.

67

PIONEER SURGICAL CASES.

Until recent times certain surgical conditions inside the thorax were beyond the reach of a Surgeon. During the past year important pioneer work, of which we are justifiably proud, has emanated from our Hospital.

In one case an œsophagus affected with malignant disease was successfully removed from a man aged 60. It was subsequently replaced by the re-construction of a new ante thoracic œsophagus.

Also in two cases a whole lung was successfully extirpated for bronchiectasis from patients aged respectively 13 and 18. This is the first time that such an operation has been successfully performed in this country.

MOTOR ACCIDENTS.

The results of motor accidents continue to immobilise a substantial daily average of surgical beds.

During the year 496 patients were admitted, of whom 73 died.

OTHER CASES OF INTEREST.

171 cases were operated upon for ruptured digestive ulcer ; 903 for appendicitis ; 73 for goitre ; while in 13 cases the phrenic nerve was avulsed.

Compared with 1913, when 51 cases of strangulated hernia were admitted, there were 93 such cases admitted in 1934. The increased number suggests that the cause may be the increasing difficulty in the admission to Hospital of ordinary cases of hernia.

The coming of the NHS

The combined Annual Report for the years 1948 and 1949 states *"on the 5th July 1948 an outwardly imperceptible but nevertheless revolutionary change took place, namely the provisions of the National Health Service Act (1946) came into being transferring the nation's hospitals to the Minister of Health"*. On that day, Princess Mary Maternity Hospital (already amalgamated with the Babies Hospital) and the Newcastle upon Tyne Dental Hospital were combined with the RVI into *"The United Newcastle upon Tyne Hospitals"*.

In essence, the RVI was one of thirty six designated teaching hospitals (consisting of single institutions or groups) to provide facilities for teaching and research. In London, there were twelve undergraduate and fourteen postgraduate hospitals and throughout the rest of England, ten provincial teaching hospitals. All were directly accountable to the Minister of Health. In the remainder of the Newcastle 'region' embracing the North East and Cumbria, some thirty two Hospital Management Committees provided 26,721 beds and were accountable to the Newcastle Regional Hospital Board.

All of the teaching hospitals were, before nationalization, voluntary hospitals but with the exception of The Hammersmith and The Maudsley being hospitals run by London County Council.

The provision of clinical teaching facilities in association with a University Medical School was an overriding requirement to be a teaching hospital but today such facilities are widespread throughout the NHS in both hospital and community settings.

The 1946 National Health Service Act defined the Board of Governors as a Chairman, appointed by the Minister of Health and such numbers of other members appointed as the Minister thought fit. Not more than one fifth were nominated by each of the following i.e. the University of Durham; the Newcastle Regional Hospital Board, and the medical and dental staff of the United Newcastle upon Tyne Hospitals. Others could be appointed after consultation with local Health Authorities and other organisations.

The duties of the Governors were:

> To manage and control the hospitals on behalf of the Minister of Health
> To provide the University of Durham and its Medical and Dental Schools in King's College, Newcastle with the facilities required for clinical teaching and research
> To appoint officers required to be employed for the purpose of the hospitals
> To maintain the premises
> To acquire and maintain equipment, furniture and moveable property required by the hospitals.

The Governors, chaired by Robert Muckle, included local dignitaries such as Lord Eustance Percy, Viscount Allendale, Viscountess Ridley, famous medical academics such as Professors Spence and Nattrass and local politicians. Their places of residence stretched from Alnwick to Durham.

The 28 appointed Governors who in addition to being Board members served on House Committees aligned to the hospitals in the group as well as standing sub-committees covering Finance, Supplies, Medical Advisory, Nursing, Building & Planning and also a new *'Joint Committee of the Regional Hospital Board and the Teaching Hospitals'*. The issue of voluntary donations were no longer a concern of the Governors but securing adequate government revenue and capital investment became the new challenge then and today the issues have a familiar ring - demand and expectations outstripping available resource.

It is to be noted that other than the hospitals making up the United Newcastle upon Tyne Hospitals, all other hospitals (but with the exception of St. Nicholas Hospital) in Newcastle including the General, Fleming Memorial for Sick Children, Hunters Moor, Throat, Nose and Ear (Rye Hill), Eye (St. Mary's Place), Northern Counties Chest (Elswick Road), TB Hospital (New Bridge Street), Walkergate, Walker Park, Isolation (Town Moor), Lemington, Ponteland, W. J. Sanderson Orthopaedic and the Ethel Watson Convalescent Home for Children (Rothbury) came within the aegis of Newcastle Hospital Management Committee. St. Nicholas Hospital (Gosforth), a mental illness institution, came under St. Nicholas Hospital Management Committee.

The introduction of the NHS in July 1948 made a major difference to the lives of the majority of the people in the UK, especially in the northern industrial conurbations such as Greater Tyneside as well as the surrounding rural areas. The latter were particularly poorly served in terms of healthcare provision and large areas of the countryside did not have any specialist Consultant services. Although there was no immediate change in terms of the number of doctors and nurses employed, nor in the scale of provision and environment of the hospitals and clinics, the community at large had for the first time, access to medical care free at the point of delivery and were not dependent on charity or the ability to pay.

The Governors by 1950 sensed an emerging reality and it was acknowledged *"state ownership has not, so far, resulted in the lavish building development which some has visualized... the much discussed project to erect a Combined Hospital Centre on the Castle Leazes site has to be shelved indefinitely."* It was not until the late 70s that the Dental Hospital and School, then Medical School and in the early 90s, the Leazes Wing, were opened. It will be sixty years and more before the vision is complete.

As the NHS developed, the beginnings of the problems that have so consistently dominated the scale and scope of the NHS became manifest. The euphoria that accompanied the reductions in infectious diseases, particularly tuberculosis (thereby enabling the closure of infectious diseases hospitals and sanatoria with all the associated cost savings), was soon dissipated by the demands of mothers for improved maternity services and hospital deliveries. At the same time, adventurous thoracic surgeons were devising operations to deal with the ravages of heart disease and orthopaedic surgeons were taking the first steps in treating worn out hip joints by surgical operations.

All this meant that, within a few years of its launch, the concept of a free NHS had to be rethought and by 1952, a one-shilling charge for prescriptions was introduced, as well as a one-pound charge for dental treatment.

The 1951 Annual Report (the year of the Newcastle Infirmary bi-centenary) revealed a formidable list of local people were involved in the running of the hospitals but in the fifties the Annual Report of the RVI diminished into a state of insignificance and not until 1992, when the Royal Victoria Infirmary and Associated Hospitals NHS Trust was established, did the presentation of an informed archive re-emerge.

The NHS entered its second decade in 1958 facing an exponential rise in medical knowledge. It is difficult for people today, including many healthcare professionals, to appreciate just how bad things were before such treatment as poliomyelitis vaccination and dialysis for kidney failure were introduced, but all these advances were achieved at a considerable financial cost. Nye Bevan, the forthright politician and Minister for Health who brought the NHS into being, always recognised that this would happen, saying *"we shall never have all we need, expectations will always exceed capacity".*

In particular, the Hospital Plan (1962), brought in an era of new hospital buildings and confirmed the rise in status of the District General Hospital which delivered in towns across the country the breadth and complexity of service only provided previously in teaching hospitals.

1968 saw the beginning of the third decade of the NHS and was accompanied by even more radical and expensive advances in care and treatment. Joint replacement surgery was perfected and its indications extended, organ transplantation became a reality and coronary artery surgery was later developed to deal with the medical problems of an increasingly affluent society which was living even longer and turning to the NHS for the management of the problems of aging.

An important and exceptional development in Newcastle took place in 1971. A consortium of the University of Newcastle, the RVI Board of Governors, Newcastle Hospital Management Committee and the Regional Hospital Board agreed to form a joint University Hospital Management Committee encompassing all the hospitals in Newcastle including the RVI. This was an interim body and forerunner to the organisational change extant in the NHS Reorganisation Act 1973 and which served to extinguish the relative independence of both the provincial and London undergraduate Teaching Hospitals who became part of a structured administration involving newly constituted Regional Health Authorities and Area Health Authorities. The Newcastle Area

Fig 15.16.

Health Authority (Teaching) (*Fig 15.16*) assumed responsibility for the RVI in 1974. Of interest was the effect of the NHS (Preservation of Boards of Governors) Order 1974, made by the Secretary of State to effect continuance of Boards of Governors of the twelve London postgraduate teaching hospitals.

By the mid 80s there was an acknowledgement that '*consensus management*' had failed to 'manage and control' and hence '*general management*' was introduced as the beginnings of a return to executive authority and more clearly defined accountability which today is taken as a matter of course. This resulted in the introduction of a much more critical approach to the running of hospitals with changes such as medical staff auditing their results and becoming more directly involved in issues of effectiveness and efficiency.

Fig 15.17.

The fourth decade of the NHS saw in the late 80s the commencement of the most significant cultural shift since the service began. The return of '*self governing hospitals*' and introduction of an internal market (with distinct separation of the 'commissioning' and service provider functions) was an endeavour to address the problem of growing waiting lists by giving budgets to the General Practitioner purchase services from hospitals and who from 1991 could elect to become 'NHS Trusts'. Between 1991 and 1995 all hospital based providers became NHS Trusts including the RVI (*Fig 15.17*) and the Freeman, the latter hospital being one of the 57 hospitals in the first wave of this change and hence the vanguard of what is now proving to be fundamental reform. By the mid 90s it was also apparent that the major demographic change of an increasingly aged population was impinging heavily on the resourcing and organisation of the Health Service.

Fig 15.18.

In May 1997, a Labour government was returned to power and pledged to abolish the internal market and instead built on what had worked previously and discarding that which had failed. The White Paper "*The new NHS Modern - Dependable*" (*Fig 15.18*) laid out a third way based on partnership and driven by performance. Since April 1998 and as the fifth decade of the NHS beckoned, the RVI came within the aegis of The Newcastle upon Tyne Hospitals NHS Trust and which includes Newcastle General Hospital, Freeman Hospital, Walkergate Hospital and facilities based at the International Centre for Life. Today in the NHS we have an ever increasing involvement of the private (independent) sector as well as the introduction of Foundation Trusts. A key governance feature of an Foundation Trust is the elected Board of Governors, almost identical to the one that was in place one hundred years ago when the RVI opened. *Plus ca change!*

Date

BANK ORDER FORM FOR SUBSCRIPTION.

To Messrs. *(Bankers).*

Please pay annually. until further notice. the sum of Guineas to the credit of the Newcastle-upon-Tyne Royal Victoria Infirmary. at Barclay's Bank. Ltd., Newcastle-upon-Tyne, and charge the same to my account.

Signature

Address

£ : :

The post of House Governor and Secretary no longer exist. However Len Fenwick, Chief Executive of The Newcastle upon Tyne Hospitals NHS Trust, carries on the tradition in the RVI centenary year.

169

Marjorie Shipton, Joan Driver, Ken Grey, Barbara Gubbins, Chris Sadler, Sheila Wheatley

Essential Support from the public and patients

Fig 16.3: Fundraising for the RVI - 1897.

Introduction

From its inception the Infirmary has depended on the generosity of individuals, both the rich and eminent and the ordinary and of caring heart. (*Figs 16.1 to 16.3*) Long before its official opening in 1906 substantial sums of money had been given by numerous benefactors to make the vision of a new infirmary for the city a reality. Amongst them were Mr John Hall and Mr and Mrs W.A. Watson Armstrong, who each gave £100,000, the latter being to perpetuate the memory of Lord Armstrong of Cragside. Many others gave for specific purposes. For instance, *'the gifts of great value bestowed for the fitting up and embellishment'* of St Luke's Chapel. Numerous fund raising events were held such as a ball organised by Mrs Albert Lord towards the cost of the Royal Doulton Tiles, which can be seen on wards, 14 and 18. In 1901 members of the public could endow an adult bed for £1000 or a child's bed for £500 (*Fig 10.2, p.100*). Even after the official opening of the RVI Sweep the dog, described in the archives as an 'unpaid member of staff', sat outside his kennel, complete with collecting box to raise money to endow further beds. (*Fig 16.4*) Yet others gave specific gifts, such as two gramophones presented by friends of the Infirmary in 1906.

Over the years a number of long-established local and national charitable organisations have continued to support the RVI. Notable amongst these are The Special Trustees, The League of Friends, The WRVS, The Fleming Children's Trust and more recently The Yellow Brick Road. Presently, there are a whole variety of charities and funds associated with specific wards and departments which are kept going by individuals who unflinchingly raise money for equipment or to generally raise the quality of life for patients. There are couples who have asked for donations to ward funds in lieu of wedding presents and parents who work fervently to raise money for the units that have helped their children. Numerous individuals have given generously to help the people of the North-East; the late Dame Catherine Cookson's name appears on many a piece of hospital equipment (*Fig 16.2*) and similarly Sir William Leech patronised many ventures.

This chapter however is not simply about fund raising achievements. We also pay tribute to individual volunteers who give of their time, to relationships formed, to practical support given, and to the personal care shown to patients and relatives. Each in their own way has helped to imbue a sense of community. Thus, what follows is an acknowledgement of all of the generosity that has gone on over the years and still goes on, often unseen, yet invaluable.

Marjorie Shipton

Fig 16.4: Sweep the dog, complete with collecting box.

Left: Fund raising 1853 and today. Fig 16.1: Charity Concert in aid of the Infirmary, January 1853.
Fig 16.2: Catherine Cookson - a major donor to the RVI. Left - Right: Dr Chris Record, Laurence Martin, Catherine Cookson, Mr Hugh Marshall.

Newcastle Healthcare Charity

The Newcastle Healthcare Charity - long known as the Special Trustees, is the oldest and best endowed of the RVI's charitable funds. As such it has an outstanding record of succesful funding of research and patient amenities over the past century. The trustees of the Infirmary's charitable funds have directed the resources, under their stewardship, in support of the Royal Victoria Infirmary since the opening of the hospital. In the early years of the Infirmary's life, the stewardship of charitable money was regulated by the hospital's *Board of Governors*. Over the years this stewardship passed to the *Hospital Management Committees*, then to *Newcastle University Hospitals Special Trustees* and in 2001 to the *Newcastle Healthcare Charity's Board of Trustees*.

The Newcastle Healthcare Charity is therefore the successor body to the Newcastle University Hospitals Charity, the trustees of which held stewardship of the NHS charitable trust funds for the benefit of The Royal Victoria Infirmary, Newcastle General Hospital, The Walkergate & Sanderson Hospitals, and the medical research departments of the University of Newcastle's Faculty of Medicine when working in partnership with the NHS.

Mrs Catherine Wood.

Professor Reg Jordan.

Fig 16.5: *The Trustees of the Newcastle Healthcare Charity. L-R: Sir Miles Irving, Mrs Margaret Carter, Mr Roger C. Spoor, Mr Ken Grey (Chairman), and Mr Richard Middleton (Co-opted).*

In 2001, the Secretary of State for Health, through the provisions of Section 11 of the NHS Community Care Act 1990, ordered that the Special Trustees of the Newcastle University Hospitals 'Special Trustees' be replaced by, what are known as, 'Section 11 Trustees' for the Newcastle Hospitals (NHS) Trust. Thus, The Newcastle Healthcare Charity trustee body was formed in April 2001 under Section 11 of the NHS and Community Care Act 1990, which established the body as independent trustees for the Royal Victoria Infirmary by appointment to the Secretary of State for Health.

The objectives of The Newcastle Healthcare Charity align themselves with the broad strategic objectives of its host NHS Trust (The Newcastle Hospitals NHS Trust). By identifying both the short & long term requirements of the local hospitals, the charity is able to target its support from charitable funds toward improving the patient & carer experience whilst in hospital, improving the workplace environment and post-qualification educational opportunities for NHS staff (particularly nurses) and *'pump priming'* innovative medical research undertaken at Newcastle University's Faculty of Medicine.

There are currently six trustees (including the Chair) and one co-opted trustee of The Newcastle Healthcare Charity. Each trustee is appointed by the Secretary of State for Health for a four-year term (which can be extended for a further term at the discretion of the Secretary of State). (*Fig 16.5*)

One of the major roles of the charity has been to support health related research in the North East especially in its early stages - so called pump priming (*Fig 16.6*). The success of this approach can be testified by fact that the highly successful Stem Cell research unit of the International Centre for Life had its origins in a project initially supported by the Trustees. Such invaluable support has been given to the *start up* stages of numerous medical research projects.

Another principal activity of the trustees has been to direct charitable funds to improve and develop the infrastructure of the hospital building.

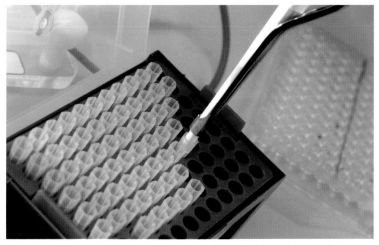

Fig 16.6: Pump priming of basic medical research is one of the most important and productive uses of the Charity's funds.

A good example of this is the support given to the hospital chapel. In May 2000 charitable funds were made available to cover the much needed restoration costs of St Luke's Chapel. Built in 1905, the Grade 2 listed building survived without the need of any major repairs for nearly 100 years. However, in 2000 engineers identified the need to carry out major structural repair to the fabric of the chapel. The chapel's roof and window frames were declared to be unsafe and in urgent need of repair. In addition, the gold ceiling mosaics, stained glass and electrical wiring all required major repair. The *Special Trustees* were asked for help, and were able to contribute £8,000 from charitable funds toward the cost of the chapel's restoration. These structural repairs coincided with the much-needed repair and renovation of the chapel's organ. The Special Trustees funded a team of organ restoration specialists to carry out the work. In addition to the restoration work a new musical keyboard was also purchased. The overall contribution by the Special Trustees to the restoration project amounted to nearly £18,500. (*Figs 16.7 & 17.26, p.190*)

The trustees also support initiatives designed to improve the total hospital experience for patients and their families. Examples are special beds for immobile patients and comfortable reclining chairs for day-cases.

Ken Grey

Fig 16.7: St. Luke's Chapel, RVI recently refurbished.

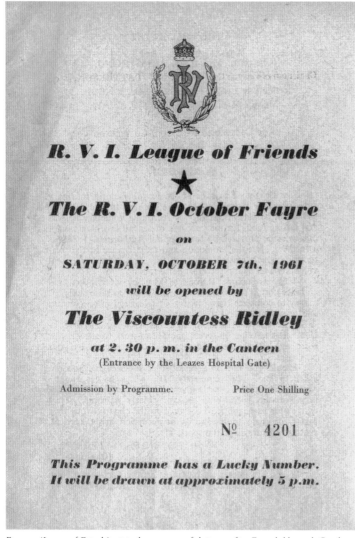

Fig 16.8: 'League of Friends' original programme of their very first Fayre held on 7th October 1961. (Chairman was Mrs C. N. Armstrong).

The League of Friends

In 1996 the League of Friends Movement celebrated 250 years of service in the care of hospital patients and the League at the RVI held a Flower Festival to mark the occasion. It was lovely - a blessing in the chapel, teas and raffles - all very successful.

Of course, the history of the movement actually goes back more than 250 years. The earliest existence of the League of Friends (hereafter referred to as LOF) can certainly be pinpointed to 1746, when Bishop Maddox (founder of Worcester Infirmary) is recorded as saying, 'Few cures are brought about by drugs alone. Proper food, necessary attendance and above all ease and tranquillity of mind have a large share in every recovery'. This embraces the philosophy of the Leagues, which is still the reason for their existence today - to care for the health, comfort and dignity of patients - in short their general welfare and comfort is the concern of LOF.

The RVI League of Friends was formed in March 1961 when Mr E.F Patterson (Assistant Librarian at King's College Library) was appointed Chairman. Membership fees were 2/6d and within a fairly short time there was a good membership consisting of wives of consultants, surgeons and doctors and many others who were offering their services to help. Indeed, Mrs C.N. Armstrong was the Chairman of the Fayre Committee when the first Fayre took place on Saturday 6th October 1961. This was a huge success and continued for many years. (Fig 16.8) When Mr Patterson resigned in 1963, Mrs Armstrong became Chairman of the League and with her band of helpers the League continued to flourish.

Many currently thriving LOF were set up after the establishment of the National Health Service in 1948 but certainly a number existed before and the origins of some go back for many years. The voluntary service that they gave and are still providing is invaluable and the list of great achievements by LOF all over the country is simply endless.

After the 1939/45 War the NHS Act, amongst other things brought voluntary hospitals and their servants under the umbrella of the new NHS, and the LOF questioned their role, if any, under the new regime. Aneurin Bevan, the then Minister of Health, gave an immediate reply to the effect that there would always be a place for personal and voluntary service in hospitals. Fundraising by voluntary effort was needed to provide extras, and LOF would always be needed 'to feel where the boot pinches and apply relief'.

As a result, on 24th March 1949, representatives from forty Leagues met in London and this historic occasion saw the birth of The National Association of League of Friends. The National Association has grown from forty Leagues to almost one thousand with a membership of over two hundred and fifty thousand, raising collectively over thirty million pounds per year as a result of millions of hours of voluntary time, to directly benefit patients.

The RVI, as everyone knows, is a huge hospital with more and more modern ideas coming along every day. Vast corridors connect the wards and departments of the old Victoria Wing to those of the new Leazes and Claremont Wings. Consequently, it was realised some time ago that it was no longer possible for LOF helpers to trundle tea trolleys from the old Tea Bar at Casualty to individual wards. It simply was not feasible. As a result on the 1st December 1995 the new Tea Bar in Leazes Wing was opened and is still being very capably operated by Mrs Ruth Gordon and her helpers. The Tea Bar remains extremely popular and raises a lot of money. Sadly, it was impossible to also keep the old Tea Bar going because of lack of volunteers, but it was good to see it manned later by the WRVS.

Fig 16.9: League of Friends Shop in Victoria Wing as it is today.

The original LOF Shop in Victoria Wing - near Peacock Hall- continues to flourish and is very proud of its many achievements. These include funding the electric shutters which are a boon to the 'recycled teenagers' behind the counter, and paying for the installation of electric cool-trays for various drinks, which pleased the customers. A tremendous variety of goods are available, including drinks, chocolates, cards, toys and toiletries, just to mention a few. (*Fig 16.9*) The Shop and Tea Bar are both very popular, judging by the comments received after Bank Holiday closures and the like! Both have a good turnover with profits being ploughed back into the hospital by way of the purchase of medical equipment, furnishings and amenities for the benefit and comfort of patients.

LOF helpers are always busy, not only serving the customers but also constantly giving them directions! Whilst the shop used to open from 9am to 7pm Mondays to Fridays, regrettably, because of staffing difficulties, it now closes at 6pm. Like all voluntary organisations the main problem is recruiting more voluntary helpers and meanwhile existing staff do more duties to fill the gaps.

The Flower Ladies form another section of the LOF and do a magnificent job in attending to flowers on certain wards with a specific group arranging the flowers in the Chapel every week, year in, year out and for which LOF provide the funding.

Every two months the Committee meet within the RVI and amongst other things discuss appeals, which come before them for various equipment etc… and which are finally approved by Mr Fenwick, the Chief Executive. New rules and regulations have been enforced over the years and 'it's all different to the old days', says a former Chairman, Mrs Jean Heppell, who had held the position for thirteen years when she resigned in1995. Mrs Heppell remembers the days of telephone trolleys and such like and never envisaged the time when you would put £5 in a machine in return for a TV card enabling patients to watch personal television, surf the net, telephone or e- mail, all at their bedside. Such is progress and it is wonderful!

Over the years many interesting characters have joined the League, not least of whom was Mrs Mary Burkett, M.B.E. who gave many years of her life to the service of LOF, mainly in the shop for which she was suitably honoured by the Queen. Mrs Burkett did not leave the shop until she was ninety-three years old and whilst she does not live in Newcastle any more, it is understood that she has recently had her one-hundredth birthday and is still going strong! A good advert for voluntary work would you say?

Joan Driver

Women's Royal Voluntary Service

During the Second World War a vast army of women who wanted to help the war effort emerged and became known as the 'Women's Voluntary Service'. After the war these women wanted something into which they could channel their experience. Amongst other targets were hospitals, the RVI being one.

Initially, they would do the rounds of the wards with trolleys filled with things the patients needed. These progressed into small static outlets of which there are now three: one in the Victoria Wing Out-patients Department which was originally in the Fracture Clinic, one in the new Maternity Department which operated previously in Princess Mary Maternity Hospital and a third in the Children's Out-patients Department. 'Comforts' for patients are still provided but these are mainly for patients attending the hospital for out-patient clinics, some of whom travel many miles and are ready for a hot drink and maybe a snack.

All of the profits from what is now the WRVS (with Her Majesty the Queen as patron and now including many men) go back into the hospital to provide 'extras' for the patients as well as helping to finance a buggy to transport patients to various parts of the hospital. (*Fig 16.10*)

In the past few years, amongst other things the following have been provided: a computer for the children's wards, comfortable chairs for dialysis patients and equipment for the Dermatology Department. (*Fig 16.11*) Along with the Freeman and Newcastle General Hospital outlets £235 000 has been given to the Trust over the last few years. Investments have included Electric Profiling Beds for all four hospitals in the Trust, a scanner for the Fracture Clinic to help in the diagnosis of Brittle Bone Disease and equipment for the NCCT.

The WRVS also has Emergency Teams which operate nationwide and which are always at the ready to help in times of crisis such as the flooding in Boscastle and Carlisle, rail disasters such as Potters Bar and Selby, and air disasters like Lockerbie.

The WRVS is always looking for more volunteers so if anyone reading this chapter has a few hours to spare, both ladies and gentlemen, the RVI Team would be pleased to see you.

Sheila Wheatley

Fig 16.11: WRVS present a hoist to the dermatology department.

Fig 16.10: A familiar sight - Buggy Service between Victoria Wing, Claremont and Leazes provided by the WRVS.

The Fleming Children's Trust

Initially this fund raising organisation was formed to support the Fleming Memorial Hospital for Sick Children. The first meeting of the Fleming Fund Committee was held in the boardroom of Barclays Bank on Thursday 27th January 1949 at 2.30pm and comprised local businessmen and women. The minutes from that meeting record that there were 120 subscribers to the fund and that Matron would be consulted about suitable purchases that would benefit the children and their families.

Over the years the name of the fund has changed, originally to 'Friends of the Fleming', the name used until 1989 when the Children's Hospital closed and the services transferred to the RVI. The children's wards were all located in the same part of the hospital and the fund was renamed, 'Friends of the Fleming Children's Wing RVI' The function of the organisation remained the same. Fund raising events continued and a greater number of children and their families benefited. The annual garden fete is now held in the grounds of the RVI and other events in and around the Infirmary.

Fig 16.12: Preparations for the annual garden fete.

The amalgamation of the children's services of the Newcastle General Hospital and the RVI increased the number of wards and departments needing support. There was a further increase when all three acute hospitals formed the Newcastle Hospitals NHS Trust and wards and departments at Freeman Hospital were included. Today this fund raising organisation supports children both in hospital and in the community.

In 2001 in order to reflect current changes and the future application for charitable status the name was changed again to the Fleming Children's Trust. The Trust welcomes support from a wide variety of people. This may be in the form of an annual subscription, help at events or as a committee member. Whatever help is given to support the Trust it is used to benefit children and their families. (*Fig 16.12 & 16.13*)

Chris Sadler   *Fig 16.13: Bouncy castle fun.*

The Children's Foundation and the Yellow Brick Road

The Children's Foundation was set up in 1990 by a group of academics, business people and community leaders in Newcastle, led by Professor Aynsley-Green, (now National Clinical Director for Children). They came together in reaction to a Government report - The Health of the Nation (1988), which identified children in the north (Northumberland, Tyne & Wear, Durham, Teesside and Cumbria) as having the poorest health of any English region.

Professor Aynsley-Green was head of the Department of Child Health at Newcastle University and he felt this challenge particularly keenly. With colleagues, he spearheaded the creation of The Children's Foundation to raise money to improve child health in the north. Their first objective was to build a centre of excellence for child health, based at the Royal Victoria Infirmary in Newcastle. (*Fig 16.14*)

Fig 16.14: Dr Hugh Jackson, Vice-President The Children's Foundation.
Lucy Winskell, chairman of The Children's Foundation.
Professor Al Aynsley-Green, National Clinical Director for Children and Vice-President of
The Children's Foundation.

The Yellow Brick Road Appeal - the public appeal of the campaign - captured the hearts and minds of people in the north of England and it was in 1994 that The Children's Foundation commissioned the Sir James Spence Institute to be built and used for the purposes of child health. (*Fig 10.10, p.105*) This facility was inspired by the memory of Sir James Spence, who made an outstanding contribution to the advancement of paediatric knowledge, services and treatment. It is now home to world class medical experts who work to improve the lives of our children through research and treatment programmes.

The Children's Foundation is a charitable company limited by guarantee with memorandum and articles of association that govern it, together with a Board of Trustees drawn from all walks of life. The Duke of York is its Patron.

The aims of the organization are:
The relief of sickness amongst children and young people,
The preservation and protection of their physical and mental health,
The promotion of research into the causes and treatment of diseases suffered by children and young persons and to disseminate the results.

Working closely with the RVI, The Children's Foundation also provides additional extras and facilitates activities on the wards to cheer up children whilst they are ill, thereby making their stay in hospital more enjoyable. This includes organising presents at Christmastime and Easter and visits by local magicians and celebrities. (*Fig 16.15*)

One particular fundraising activity with celebrity chefs from across the country, resulted in a new water treatment plant being secured for the Children's Kidney Unit at the RVI in partnership with the Newcastle Healthcare Charity and a contribution towards the development of a prototype machine to dialyse premature babies.

Another project supported by The Children's Foundation and based at the Sir James Spence Institute at the RVI, provides children with cerebral palsy with specially adapted equipment and a range of toys to determine therapy programmes.

Fig 16.15: North East actor Tim Healy, in costume as Captain Hook, visits children on the wards of the RVI with some of the other members of the Theatre Royal panto cast.

The charity is considered to be the leading children's healthcare charity in the region and works in partnership with other organisations to develop innovative projects within the regional community and, in some cases, support projects by finding national partners. Some key regional projects have been funded through The Children's Foundation by sourcing external funding providers, and managed in partnership with other local and national organisations. These include: *The Golden Freeway* - an internet-based support system for children with life-limiting diseases; *The Gateshead Child Safety Project*, or 'Whoops!' as it is known, a new way of approaching the safety message through art, drama and direct marketing techniques; and *Baby Express* - an age-paced newsletter to build better relationships between new parents and their baby.

The Children's Foundation is determined to tackle child health issues in the North East but recognizes the need to work in partnership with others from all sectors and with the continued support and generosity of the people in the region.

Barbara Gubbins

Radio Lollipop

Radio Lollipop Newcastle was founded at the RVI in 1983 and has been cheering up children on the wards ever since! As part of a larger national charity that spans the globe, we provide play, comfort and care to children at times when they need it most.

Although sick children may not have the chance to control the time they spend in hospital or the treatment they receive, Radio Lollipop gives them an outlet for fun, enjoyment and activity and the chance to take part in on-the-ward games and competitions. At the moment, games and activities on the wards are our main services to the children. We are in the process of returning the radio service to the airwaves and trying to get it up and running on as many of the children's wards as possible.

Based at the crossroads opposite the WRVS shop, the Lollipop radio service gives sick children the chance to request their own songs, phone in and on air and engage in some lively chat with the Lollipop DJ's.

We currently operate ward rounds on a Tuesday and Friday night from 5.30 pm to 7.30 pm in wards 1, 2, 6, 7, 9 and 16, reaching out to many children with a wide range of illnesses including cancer, kidney disease, severe burns, cystic fibrosis, cerebral palsy, post-surgery patients and patients in the general wards.

Radio Lollipop is an entirely voluntary organisation. All of those involved give their time freely because they know the positive difference that they can make to each sick child's health and emotional well being. The future outlook for Radio Lollipop is uncertain. We have secured a studio space in the new wing of the hospital but funding is low and

Fig 16.16: Training the next generation of broadcasters for Radio Lollipop.

help is needed to make sure that Radio Lollipop can continue to provide its valuable service free of charge to as many sick children as we can.

As well as fundraising, the best way you can help is by supplying small gift items like key rings, stationery, unwanted toys, CD's, videos, DVDs, console games and children's clothing. We will make sure that these items are used wisely and given to children who really need their frowns turned upside down.

Conclusion - A Glimpse of the Future

These accounts depict just some of the activities that volunteers have played in fund raising and providing services to patients and their relatives in the RVI. They have been an integral part of the Infirmary's life during the last century but what will be their role in the next? The document, 'Making a Difference: Strengthening Volunteering in the NHS', (Report of the Working Group on Volunteering in the NHS, Department of Health 1996) affirmed the necessity for volunteers well into the future. Further, their role is widening. Many existing volunteers have enrolled as members of the Trust as it seeks Foundation Hospital Status and indeed some may have key roles. The Patient Advice and Liaison Service relies on volunteers to support its full time staff in dealing with enquiries from patients and relatives. Chaplaincy volunteers are being trained on a regular basis to listen to patients' emotional, spiritual and religious needs. The organisations highlighted above continue to extend their membership and increase their fundraising achievements, whether it be to provide high-tech equipment, improve the quality of life for in-patients, develop a new service or ferry patients and relatives along the vast network of corridors linking the original Victoria Building and the emergent state of the art hospital that will serve the people of the region in this century and beyond. Whilst the RVI continues to provide vast numbers of people with healthcare of the highest standard it seems that there will always be that need to 'give something back', be it through volunteering or fundraising, either by individuals or groups and be it high profile or unseen.

Chapter 17: *The Treasures of the RVI*

Gary Enever, Martin Barrett, Derek Tacchi

The Royal Victoria Infirmary has, itself, always been one of Newcastle's treasures. Built to replace the old Infirmary on Forth Banks, beautiful works of art became part of the fabric of the hospital from the very beginning. The new Infirmary also became a repository of the treasures of its predecessor. In the following pages, we hope to show a little of the rich heritage that is still an integral part of the Royal Victoria Infirmary.

Chronologically, it might be best to start with the oldest treasures first, and these came from the Newcastle Infirmary, opened in 1753 and closed in 1906. The most striking are a collection of paintings, depicting the Infirmary's benefactors.

The Boardroom Paintings

The Boardroom, looking out over the statue of Queen Victoria, houses a collection of eight large eighteenth and nineteenth century portraits. The eyes of the benefactors gaze down on the meetings that still take place in the Infirmary's most impressive room.

Fig 17.1: Portrait of Mathew Ridley.

Fig 17.2: Portrait of Sir Walter Blackett.

Mathew Ridley (*Fig 17.1*) was Mayor of Newcastle in 1751, on the founding of the Infirmary. He was rich from coal, and a great benefactor to the poor of Newcastle. His staunch support of George III earned the populace the nickname "Geordies". The painting is by Westfield Webb, a London portrait painter, and shows Ridley pointing to the plans of the Infirmary, with the Newcastle Corporation Mace and Sword behind.

Sir Walter Blackett (*Fig 17.2*) was one of eighteenth century Newcastle's most prominent citizens. He represented the city in Parliament for many years, and was renowned for his generosity to all. He gave substantial amounts to the Infirmary, the poor, and the debtors in Newgate Street Prison. His portrait was presented to the Infirmary after his death in 1777, and is reputed to have come from the studio of Sir Joshua Reynolds. This did not stop the House Committee having the painting altered and the colour "touched up"!

Left: Fig 17.19: Detail from Royal Doulton nursery rhyme tiles.

183

Fig 17.3: Portrait of Martin Benson, Bishop of Gloucester.

The portrait, by the London artist John Taylor, shown in Figure 17.3, is of Martin Benson, Bishop of Gloucester, another of the Infirmary's founding benefactors. He was a great friend of Joseph Butler, Bishop of Durham, (Fig 17.4) who laid the foundation stone of the Infirmary in 1751. Neither Bishop survived to see the opening in 1753. Butler died in Bath in 1752, and Benson died soon after, exhausted after attending his lifelong friend during his last illness.

In the mid nineteenth century, Algernon, the 4th Duke of Northumberland, donated £1000 to fund the building of the Dobson Wing in the old Infirmary. He served in the Navy from 1805, being a midshipman under Collingwood, and finally reached the rank of Admiral. He was an Egyptologist, an astronomer, a historian, and much more.

This portrait, (Fig 17.5) by Sir Francis Grant, shows the Duke in the uniform of a captain, and was painted in 1855. It depicts him in his Ducal robes with his Knight of the Garter sash and star.

Fig 17.4: Portrait of Joseph Butler, Bishop of Durham.

Fig 17.5: Portrait of the 4th Duke of Northumberland.

Before leaving the Boardroom, it is worth noting works of art created for the new Infirmary, in particular, two beautifully carved chairs. (*Figs* 17.6 & 17.7)

More from the old Infirmary

Within the entrance to Peacock Hall, a wide staircase ascends to the first floor. On its first landing stands a magnificent eighteenth century clock, (*Fig* 17.8) that originally kept the time in the Infirmary on Forth Banks.

Fig 17.6: *The Medical Society Chair.*

Fig 17.7: *The RVI Chairman's Chair.*

Fig 17.8: *Clock from the Newcastle Infirmary.*

As one looks up, the window sills are occupied by the busts of prominent surgeons and physicians of the nineteenth century.

The bust shown here (*Fig* 17.9) is that of Thomas Headlam, a physician to the Infirmary between 1805 and 1840. It was donated by a Miss Bates, of Milbourne Hall.

Fig 17.9: *Bust of Thomas Headlam.*

Fig 17.10: Portrait of John Fleming.

Fig 17.11: Portrait of Mrs Fleming.

Fig 17.12: Frampton's Statue of the young Victoria.

There are many other artefacts around the RVI that originated in the old Infirmary, and some that originated in other hospitals. Particular mention should be made of the "Flemings", whose portraits can be found on the top floor of the Victoria Wing, near the children's operating theatres. (*Figs 17.10 & 17.11*)

John Fleming was a prominent solicitor in Victorian Newcastle, and in 1886 he funded the building of a children's hospital in the fresh air of the Town Moor, as a memorial to his wife. The Fleming Memorial Hospital for Sick Children opened in 1888, and became closely associated with RVI until its closure nearly 100 years later.

Fig 17.13: Queen Victoria's night apparel.

The New Infirmary

As a celebration of Queen Victoria's Diamond Jubilee, the RVI was not only intended to be a state-of-the-art hospital, it was also a work of art. The architecture has been discussed elsewhere, but consider approaching the Infirmary from the direction of Leazes Park. The gleaming white statue of a young Victoria (*Fig 17.12*) stands before the red brick and honeyed sandstone of the south-facing facade.

Windsor Castle

This Petticoat was worn by Her Majesty the Queen in May 1899.

Fig 17.14: The note accompanying the donation of Queen Victoria's petticoat.

The statue of Queen Victoria is remarkable for a number of reasons. It was commissioned by Riley Lord, the Mayor and instigator of the new hospital, and he was able to engage the services of one of the most famous sculptors of the era, George Frampton. Frampton, who was a friend to the Prince of Wales, was able to carve an image of the Queen as she was on her accession to the throne. Nearly all other statues of the era show her as the elderly Empress of the British Empire.

Frampton's most famous piece was a result of his friendship with J.M. Barrie. For him, he carved an image of Peter Pan, which was secretly placed next to the Serpentine in London, for the benefit of nannies walking their charges in the Park.

As well as her statue, the Infirmary is in possession of more intimate mementoes of the late Queen. After her passing, the house committee was presented with a set of her petticoats and a shawl. (Figs 17.13 & 17.14) Why such intimate apparel should have been left to the hospital is not clear and is the source of much interesting, if unfounded, speculation.

Fig 17.15: RVI foundation stone.

As we pass through the Peacock Hall entrance to the RVI, it is interesting to note the engraved stones celebrating the construction (Fig 17.15) and opening of the Infirmary, both ceremonies attended by Edward, as Prince of Wales in 1900 and then King in 1906. There are also long lists of committee members and subscribers on handsome metal plaques.

The Peacock Hall itself is a marvellous memorial to the Edwardian Age. With its wooden panelling, (Fig 17.16) wallpaper, stained glass (Fig 17.17) and beautiful plasterwork, it is like entering a stately home rather than a hospital. The original wallpaper, depicted in Chapter 20, (Fig 20.5, p.214) has now been replaced.

As we enter the Infirmary from Peacock Hall, we reach the "crossroads" of the Victoria Wing. Turning right, and proceeding to the very end of the corridor, we reach Ward 14, which houses a remarkable collection of tiled panels. Originally, these were children's wards, and to make them happier places, the walls were covered by wonderful landscapes and nursery rhyme characters. (Figs 17.18 to 17.25)

Fig 17.17: Details of Peacock Hall windows.

Fig 17.16: The entrance to Peacock Hall.

Fig 17.18: *Royal Doulton nursery tiles.*

The tiles were created by the Doulton Company Ltd (Edward VII granted its charter in 1901 and it became Royal Doulton), then based in Lambeth in London. There are a number of hospitals in the country and overseas, built at about the turn of the last century, with similar collections, but the RVI boasts the largest collection in the world, at around sixty panels.

Fig 17.19: *Details from nursery tiles.*

Fig 17.20: *Details from nursery tiles.*

Fig 17.21: *Details from nursery tiles.*

Fig 17.22: *Margaret Thompson's mark.*

Many of them carry the marks their artists, including Margaret Thompson (*Fig 17.22*) and W Rowe, then two of Doulton's most talented artists. Every tile is hand painted, and there are several thousand of them. Most of Doulton's artists came from the Lambeth School of Art, which interestingly also trained George Frampton.

Fig 17.23: Little boy blue.

Fig 17.24: Little Miss Muffet.

Fig 17.25: Simple Simon.

When the ward is demolished, these, and other tiles will be saved for posterity. They would certainly grace a new paediatric wing.

189

Fig 17.26: St. Luke's Chapel, RVI.

St. Luke's chapel

The builders of the new Infirmary showed admirable concern for the spiritual as well as the physical well-being of its patients. With a domed golden ceiling, carvings and stained glass, the chapel is another self-contained wonder. (*Fig 17.26*)

The work of the chaplaincy service is of great benefit to both staff and patients. St Luke's Chapel itself provides a unique place of worship, contemplation and spiritual support, which is enjoyed by hospital patients, visitors and staff alike. The charity trustees recognised the importance of this role and willingly supported the Chaplaincy in its times of need.

The collections

Throughout the Infirmary are a number of small collections, often held in departments, which reflect its history. The Radiology Department has a wonderful collection of equipment and documents that chart the development of the speciality. (See chapter 11).

The University Department of Surgery in the Medical School has a wooden operating table and a Lister antiseptic spray, as well as many old surgical instruments. (See chapter 5). The Anaesthetic Department of the University is in possession of one of the largest collections of old books and equipment in the country, as well as archive material relating to past members. (*Fig 17.27*)

Most Departments have similar treasures, and the Infirmary itself has many documents and year-books that make fascinating reading.

There are other works of art throughout the Infirmary, including the paintings and photographs in the Leazes link corridor, the plaques of famous surgeons on the Leazes third floor, and the First World War bedspread near Leazes outpatients (chapter 19).

Fig 17.27: Articles in the Anaesthetic Collection.

The Conservatory, Derek Tacchi

Fig 17.28: The Conservatory, RVI.

To the west of Peacock Hall stands the conservatory, originally built as a covered connecting link between the Nurses' home and the old main corridor of the RVI. (*Fig 17.28*)

The conservatory, or Winter Garden, as it was known, was meant as a place of repose for patients, visitors and staff alike. It was also a protective barrier between the young (male) doctors and the even younger nurses, who were the responsibility of the Home Sister. In its early days the Winter Garden was a trysting place, and many tender farewells could be witnessed before the doors of the home were locked at 10 p.m.

The conservatory was a unique glass structure made of a flitched steel and timber superstructure comprising girders, trusses, T-section bowstrings, plates, bars and timber opening windows (with opening mechanisms). Early 20th century glazing, some curved and all slightly ribbed, complete the effect.

Inspection in 1996 showed the superstructure was basically sound, but to restore it completely required the conservatory to be dismantled, all surfaces cleaned and lost material replaced before re-erecting the structure in its entirety.

The Special Trustees of the hospital funded the project, at a cost of over £150,000. The work was carried out by Stephen Easten Ltd, between June and October 1996. As well as a full restoration, an external rail was added to aid window cleaning. Also added were modern lighting and a shield for the heating pipes.

The final result is both elegant and pleasing, and the building certainly does induce a sense of repose. Re-stocking with exotic plants was achieved following an open day in September 1997, when staff and the public loaned plants for a temporary display. The response was overwhelming and, thanks to many generous donations, the conservatory is now full of beautiful specimens. The restoration of this important link with the history of the RVI was a worthwhile and successful exercise.

Postscript

But despite the worth of all these accumulated objects, the RVI is a living, working hospital, and not a museum. The treasures give a richness, and a sense of history, to all those that look on them. We hope this chapter will help staff and visitors understand what they see a little better, but they must remember - it is its people and not its possessions that are the true treasures of the RVI.

Chapter 18: *The Spirit of the RVI*
A Pictorial Glimpse Ann Clouston

For some of us who walk into the RVI through Peacock Hall, there sometimes can be a feeling of the sense of history, and maybe even a shiver of excitement as we recall what has gone before. Whilst there is a definite recognition of the atmosphere created by the building, the real presence and value comes from the people who now work and have worked there.

Sadly, there are not many photographs of such people in the archives but in 1993 Simon James produced a collection *'Signs of Life'.* Many of these images include the *real* RVI, capturing the spirit of the place, using oft forgotten departments whose functions provide the backbone of the organisation.

The following pictures depict a few of the many people who provide the essential support to the doctors, nurses, professions allied to medicine and managers who of necessity have the highest profile within the hospital. Without the support of such individuals the hospital could not run as smoothly as it does and this chapter serves to remind everyone, patients, visitors and staff of the importance of their roles.

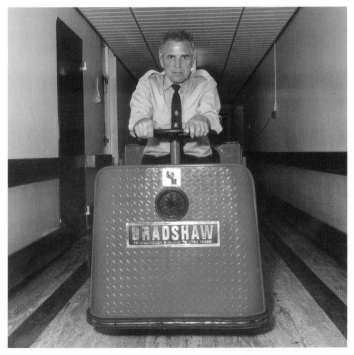

Fig 18.2: *Stuart Douglas driving one of the familiar orange workhorses.*

Portering

The innumerable tasks demanded of our portering staff are too widespread to document, but without their services patients and staff would not be fed, would not have the equipment needed for their treatment, would not be taken to the operating theatre, would not receive any post, and would not be secure.

* By kind permission of the RVI trustees

Fig 18.1: Robert Alan Taylor (RAT), the Estates Department.

Accident & Emergency (A/E)

Fig 18.3: *From the trivial to the desperate. A/E has always taken in whatever is presented to what is truly the Infirmary's front door.*

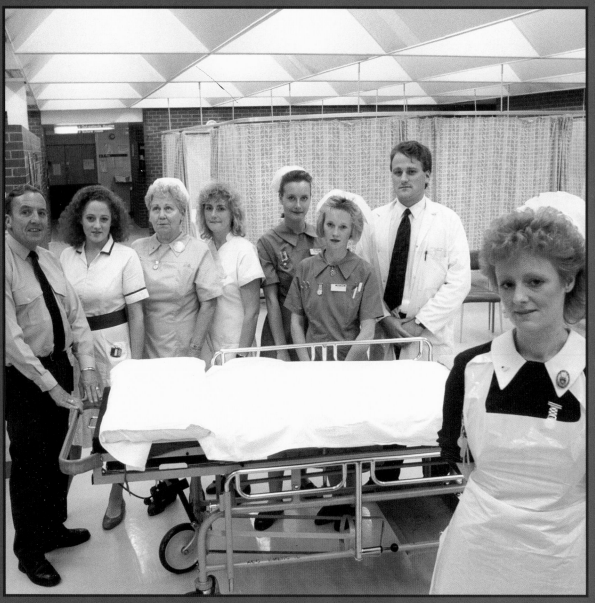

Fig 18.4: *Team working is today's in-word. This picture, from 15 years ago, shows that teams made up of doctors, nurses, radiographers, porters and others have always been a feature of A/E.*

Catering

Just as an army marches on its stomach, so a hospital is only truly at ease with itself if patients, visitors and staff are well fed.

Fig 18.5: Jacquie the supervisor in the Victoria restaurant.

Fig 18.6: RVI catering staff.

Fig 18.7: RVI catering staff.

Fig 18.8: RVI catering staff.

Domestic Services

Cleanliness is next to godliness and ever since the days of Florence Nightingale a hospital has been judged on its cleanliness. The army of those who keep the RVI spotless have many thankless tasks but occasionally looking after our treasure is a small reward.

Fig 18.9: Domestic Services.

Laundry

Clean sheets on the bed and spotless linen are a luxury that everyone expects at home and in hotels. The laundry department of the RVI, until the service was transferred to Gateshead, ensured that the same degree of service was provided to our patients.

Fig 18.10: Past days on the Calander machine.

The Sewing Room

Thousands of staff and patients owe grateful thanks to the staff of the sewing room who alter uniforms and undertake many other tasks which help create a professional and dignified appearance.

Fig 18.11: A seamstress at work.

Medical Records

The millions of patients who have been seen at the RVI over the past century have generated mountains of records. Until the computerised paperless society we all hope for becomes a reality, the medical records department will underpin the keeping of accurate information about those who seek the services of the hospital.

Fig 18.12: Filing medical records.

Dental Hospital

The Dental Hospital, although providing separate services and student education, is functionally intergrated with the RVI.

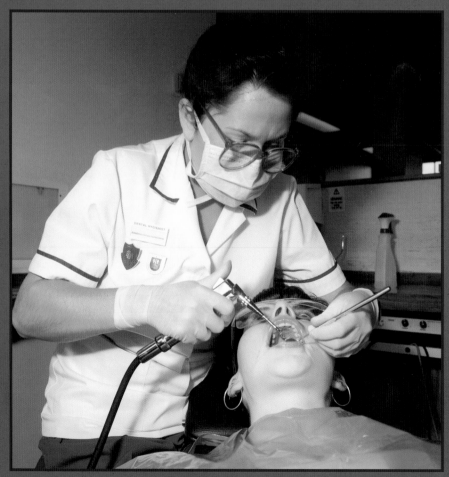

Fig 18.13: Dental Hygienist at work.

The talented staff presenting the Christmas concert

Maintaining the morale of the staff is essential to a happy hospital. The RVI concert was a tradition of the past and continues in a modified form to this day with charity concerts in the Peoples Theatre using the talents of the Trust staff. Similarly the ensuring of a warm atmosphere at Christmas time remains a vital hospital tradition.

Fig 18.14: The talented staff presenting the Christmas concert.

Making Christmas special for the Children's Ward, 1990s

RVI Crêche

Kindervision was a pioneering development recognising the growing need for staff childcare. Many staff have found reassurance from the knowledge that their children are being cared for nearby.

Fig 18.15: Making Christmas special for the Children's Ward, 1990s.

Fig 18.16: Children of RVI staff being looked after whilst their parents work.

Bereavement Services

Sadly death will always be a part of hospital life and the way it is handled will leave lasting impressions for those who have been bereaved. All staff have a role to play but bereavement services and the chaplaincy have a special responsibility at this time.

Chaplaincy

Alan Maude has been part of the RVI for over 30 years. Small in stature, huge in presence, his office is the corridors of the RVI. He has offered a listening ear, appropriate support and comfort to many staff, patients and relatives.

Fig 18.17: Julie Mcfarlane, who works with relatives and staff as part of the Bereavement services team.

Fig 18.18: The Hospital Chaplain.

Thank you

Undermining the NHS seems to be a national pastime! Hooray for the thousands of patients and relatives who take the time and effort to send their grateful thanks for the care they have received from RVI staff.

Fig 18.19: A typical ward notice-board festooned with thank you cards.

Princess Anne at the opening of the Leazes Wing

Fame and recognition regularly come to the doctors, nurses and other professions. The RVI ensures that when dignitaries visit those who make the hospital tick are high on the list to meet all Royal Visitors.

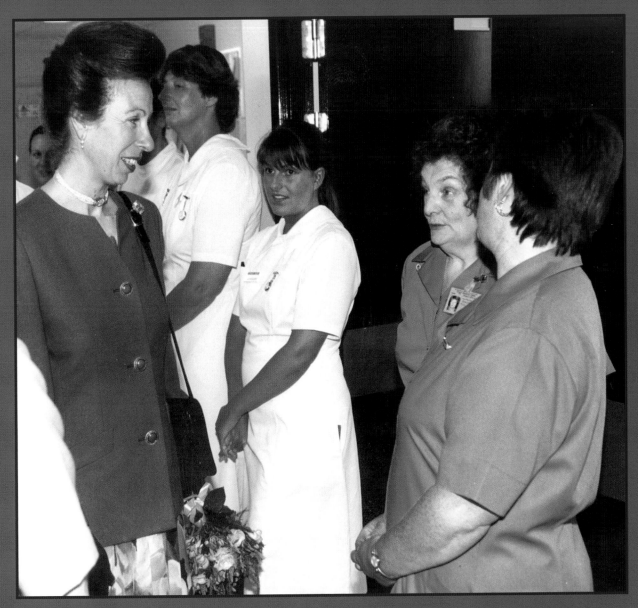

Fig 18.20: Princess Anne at the opening of the Leazes Wing.

Doctors

Although consultants provide the leadership and continuity the future of medical care lies in the hands of the students and doctors in training, many coming from far flung parts of the world.

Fig 18.21: Doctor in training.

Nurses

The backbone of any hospital is the nursing staff who care for patients day and night, 365 days a year. Upon their shoulders rests the reputation of the RVI as a caring institution.

Fig 18.22: RVI Nurse.

11 LANCS FUS

FOR KING AND
COUNTRY
1914   1918

12 YORKS

W FOX

2 YORKS

THOMPSON.

204

Chapter 19: *The RVI in Wartime 1914-18 and 1939-45*

John Walton, Jeremy Feggetter

The 20th Century witnessed two horrific world wars which inevitably impacted upon the Royal Victoria Infirmary. *(Fig 19.2)* During these times the hospital was heavily tested by having to deal with the injured repatriated from the war zones and a small number injured by enemy action locally. In addition the Infirmary had to maintain normal peacetime services for the people of Newcastle and the North East. As expected the hospital rose to the occasion during each war despite the problems imposed by having many of their staff away on war service. Not surprisingly we have been unable to identify any staff with personal recollections of the 1914-18 war, but this period is commented upon both by William Hume in his *History of the Infirmary 1751-1951* and by Grey Turner and Arnison in their *History of the Newcastle upon Tyne School of Medicine (1834-1934)*. Relevant reference is also made by David Shaw in chapter 14 on *The Universities and the RVI* in this book.

Fig 19.2: 1914-1919 War memorial (RVI staff).

Fig 19.3: The Armstrong Building.

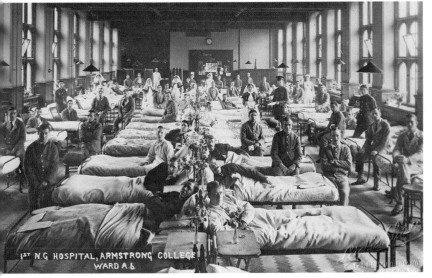

Fig 19.4: A military ward.

Hume pointed out that in the eight years prior to the outbreak of the First World War there had been significant improvements in the accommodation and facilities available at the RVI, but when the war broke out the Infirmary had to share the work resulting from illness and casualties in the forces in France and other theatres of war. This it did in collaboration with the 1st Northern General Hospital (Territorial Force) *(Fig 19.4)* which had been founded in 1912 and was the first Territorial General Hospital in the United Kingdom. This hospital took over the principal buildings of Armstrong College, *(Fig 19.3)* providing thereby much increased accommodation and other facilities for patients and staff. Indeed, until 1955, anyone visiting the University Department of Zoology in the Armstrong building could still see a notice in the main lift which read *"This lift is for stretcher cases only"* 1(N) General Hospital (TF). *(Fig 19.5)*

Left: Fig 19.1: The Leazes Bedspread created by servicemen injured in the 1914-1918 war.

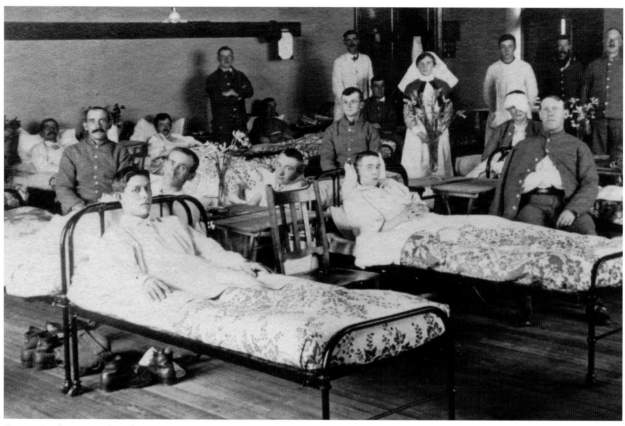

Fig 19.5: A military surgical ward.

The honorary staff of the RVI, and in particular its surgeons, undertook the increased work which necessarily resulted, and to meet the additional demand for surgical accommodation two temporary wards were added to the hospital. Many members of the senior and junior staff joined the forces at home and abroad, and some recently retired members of the honorary medical and surgical staff were recalled to fill some of the gaps. Towards the end of the war, the Ministry of Pensions Hospital was built adjoining the Infirmary buildings, consisting of three brick pavilions and wooden huts, for which the RVI provided all the X-ray and laboratory facilities. (Fig 19.6) When the Ministry of Pensions Hospital was ultimately removed to Dunston Hill, the three brick pavilions, after a time, were converted into pay-bed wards for patients able to pay for hospital maintenance and treatment. In total, 86 beds were provided, together with an operating theatre, and the whole unit became known as the Leazes Hospital.

Fig 19.6: Ministry of Pensions Hospital.

Hume comments that medical knowledge gained during the 1914-18 war made important contributions to the physiology of medicine and surgery, and influenced civilian practice in many directions. Thus, the experience which physicians and surgeons gained from treating gunshot wounds of the chest during war gave an impetus to the development of chest surgery in civilian practice. There are many more examples of improvements in treatment resulting from war experience.

Turner and Arnison, in their history of the Medical School, said that the moment war was declared, the place was a whirl of excitement and activity, for many members of both staff and students were under military obligations (some being in the Territorial Force), the OTC was very active, and all the young bloods were keen to be "in the swim". More particularly, from the moment that Armstrong College was evacuated in order to accommodate the Territorial General Hospital, the Medical School felt compelled to offer students from Armstrong College access to many of their facilities. This resulted in considerable overcrowding and re-organisation of the Medical School's own work. Some students at once left their studies to join the forces, but others who remained carried out double, and often treble duty while doing all that they could to speed completion of their Medical Studies so that they might themselves qualify and join one or other of the medical services. The College nevertheless carried on its duties of teaching and examining throughout the whole of the war, although this meant continuous overwork for the staff and great inconvenience for the students.

Fig 19.7: Mr G. Y. Feggetter, FRCS.

Turning to the Second World War, Hume points out that in September 1939 the Infirmary had to make preparations for the reception of convoys of the wounded and sick, and for casualties amongst the local population. Gas attacks were expected and a temporary building was erected for the decontamination and treatment of casualties. Shelters were also built as protection from aerial bombardment. As in the 1914-18 war, the honorary and resident staff became seriously depleted because of the demands of the services, and in addition to their work in the Infirmary members of the honorary staff who were too old to undertake military service were called upon to undertake duties in other hospitals in the region. In the event aerial bombardment did affect parts of Tyneside, but was much less severe than in other parts of the United Kingdom, and no gas attacks took place. There were, however, sufficient numbers of casualties to allow Grant and Bywaters, who worked for the Medical Research Council in London, to come to Newcastle to study the clinical effects of what later became known as *"Crush Syndrome"* resulting from severe crush injuries during air raids. It was at this time that Ludwig Wittgenstein, (see chapter 11) *(Fig 11.6, p.111)* the famous philosopher, and also a noted mathematician, spent a year in Newcastle with this team. The late Mr G. Y. Feggetter, *(Fig 19.7)* father of one of us (J.G.W.F.) and for many years a consultant surgeon at the RVI, kept a diary just before and in the early years of WW2. An edited extract from this diary follows which clearly demonstrates the effects of the war upon medical practice in the RVI.

I was appointed on 3rd March 1938 as Honorary Assistant Surgeon at the RVI. The surgical staff consisted of 12 consultant surgeons divided into six firms (clinical teams) each of two, a full Honorary and an Assistant Honorary who was appointed to the Infirmary and worked harmoniously with his chief. The full honorary was in charge of the wards, usually one big ward for men and half of a ward for women with beds in the children's ward as required. When the senior consultant retired it was usual for the senior honorary assistant to move up to become the full honorary. I worked with Mr Hedley-Whyte who had just been promoted to full consultant and we worked in the recently built surgical wards 19 (Morison) and 20 on the top floor of the RVI. Mr Hedley-Whyte was officially in charge of the wards and responsible for the patients under his name and for administration. He did not do any out-patient consultations but held two operating lists a week and did two ward rounds, one of which was for teaching students, and internal hospital consultations when requested by physicians. The contract for honorary assistants specified one day a week for GP-referred out patient consultations. This was always a long day beginning at 08.30 and continuing until late afternoon after dictating all letters. In those days there was no appointments system. Out patients arrived early in the morning and were registered by the clerks who gave them their documents. They then took their seats in the Great Hall where there still hung the board describing in gold letters "Pigg's Charity" (described by Pigg in Jorrock's Adventures by Surtees). I usually started the clinic punctually and the efficient sister in charge could usually estimate the time by which an early patient or late arrival would be seen, in the latter case advising the person concerned to have one or more cups of coffee and to return later. The important point was that a GP could tell the patient to attend on the day he felt the need for a consultation. There were no waiting lists. I was also responsible for all surgical emergency admissions for 24 hours one day a week and every 4th Sunday. There were no other Teaching Hospitals between Edinburgh and Leeds and we always had 10-15 surgical admissions on these days. Operating on emergencies began at 5.00pm and continued through the night. Other hospitals such as Sunderland, Carlisle and Berwick helped by dealing with less serious emergencies. Often general practitioner surgeons undertook immediate life-saving operations - subsequently referring the patients to the RVI for later elective surgery. I had one operating list, lasting all day, on one day a week but I soon arranged a second day for outpatient cystoscopies and a bougie clinic. I was also on the staff of the medical school giving lectures and teaching in out-patients, the wards and operating theatres. I started a programme of meetings with my student surgical dressers, house surgeons and registrars to assess the circumstances whenever a patient died.

During the first years of the war I was very busy indeed. I had all Mr Hedley-Whyte's duties as well as my own to fulfil in the RVI. I had complete charge of my firm's wards, all the usual emergencies and an increased number of lists in addition to duties at a Hartlepool hospital. To assist me I had one house surgeon who changed every six months, and one junior registrar who changed after a year. Students acted as house surgeons and undertook much responsibility. I was always on duty during air raids and also on a mobile team to operate in distant hospitals if the local surgeons could not cope. During raids I would be called to the hospital when necessary any day or night and when not called I would undertake fire watching duties in the street where I lived. Fortunately the heavy air raids that had been expected never materialised except for some on the High Level Bridge and adjacent marshalling yards. There were some nuisance raids during the day and many at night and others on South Shields and Sunderland. Mobile teams were required in South Shields but all casualties could be treated in local hospitals.

The only big bomber raid destined for Newcastle took place during the heavy bombing of London but the raiders were caught and attacked over the North Sea with such a loss of bombers and crew that no more daylight raids on this scale were repeated. There were, however, raids with 'planes dropping mines in the sea and attacking fishing boats. Despite my heavy work load in the RVI and elsewhere I had to earn a living by private work, since my hospital work was honorary and without any form of remuneration. However, in 1942 when preparations began for a Second Front there was a new demand by the army for Surgical Consultants and I was released from civilian practice to serve in the RAMC on 12th May 1942.

Just before war was declared in September 1939 and after Munich in 1938, the whole medical profession was prepared for war service. Local war committees were set up to assess medical requirements to deal with bombing casualties and the needs of civilians in the local area plus those civilians evacuated from cities at risk of heavy bombing. Based on experience from the bombing of cities in the Spanish Civil War it was estimated that there might be 25,000 casualties in the first month. Accordingly hospitals were prepared on the declaration of war to empty some wards through sending home patients awaiting investigation or who were ambulant. Additional hospitals, called EMS (Emergency Medical Services) were built in the grounds of mental hospitals and sanatoria in the periphery of towns and big cities. Cottage hospitals were enlarged, staff were recruited and resident doctors appointed. Consultants were warned that in the event of war they would be called upon to deal with casualties and additional RSOs were appointed. At national level there was a Central Medical War Committee set up to deal with the needs of the expanding armed services and to balance the needs of the services with those of the local committees. The Central Committee would demand from the Local Committee a certain number of surgeons and other consultants, sometimes giving the names of individuals. Such practitioners were usually released but the requests could be refused if they were required more urgently at home. As the war progressed and casualties in the forces increased and civilian casualties from bombing diminished, many more consultants were released. On the first day of the war there was a general mobilisation and all doctors in the TA, RNVR, and the RAAF and Reservists were called to the colours. This involved some of the RVI staff. Mr Hedley-Whyte was called up, together with one physician and several registrars from a variety of departments. Newly qualified doctors were called up immediately but were allowed six months' deferment if they had a junior hospital appointment. During the "phoney war" in 1939-40 many of the forces had very little to do while civilian doctors were overworked. After the defeat at Dunkirk service doctors had even less to do in the UK and Ireland. However this did not apply to those in the Royal Navy, RAF and those serving abroad in Africa, India and the Middle and Far East.

(Editors' note. Mr Feggetter went on to serve with distinction in North Africa with the 69th General Hospital, subsequently returning to the RVI as a consultant surgeon when the war finished). The wartime experiences of Mr J. D. T. Jones have been published in the Medical Graduates Newsletter (2005)

Mr Hedley-Whyte commanded the rear guard of the 8th British General Hospital at Rennes in June 1940. When it came under attack with high explosive bombs and machine guns he moved the remaining patients and staff to St. Nazaire. With 52 survivors of the sinking of the SS Lancastria he arranged their evacuation on the SS Glenariffic to Portsmouth. On landing he was awarded an immediate DSO and was then posted to Ireland to command 31st British General at Musgrave Park.

The experience of the students during this time also can be clearly recalled as one of us (J.W.) was a medical student in Newcastle from 1941-45 and thus had some experience of the RVI in wartime, for it was in this hospital that most clinical teaching and experience was offered. In the pre-clinical years (1941-42) service in the Senior Training Corps was compulsory for all male students who were medically fit and all undertook fire watching duties in rotation in the medical school. They also undertook training in the first instance to take the Infantry Certificate A and, later, on joining the Medical Unit of the STC, they were required to undertake Medical Certificate B. The Unit was organised as a Field Ambulance and was required to be available to support, in the event of an invasion, the 51st Scottish Division which was bivouacked in Northumberland.

Fig 19.8: Professor Authur Bernard Shaw.

After passing the 2nd MB examination in April 1942, clinical training began in the RVI alongside the memorable pathology teaching of Professor Arthur Bernard Shaw, *(Fig 19.8)* who, when asked if he was any relation to the Bernard Shaw, used to say *"I am the Bernard Shaw"*. (In fact GBS was his uncle.) Microbiology was taught by Professor Ernest Dunlop and Alan Emslie-Smith, whilst lectures and clinical teaching on the wards and out-patient department were provided by Professor Fred Nattrass, whose teaching was a model of clarity. Others involved were Dr C.N. (Natty) Armstrong (a world expert on intersex, who lived until the age of 102), Charles Ungley (a world expert on pernicious anaemia), Dr Alan Ogilvie (the Og), Dr R.B. Thompson, an internationally recognised expert in haematology and Dr Tom Boon (who took a special interest in blood transfusion). Alan Ogilvie was a charming, if eccentric and forgetful physician; his fierce percussion of the chest was unforgettable. In surgery clinical students were taught by Professor J. Hamilton Barclay, the inimitable Professor Norman Hodgson and other notable figures such as John Gilmour, John (Daddy) Brumwell, the elegant T.A. Hindmarsh and Mr W. A. Hewitson. In child health, the teaching of James Spence (subsequently Sir James) was compelling, sometimes even electrifying, and his colleagues such as Dr Freddie Miller, also greatly enlivened that subject. In obstetrics and gynaecology the first professor was the dogmatic Farqhuar Murray who was succeeded by the flamboyant and memorable Harvey Evers, whose elegance of dress and behaviour was matched by the clarity and organised content of his lectures.

A number of outstanding features of the wartime clinical training stand out. Every student was required personally to deliver 20 babies before qualification; many such deliveries were undertaken at the Princess Mary Maternity Hospital where, because of the lack of medically qualified staff, all the anaesthetics for forceps deliveries, and even for Caesarean sections, were given by medical students, an experience which was challenging but, so far as one can tell, successful. There was also "the district". When a district call came in, two students would go by taxi to pick up the obstetrics bag on Jubilee Road and then, either by taxi or sometimes by bicycle, would go out to the domiciliary delivery. Usually a midwife was available to come along, but not always, and several medical students, including the author (J.W.), were challenged by having to conduct deliveries on the district unaided including, on one occasion, a breech delivery, which happily was successfully achieved. VE day (8th May 1945) fell when many medical students, the author (J.W.) included, were delivering babies at the Princess Mary Maternity Hospital. A celebratory party was organised by Mr Stanley Way, a noted gynaecologist, and a bonfire was lit which contained parts of a derelict chicken hut purloined by a student from a nearby allotment. He was duly arrested for this offence but the magistrates were understandably sympathetic and dismissed the case. Not surprisingly the medical course during the war years had to be modified to take account of the shortage of qualified housemen in all the Newcastle Hospitals caused by the demands of the armed services. At one time there were only six qualified house doctors working in the RVI, all of the other house jobs being held by senior students supervised by Dr John Craig as Resident Medical Officer (RMO) and by Mr Mac Stewart from South Africa as Resident Surgical Officer (RSO). Stewart was succeeded by "Taff" Evans (subsequently a distinguished thoracic surgeon in South Wales). Practically all students did at least three, and often as many as four or five, months in resident appointments during a shortened wartime course of four years and three months, before the final examination. The author (J.W.) worked for four months in all as a student houseman in paediatrics supervised by a registrar, Brenda Morrison.[1] Other students were called upon to suture perforated peptic ulcers and occasionally to remove inflamed appendices with only minimal supervision. The experience that students gained during that time was extraordinary; most were ready for it and responded well to the challenges under the supervision of the harassed and overworked qualified housemen and the RMOs and RSOs.

One particularly notable experience was when, following D Day and the invasion of France, a hospital train carrying many sick and wounded came to Newcastle, where its unloading was supervised by the then Tuberculosis Medical Officer in the City of Newcastle, Dr George Hurrell. During this process medical students were called upon to assist in offering such first aid as might be needed by the patients on being disembarked. They were also called upon to assist in seeing that the soldiers were suitably housed in wards at the RVI, the Newcastle General Hospital, or elsewhere. Despite the inevitable disruption resulting from war, the RVI continued, although under very considerable pressure upon all concerned, to offer what seemed to be an outstanding level of care to the residents of Newcastle, and the North-East. Fortunately, neither the RVI nor any of the other hospitals in the area were directly affected by aerial bombardment or by any of the other direct consequences of warfare.

Nursing during the two world wars (Fig 19.9)

Nurses from the RVI played a major role in treating the sick and injured resulting from the two world wars. Indeed the RVI was so proud of its efforts that in the midst of the First World War it produced a poster entitled "what the Royal Victoria Infirmary has done and is doing in War Time. It listed seven areas of activity and made particular reference to nurse activity stating *A large Nursing Staff, organised by the Matron in time of peace and maintained since the outbreak of war has been available for work in the 1st Northern General Hospital and many Sisters and Nurses from the regular staff have joined the Navy and Army Nursing Services"*.

The poster also listed the activities of the St. John Ambulance Brigade and the British Red Cross Society in providing support services under supervision on the wards of the RVI. It comments that the skills the members acquired enabled them to provide services elsewhere in England and in Flanders and the Dardanelles.

In the Second World War nursing services were provided nearer to the scene of combat. Brenda McBryde has given an account of this time in her book, *A Nurses War* published by Osprey. She was born just 10 days before the armistice ended the First World War. In 1911 she started a four year course of nurse training at the RVI qualifying in April 1943.

[1] Lord Walton of Detchant (1993), The Spice of Life, Heinemann, Royal Society of Medicine.

She was then commissioned into the Queen Alexandra's Royal Army Nursing Service and underwent further training at the 75th General Hospital in Peebles. Within a fortnight of D Day the hospital was redeployed to the village of Rys in Normandy close to the coastal town of Arromanches. There she was involved in treating the casualties from D Day and from both sides. In addition to treating allied soldiers, she had the task of managing a ward full of German soldiers who, although recumbent, would click their heels together whenever a nurse entered their ward in response to a shout of "achtung" from the duty officer on the ward who she labeled "the tent meister".

Another nurse, Kitty Brown recalls working as a staff nurse at the RVI during the Second Word War helping to restore injured soldiers back to health. She recalls soldiers suffering from shrapnel wounds, and shell shock and other mental scars of from fighting in the war. Despite the anxieties of wartime nursing she described spirits as remaining high and that there was a lot of fun at work which helped ease the pain of being at war. Overall, RVI nurses have a proud record of service during wartime though sadly most of it was undocumented.

The Newcastle Territorial Army Hospitals

The First Northern General Hospital (Territorial Force), established in 1912 before the outbreak of the First World War, subsequently became the No 1(N) General hospital (TA), and later still the 201 (Northern) General Hospital. These hospitals have always had close links with the RVI and previous commanding officers have included such notable members of the RVI staff as Grey Turner, George Feggetter, Bill Ross, Len Constable, Hugh Brown and Ann Clouston as well as both authors of this chapter. The Hospital received the Honorary Freedom of the City in 1990 and has functioned with distinction in the 1992 Gulf War, as well as in recent conflicts in the Balkans, Afghanistan and most recently in Operation Telic in Iraq. In all these campaigns members of the RVI staff, medical, nursing and professions allied to medicine, have been deployed with distinction. The tradition of linkage between the two organisations is continued by the current chairman of the Newcastle Hospitals NHS Trust, Sir Miles Irving, who is Honorary Colonel and the commanding officer Colonel Ian Goulborne who is an honorary consultant at the RVI.

Fig 19.9: World War 1 nurses serving the RVI and the armed forces.

The King unveiling Statue of the late
QUEEN VICTORIA,
Royal Victoria Infirmary,
NEWCASTLE-ON-TYN
July 11th 1906

212

Chapter 20: *The Architectural Evolution of the RVI* Ian Ward, James Gallantry
New Buildings - Better Health

The RVI is like a family. In that respect its constituent parts change over time but it stays basically the same. The RVI's buildings have changed greatly in the last 100 years and this chapter invites the reader to consider what has changed and what is essentially the same.

Fig 20.2: View of the RVI from the North West showing the Nurses' Home on the right, Ward 11 centrally and Ward 12.

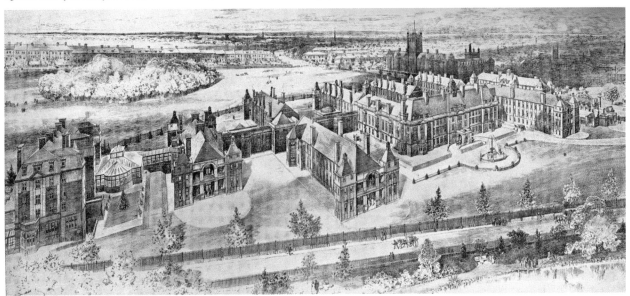

Fig 20.3: Bird's Eye View of the planned Royal Victoria Infirmary. Note the fountain where the statue was eventually positioned.

The best place to start our tour through time is at the entrance to Peacock Hall, looking at the front of the hospital that is familiar from newspapers and TV screens. The RVI was originally constructed between 1900 and 1906 to a design by W. L. Newcombe and Percy Adams. The Edwardian RVI did not exist in a vacuum; it was in fact the apogee of the design competition system as applied to pavilion hospitals in the Victorian and Edwardian eras. Best practice at the time in hospital planning was the pavilion system, which provided effective circulation patterns and, of greatest importance then, fresh air to the wards. (*Figs* 20.2 & 20.3)

A design competition for a new hospital at the Forth Banks site had been held in 1897 but this was abandoned because that site was under pressure from rail, road and cattle-market traffic. A 10-acre site near Leazes Park became available instead. A new design competition was held in 1899, entrants being required to lay out 400 beds and supporting departments. The Leazes site was complex in that it was triangular and sloped! It was quite a challenge to locate the pavilion wards and to place the main entrance effectively.

The commission was awarded to H. Percy Adams of London and W. Lister Newcombe of Newcastle. Their design provided an east-west route across the widest part of the site with the pavilions off this spine and the administration block placed in the centre, facing south. The Nurses' Home was placed at the far west side and linked to the corridor by a large conservatory. (*Fig* 17.28, p.191) The use of conservatories to link buildings was a typical feature of Edwardian hospital architecture.

Fig 20.4: RVI Administration building.

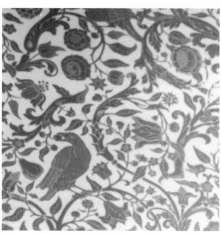

Fig 20.5: Handmade leather wallpaper that gave the Peacock Hall its name.

The most striking building was Administration, known today as Peacock Hall. The entrance was approached by a curved drive, as if it were a large country house. The architecture and the internal decoration sustained that illusion as much as was possible. The materials were bright red brick, stone and grey-green slates from Borrowdale, known as Honister slate. The overall style was mainstream Edwardian classicism. (Figs 20.4 & 20.5)

The internal appearance and arrangement of the original RVI was functional but meant to impress. The wards were traditional Nightingale wards, which included splendid fireplaces and dining tables down the middle of each ward. This will have given the senior nurse control over heating, meals etc. as well as the clinical care. The "Modern Matron" of today would have found this aspect familiar! (Figs 20.6 & 20.7)

The corridors were light and airy by comparison with many modern hospital corridors. Perhaps the most striking local feature was the collection of sixty-nine Royal Doulton nursery rhyme tiled panels on walls of the original children's wards. These were the gift of the Lady Mayoress and her friends and were executed by the artists J. H. McLennan, William Ross and Margaret E. Thompson. A former patient on the wards recalls being "scared stiff" of being in hospital but finding the tiled panels re-assuring 43 years later!

It is interesting to compare the costs of hospital architecture between then and now. The Adams and Newcastle building cost 9 pence per square foot while the planned new facilities at the RVI will cost £2,500 per square metre or £236.69 per square foot! Even after allowing for inflation, this difference indicates that hospital architecture has become much more complex and is concerned with creating a total infrastructure for health.

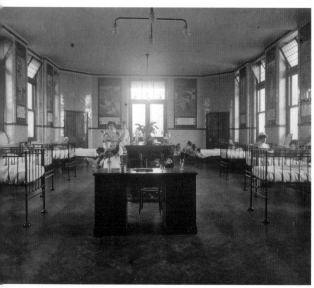

Fig 20.6: A children's ward, with the Royal Doulton nursery rhyme tiled panels.

Following the completion of the new building in 1906, a major addition to the Infirmary was built by the Government for the care of wounded and disabled soldiers, towards the end of the First World War (see chapter 19). Known as the Leazes Hospital, it was located at the north end of the site. This Hospital consisted of three pavilion wards (later to be known as pavilions 1, 2 and 3), a twin operating theatre, plus some other ancillary accommodation, later to be used as the Leazes kitchen and dining room, plus supplies and stores accommodation. These buildings were fully incorporated into the Infirmary in the 1920s. Today none of these buildings exist. Pavilion 3 was demolished in 1979 to create space for the new Medical School, and Pavilions 1 and 2, plus the theatres, were demolished in 1994 to create space for the Claremont Wing. The remaining original buildings (except for a small portion of the stores building) were also demolished in 1994 for the construction of the new catering block.

During the 1930s there were further major additions to the Infirmary. A large extension to the Nurses' Home was constructed in 1932, which doubled the size of the original 1906 building. This 'new' extension can still be identified today by the lighter coloured stonework and differences in the architectural detail. Additional clinical facilities were also provided by the provision of an additional floor to one of the original 1906 buildings to provide two wards (now Wards 9 and 10) plus an operating theatre, and the Orthopaedic block. The Orthopaedic block was constructed in 1933, and was located between the Leazes Hospital and the original Infirmary buildings. This building, which provided accommodation for two wards, an operating theatre, Fracture Clinic, Out-Patients and Physiotherapy, was demolished in 2002 as an enabling measure for the major redevelopment of the Infirmary. (*Fig 20.8*)

Pavilion wards were refurbished many times to provide modern medical services. Out went fireplaces and oak desks. In came central heating, medical gases, nurse call systems and increasing demands for the architecture to support rapidly changing healthcare.

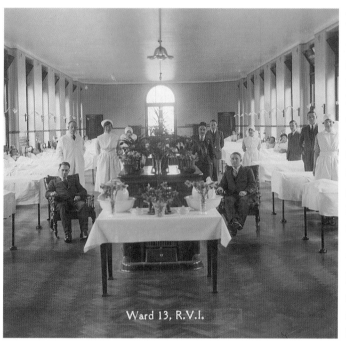

Fig 20.7: Ward 13, RVI.

As medicine expanded and the NHS was established, the RVI's building stock grew in less attractive ways. The spaces between the pavilions were gradually filled with new departments and additional buildings were added, mostly behind, but sometimes in competition with the splendour of the Edwardian frontage. Examples are the day rooms built towards the end of the 1960s on to most of the original wards, the western extension to the Nurses' Home, the extension to the out-patients department, the Wellcome research laboratories, the Ridley extension to the then children's wards (now Wards 14/18), the 'new' Accident and Emergency (A&E) department (which was demolished in 2004) and the Intensive Care Unit which was built between the Administration block and the adjacent surgical ward.

The next architectural intervention at the RVI site was the Dental Hospital and School. The new building opened in 1978 and was the first building block in the medico-dental teaching campus that today consists of the Leazes Wing, the Medical School and the Dental Hospital. The Dental Hospital has since proved an adaptable building in terms of the space and functions needed to provide modern dentistry.

The RVI's architectural relationship with its neighbours also changed. The Hospital had always had a close relationship with the Medical School and in 1985 the Medical School moved from the Queen Victoria Road site to where it is today. From this point onwards, the Hospital could not consider itself in isolation. The next logical step in the process (if the reader believes that these things are logical...) was to link Hospital and Medical School facilities much more closely. This was achieved by the concept of the "First Ward Block".

As early as 1961 (the year in which one of the authors was born!) the "First Ward Block" began to be discussed. This was envisaged as the first of two buildings that would ultimately replace virtually all the old buildings at the RVI. The very purpose of the building and its design were

Fig 20.8: Royal Victoria Infirmary, 1949.

215

repeatedly examined and often modified until 1987 when construction finally started. The building was called the Leazes Wing, following a competition to name it, and the first patients moved in on 7th April 1992. (*Fig 20.9*)

Fig 20.9: *Leazes Wing, 1991.*

The Leazes Wing was the most significant architectural intervention at the RVI since the construction of the Edwardian buildings. It was a major change as wards moved from the Nightingale pattern to the NHS "racetrack" design. The Leazes Wing plan form was based upon tried and tested NHS standards and interiors were functional and pleasant but not especially uplifting. The design of the Wing was a simple block form. In terms of size, the Leazes Wing was a very large building, being half the size of the whole Freeman Hospital, for example. Architecturally, function led form.

The Leazes Wing allowed clinicians to expand services and released considerable space in the Infirmary for other developments. Perhaps the greatest impact on practice was standardisation and consolidation. For example, operating theatres went from being unique to being in a suite of several identical theatres.

During the 1990s the RVI family of buildings underwent further change, driven partly by the Newcastle Strategic Review (the NSR). The immediate aim of the NSR was to bring clinical services from the NGH to the RVI. The architecture evolved accordingly.

In 1996 the Claremont Wing opened to ophthalmic patients as Ophthalmology services were centralised at the RVI after nearly fifty years in temporary accommodation! They say that nothing endures like the temporary…

The Claremont Wing was designed by the clinicians who were to use the building. It reflected some aspects of the Leazes Wing, its "form follows function" ethos, but was a more imaginative building. The external appearance was unusual by RVI standards as it used shiny metal cladding combined with brickwork at some very jaunty angles! The inside of the building was unusual for its detailed design in that the specialized ophthalmic spaces were all "mocked-up" in full scale before construction. The Wing also saw the RVI's first major programme of visual arts, including the needle sculptures in the courtyard by the local sculptor Colin Rose. (*Fig 20.10*) Interestingly, these were the first major sculptures commissioned at the RVI since the original art nouveau statue of Queen Victoria in 1906.

Fig 20.10: *Claremont Wing Courtyard with sculptures by Colin Rose.*

The Claremont Wing included "shell" space to accommodate General Medicine services that would move from the NGH to the RVI in 1997. Shortly afterwards, General Surgery made the move. In this process the external architecture of the RVI did not change much but the existing buildings were altered internally and clinical services reconfigured in order to accommodate ever-more clinical activity on the site. The watchword of the late 1990s was "density" as it became obvious that this trend would increase.

During this period, the pavilion wards were altered to meet different needs. One went from being a Coronary Care Unit to a Personnel Department to a Children's Oncology Ward inside four years!

A significant addition, completed in 1994, was the Sir James Spence Institute for Child Health, not least because of the proximity of its location next to the Administrative Building and the Main (Peacock Hall) Entrance. Funded largely from charitable donations, this building was built in a character sympathetic with the original 1906 building.

The supporting services also required architectural interventions in the 1990s. A new Catering and Restaurant block was opened in the "Industrial" quarter of the site in 1996. The lack of car parking facilities on site, a major problem since the beginning of the construction of the Leazes Wing, was addressed with construction of a 574 place multi storey car park. The new car park was opened in 1998 and was funded by the then novel method of private finance (PFI).

Because over the intervening years the Infirmary site had become full of buildings, space for expansion and new buildings was at a premium. To overcome this difficulty a range of projects known as the Newcastle Strategic Review (NSR) Enabling Schemes was carried out to create space in the middle of the site for the projected new building. The major projects associated with this programme were the relocation of the Ante-Natal Clinic in the Leazes Wing, the development of laboratory accommodation (for Clinical Biochemistry, Microbiology, Immunology and Haematology) in the Medical School and the provision of a building which provided for pharmacy manufacturing and stores, as well as a decanting store, sewing room and delivery point for the hospital. All of these projects were completed in 2003.

Fig 20.11: Construction underway of the new Victoria Wing and Children's Hospital (2005-2013).

Fig 20.12: Royal Victoria Infirmary aerial view. How it will look with the new development.

The upshot of all of this new building was the eventual demolition programme to create the space for the *'Transforming the Newcastle Hospitals'* (TNH) building project. Buildings demolished included the C.N. Armstong Lecture Theatre, the former Haematology laboratories, the former Ante-Natal Clinic and the former A&E Department.(*Fig 20.11*)

At the time of the RVI Centenary, the hospital is due for the largest architectural change in its history. The TNH project is set to provide new buildings of an unprecedented scale and complexity. The new RVI will provide some 60,000 square metres of accommodation in discrete zones for adults, children and high technology services. These will be linked by a spectacular atrium which will in fact be the largest room in Newcastle. At 110 metres in length, it could comfortably accommodate two Olympic-standard swimming pools! The new development will almost entirely replace the 1906 Infirmary with state-of-the-art facilities. The project is being procured through the Private Finance Initiative (PFI) at an approximate cost of £300 million. (*Figs 20.12 , 20.13 & 20.14*)

Fig 20.13: New Main Entrance and children's hospital.

Fig 20.14: New RVI Atrium looking towards Queen Victoria Road.

This may be the newest member of the family (with a formidable gestation period…) but it will make its presence felt for generations to come.

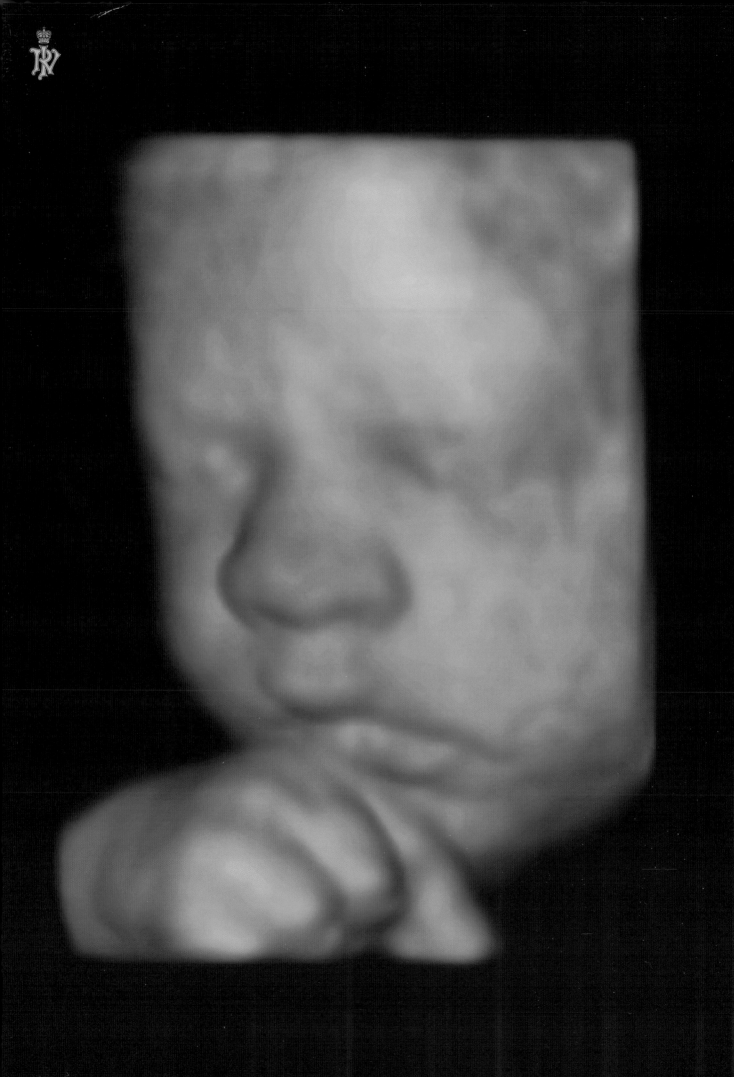